Joe D'Ambrosio

PSYCHOLOGICAL TECHNIQUES
IN
NEUROLOGICAL DIAGNOSIS

PSYCHOLOGICAL TECHNIQUES IN NEUROLOGICAL DIAGNOSIS

BESSIE B. BURGEMEISTER, Ph.D.

Formerly Research Assistant,
Department of Neurology,
Columbia University College of
Physicians and Surgeons,
New York City

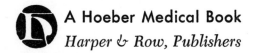 **A Hoeber Medical Book**
Harper & Row, Publishers

Contents

Preface

It is understandable that psychologists have emphasized psychogenic elements of dysfunction and maladjustment; more patients present themselves with emotional than with neurological problems. But the incidence of neurological disorders may be greater than is supposed, and with improved techniques many so-called functional behavior deviations may be shown to have neurological origins or components. By not realizing the full potential of their test instruments psychologists overlook evidences of neurological disorder. At the same time, through an inadequate understanding of such tools, neurologists often disregard these significant aids to diagnostic examination.

The contribution of psychological techniques to the diagnosis of neurological disorders deserves and needs further study and development.

This book is written as a guide and a challenge to the clinical psychologist interested in neuropsychology. By consolidating current information on neuropsychological testing, it presents both the assets and the limitations of psychological methods in diagnosing neurological disorders. The material focuses upon numerous aspects of practice in clinical psychology, since central-nervous-system disorders are found wherever human behavior is being evaluated—in child guidance clinics, hospitals, nursery schools, educational centers, courts, and penal institutions. Recent psychopharmacological advances, moreover, make a neuropsychological orientation for the clinical psychologist seem especially timely.

The bulk of work on this book was done by the author as Research Assistant in the Department of Neurology, College of Physicians and Surgeons, Columbia University. I wish to express appreciation for the valuable assistance of several of my colleagues: to Dr. H. Houston Merritt for reading the manuscript; to Dr. L. Vosburgh Lyons, Dr. Frederic T. Zimmerman and Miss Louise R. Hewson for their interest and cooperation; to Dr. Leonard Small and Verna Small for their most helpful comments in preparation of the text and editorial work; and to the publishers of journals and books for permission to reproduce their material. Most of all, I wish to thank Dr. Leonard Small for his initial suggestion that the book be written and for his continued encouragement during its evolution.

B. B. B.

New York City

I

>>

Relation of Psychology

to Neurology

Use of psychological techniques in the diagnosis of central-nervous-system disorders assumes a demonstrable relationship between neuro-anatomical functioning and psychological expression. Evidence is unequivocally favorable to this hypothesis in its broadest sense. But in attempting precise definitions of interactive and integrative processes, one enters a more speculative realm. As questions become more precise, problems of delineation involve more of the unknown than of the known.

Solutions to neuropsychological problems have been sought in many areas, but despite considerable progress, many questions remain unanswered. Controversies continue among investigators about the nature and influences of numerous basic variables.

NEUROPSYCHOLOGICAL THEORIES OF LEARNING

Inadequate knowledge of neuropsychological mechanisms in the intact organism hinders measurement of the alterations in thinking, affect, and behavior which may result from neurological disturbance. The obscurity of many aspects of the dynamics of cortical activity and its expression at the behavioral level is widely admitted. Among psychological theorists, Leeper[22] points out that Hebb's interpretation of neural function[10] is diametrically opposed to the stimulus-response theory of learning. The S-R theory assumes cortical mechanisms which, activated by stimuli, satisfy basic physiological needs. Even though operation of these mechanisms may be elicited at a later time by learning, they precede learning itself. Hebb, on the other hand, believes that the conduction of

1

impulses along the fibers of cortical neurons results in localized synaptic changes, and that learning must create linkages between cortical cells so that structural and functioning units are produced in the brain.

Halstead's theory[9] relies upon four factors as components of "biological intelligence": 1) a C factor (a central-integrative-field factor which assumes ability to associate and synthesize); 2) an A factor (basic ability for abstraction); 3) a P factor (power or drive factor), and 4), a D factor (directional factor or selective medium by which processes become exteriorized).

Kohler's "electrical field" theory of cerebral integration[16] of several decades ago accounts for the phenomena of generalization in terms of diffuse electrochemical states that permeate cortical tissue. (Lashley, Chow, and Semmes[21] do not consider this theory valid.)

In Goldstein's "organismic theory"[8] the qualitative and holistic functioning of the organism is maintained; it denies that a response may be explained as a quantitative summation of parts. Instead of complicated neuropsychological processes being built upon primary sensations, according to this theory such complex units are considered an integral part of the sensations themselves.

All these attempts to explain both neurological and psychological components of cerebration offer possibilities for study. The nature of neural mechanisms underlying learning remains a subject of controversy.

LOCALIZATION STUDIES

After neurologists demonstrated a considerable amount of functional localization in the human brain, psychologists began to hypothesize that behavioral aberrations or deficiencies might be identified with discrete areas of the brain. The sections below are a summary of current information on localization.

FRONTAL LOBES

Uncontrolled behavior, difficulties in abstract thinking, and poor judgment are prevalent among individuals with damage to the frontal lobes. It is furthermore generally agreed that in the intact brain the frontal lobes act as integrators and regulators, or inhibitors, of the less highly-developed components of psychological expression. In some conflict with this generalization is the fact that epileptics, for example, may perform automatic acts of a very complicated nature while displaying no consciousness of them. Brock[4] compares these to a somnambulistic phenomenon, the exact nature of which is unknown, but which appears related to disturbances in transcortical associations involving not only the prefrontal but also other areas of the brain.

Although the "automatic" individual is confused, and his behavior shows lack of insight, Penfield[28, 29] stresses that automatism is not associated with complete loss of consciousness but with amnesia. The patient's major defect is that he seems to be deprived of the ability of making a memory record. Thus, these reactions suggest the existence of a separate portion of the "centrencephalic" system (Penfield's term) which is specific to memory recording.

TEMPORAL LOBES

Psychological manifestations of disturbances of the temporal lobes include many visual, auditory, olfactory, and gustatory deviations. Penfield refers to the temporal area of the cortex as the "interpretive" or "perceptual" area to distinguish it from the motor or sensory areas involving less complicated neural processes. On the basis of extensive research he reports that the hippocampal zone which occupies the mesial surface of the temporal lobe has an important function in recording current experience. According to Penfield,[29] epileptic discharge or electrical stimulation in the temporal area has been found to produce many interpretive illusions regarding perception of the present. These are reflected as errors in judgment of distance, or of loudness, in the sense of familiarity, strangeness, or unreality, or in emotionally tinged or affective responses (e.g., feelings of loneliness, disgust).

Experiential, or psychical, hallucinations, in which past incidences are reactivated, may likewise be elicited by stimulation in this area. One of Penfield's most important contributions has been to provide evidence that the superior and lateral surfaces of the temporal lobe are centers for Jackson's "dreamy states," or "psychical states,"[13] which are more elaborate than crude sensations.

Differences in the responsiveness of the hemispheres, as well as suggestions regarding the important function of the temporal cortex controlling the minor hand, are indicated in Penfield's work. Temporal lobe functioning in the hemisphere which controls the minor hand seems dominant in interpretation of shape, position, clearness, speed; illusions of familiarity (déjà vu) originate most often in the hemisphere minor for speech and handedness. In contrast, illusions of things heard and feelings of fear may be produced equally by discharge in the temporal cortex of both sides. These findings indicate that considerable specificity of function may be associated with temporal lobe discharge.

PARIETAL AND OCCIPITAL LOBES

The parietal and occipital lobes are important association areas of the cortex, concerned with sensory-perceptive discriminations. Pathology there affects visual, auditory, and language functions as well as sensory-perceptive judgment of objects, intensity of stimulation, and orientation. Discrimination in touch is especially sensitive to parieto-occipital malfunction. Distortions in the perception of body image are common, with accompanying disturbances of motor function, classified as apraxias.

Because they are unaware of them, many patients completely deny behavioral deficiencies or aberrations traceable to such pathology. In general, when lesions of these two lobes effect behavioral changes, patients reveal varying degrees of defect-awareness.

MOTOR AREAS

According to Jackson,[13] the motor areas of the brain are sharply defined. Three motor levels are identified in the central nervous system, with the highest pre-motor, or psychomotor, level located in the frontal cortex. Motor engrams are assumed to be formed in the psychomotor area, and impulses from this area may be transmitted to the middle motor level, the pryamidal cells of the pre-central area. There impulses are elaborated upon and transmitted further downward by way of the pyramidal tracts which lead to the lowest motor level, the anterior horn cell.

VALIDITY OF LOCALIZATION THEORIES

Accreditation of pre-motor syndromes in the human brain is not always certain. Forced grasping and apraxia seem to be due to disturbances in the pre-motor area. Destruction of pyramidal tract fibers usually produces paralysis (on the opposite side of the body). Spasticity, increase in deep reflexes, weakening, or loss of abdominal reflexes, appearance of the extensor toe sign (Babinski), and other neurological signs result from upper motor-neuron, or pyramidal tract, lesions. Sometimes subfrontal pathology produces frontal lobe (prefrontal, pre-motor, or motor area) symptoms.

In general, subcortical lesions involving conduction pathways to the cortex may effect the same behavioral changes as cortical lesions themselves. This is one of the reasons why efforts at localization frequently have been unproductive. Bostroem,[3] for instance, reported psychotic symptoms of no localizing value, while Von Monakow[26] offered the generalization that psychotic symptoms may be a result of lesions anywhere in the brain. In some cases similar lesions do not produce a psychosis. All of these hypotheses still appear to be true, according to Nielsen.[27]

Studies indicate that the degree and specificity of localization vary considerably from individual to individual and according to the particular function under consideration. Conclusive neuroanatomical research is also difficult because lesions rarely occur in areas identical with formal neuroanatomical structures. Psychological interpretation is controversial

when identical symptomatology arises from different neurological conditions, or when identical neurological pathology produces different
psychological conditions. Serious limitations in psychological techniques
add to the complexities of diagnostic localization.

Recent neurophysiological investigations of cerebral organization and
function necessitate revision of many former notions. At present emphasis
has shifted from horizontal to vertical analyses of neuropsychological
reaction. With this trend, explanations based upon concepts similar to
the S-R and association-center theories have been discarded in favor of
more complex syndromes. Studies of properties at the mesencephalic
level,[23] at the diencephalic level,[14] and of the medial and basal "limbic"
formations of the forebrain[1, 7, 15] suggest hypotheses embracing such
ideas as feedback systems to receptors, graded responses, and more complicated sequences of action than any hitherto proposed. Among the
more important findings is the identification, as excitatory or alerting
centers, of certain nonspecific neural mechanisms in the brain stem and
large areas of the neo- and paleo-cortex. These mechanisms appear concerned not only with regulating and equilibrating drives, but also with
determining the selection of stimulation to be heeded. Hence, under such
a theory, the organism assumes a more active role and is less "stimulus
bound" than was previously supposed. Independence of subcortical centers from complete cortical domination likewise requires revision of
theories emphasizing action of the highest integrative centers as signal
transmitters. At the same time, information suggests a possibility for
reconciliation between localization and more global theories of cerebral
organization such as those proposed by Lashley.[19] Failure to recognize
the action of different levels appears to underlie much of the earlier
integration controversy.

A current study reported by Chapman and co-workers[5] illustrates this
point. Subjects sustained a loss of known amounts of tissue from the
neopallium of the cerebral hemispheres. Findings show evidence both
for localization theories and for mass-action concepts, inasmuch as location of damage seemed important in its effect upon lower- and inter-
mediate-level functions (sensation, motility, speech, writing, reading,
etc.). Yet reduction in intensity of defense mechanisms involving impairment of the highest integrative functions was independent of site of tissue
loss. Such results raise challenging research possibilities.

In a review of physiological psychology, Pribam[30] summarizes current
speculation on problems of cerebral organization: "Reinforcement by
cognition, based on a mechanism of hierarchically organized representations; dispositions and drives regulated by multilinked and biased
homeostats; representational organization by virtue of graded, as well
as all-or-nothing, neural responses; spontaneously generated, long-lasting

intrinsic neural rhythms: organisms thus conceived are actively engaged, not only in the manipulation of artifacts, but in the organization of their perceptions, satisfactions, and gratifications." Certainly complexity of structure and function is unmistakable in such a notion.

The present trend in clinical psychology therefore is to interpret findings against configurations broader in concept than earlier ones. Progress requires consideration of psychological factors, such as intellectual endowment, environmental deprivations, premorbid personality, and differences in learning ability and aspiration level, as well as socio-economic pressures. Research so broadly based is necessarily intricate.

POSSIBLE PSYCHOLOGICAL CORRELATES OF NEUROPATHOLOGY

A useful approach to understanding neuropsychological relationships is offered by neuropathology. The clinician becomes acquainted with the number of neurological conditions which may produce behavioral changes; he learns to isolate behavioral symptoms and signs characteristic of, if not pathognomonic of, certain disease entities. This section outlines central-nervous-system disorders which may affect behavior in varying degrees.

DEVELOPMENTAL DEFECTS

These, typically, are malformations of the spinal cord and brain, hydrocephalus (excess fluid in the cranial cavity), premature closure of cranial sutures, cerebral palsy (not a disease entity, but a term for cases with damage to the central nervous system in utero, at birth, or in the early part of life). These often produce degrees of psychological impairment affecting motor and sensory centers. Mental retardation is common.

INFECTIONS

Infections of the meninges, subdural and epidural infections, those of cerebral veins and sinuses, brain abscesses, virus infections such as poliomyelitis and encephalitis, syphilis, and infections caused by other micro-organisms are often associated with a variety of psychological symptoms, especially in acute stages. Simultaneous or more permanent manifestations frequently are sensory and motor defects, intellectual losses, and personality alterations (irritability, hyperactivity, and listlessness—i.e., exaggerations of affect).

VASCULAR LESIONS

Circulatory changes or dysfunction (as in cerebral blood-vessel diseases, intracranial aneurysms, primary subarachnoid hemorrhage, or vascular diseases of the spinal cord) can produce a variety of both diffuse and focal motor and sensory disturbances, such as paralysis and aphasia, mental changes with confusion, loss in functioning ability, and weaknesses in emotional control.

TUMORS

Intracranial tumors (all neoplasms arising from the skull, meninges, blood vessels, ductless glands, cranial nerves, brain tissue) may likewise precipitate varied mental and emotional changes. These include losses in perceptual ability and in abstract thinking, deficits in organizational ability, weaknesses in emotional control, and such personality changes as poor judgment and egocentricity.

TRAUMA

Head and spinal injuries, including closed head injuries—i.e., simple concussion, cerebral edema, cerebral contusion and laceration, simple depressed fractures of the skull, and compound fractures of the skull may be reflected in ways closely correlated with psychological functioning. In the so-called postconcussive syndrome, losses in mental functioning ability, especially immediate memory and abstract thinking, are common, along with affective exaggerations in the form of anxiety, hypochondriacal tendencies, obsessive preoccupation with trivialities, and the like. Psychological components, in fact, are often the more prominent and lasting aftereffects. In many instances they grow progressively worse, after neurological symptoms have disappeared.

METABOLIC DISEASES

Endocrine-gland and blood diseases are included in this category, as are diseases of the tissue and bone, peripheral nerve disorders, and deficiency states. Mental retardation, behavioral aberrations, personality changes (irritability, refusal to cooperate, confusion, paranoid trends, sometimes psychosis), memory loss, and motor weakness (muscular) are possible concomitants of disturbances in metabolism.

DISEASES CAUSED BY TOXINS

Bacterial (diphtheria, tetanus) toxins, metallic (arsenic, lead) toxins, and toxins derived from other organic compounds (such as alcohol, barbiturates, bromides, hydantoins, carbon monoxide) cause this group. Psychological dysfunctioning is often prominent, with losses in mental ability (confusion, memory impairment), psychotic-appearing symptoms (stupor, lassitude, somnolence), exaggerations of affect, restlessness, inattention, distractibility, refusal to cooperate, or surface cooperation, motor and sensory difficulties.

DEMYELINATING DISEASES

Disorders involving myelinization include multiple sclerosis, diffuse sclerosis, acute encephalomyelitis, neuromyelitis optica, progressive subcortical encephalopathy, and the like. Progressive mental changes involving memory impairment, and perceptual and organizational difficulties often appear, as well as personality changes, hysterical tendencies, loss of insight, weakening of emotional control, and poor judgment.

DEGENERATIVE AND HEREDODEGENERATIVE DISEASES

Diseases producing irreversible changes include neuromuscular diseases (mongolism, dystonia, dystrophy); cerebrum and cranial nerve involvement; disorders of the basal ganglia, cerebellum, and spinal cord. Psychological components comprise many motor and sensory losses, progressive mental-ability changes, mood changes, and personality alterations. In terminal stages mental deterioration and noticeable weaknesses in emotional control are frequent.

DISEASES AND FUNCTIONAL DISTURBANCES OF UNKNOWN ETIOLOGY

Convulsive disorders, migraine, and other forms of headaches, Meniere's syndrome, myasthenia gravis, narcolepsy, and familial periodic paralysis constitute entities in this classification. Again, a variable influence is felt in ideation, affect, and behavior.

Neuropathology evidently produces a number of psychological abnormalities and deficiencies. Equally, alterations in cerebration will vary with the individual undergoing change, as well as with the pathology. Hence *success in the evaluation of central nervous system disorders by psychological techniques will be determined in the individual case by type, location, and extent of pathology, as well as by accurate assessment of abilities, and of defense mechanisms used in adapting to organic limitations.* Under these conditions the psychologist's contribution necessarily varies from one disease entity to another and from one individual to the next.

Many techniques available to the neurologist for diagnosis of neuropathology are of interest to the psychologist. Sometimes diagnosis rests upon technical evidence having little in common with psychological-test materials; sometimes a closer relationship exists. Routine neurological examination, for example, leans heavily upon evaluation of sensory and motor systems, including levels of function, symmetry of reflex action, muscle tone, strength, coordination, abnormal movements, station, and gait. Disturbances give clues to the nature and location of pathology in brain centers and controlling mechanisms. The electroencephalogram is a device for recording electrical activity of the brain, which possesses rhythmic properties disturbed by pathology. The lumbar puncture (spinal tap) provides information about the chemistry and pressure of the spinal fluid, and how they are affected by certain disease entities. X-ray of the skull is a visual means of detecting malformations, growths, or destructive changes in cerebral centers. Sometimes a pneumoenceph-alogram assists in diagnosis; air is pumped into the ventricles of the brain to obtain x-ray evidence of pathology which would be invisible other-wise. Since alterations of blood and urine often accompany neurological disorders, biochemical studies are also helpful.

Certain approaches used by the neurologist seem to supplement each other naturally. This is true of the electroencephalographic method as an adjunct to neurological examination. Even though the quality and quantity of electrical change is most individualized, high positive cor-relations have been obtained between clinical neurological abnormality and electroencephalographic irregularities.

Significantly, both the neurologist and electroencephalographer make use of the idea of symmetry of brain functioning in diagnosis; gross lateral differences in reflex action and electrical activity indicate abnor-mality. Only in rare instances, however, such as those involving motor coordination, hand dominance, visual handicap, speech impairment, or the like, is this concept used by the clinical psychologist. Further explora-tion by psychologists of psychophysiological concepts such as symmetry of functioning should prove profitable.

Neurology itself depends upon information from many sciences—anatomy, biochemistry, physiology, psychiatry, psychology, which con-cern various levels of awareness and complexity of neural action. These sciences together form an inseparable unit for understanding behavioral mechanisms, with unlimited possibilities for further research. Application of biochemical methods to the treatment of mental disorders is an illus-tration of this fact.

PSYCHOPHARMACOLOGY AND NEUROPSYCHOLOGY

Psychopharmacologic agents, widely used in the treatment of func-tional disorders, have also attracted the attention of the neurologist to their action in organic syndromes. Hoch[12] reports amelioration of con-fused states in organic psychoses such as alcoholism and arteriosclerosis. Until now symptomatology in advanced cases was considered irreversible. As Merritt[25] points out, the application of biochemical methods to the study of disease promises help in many disorders previously called degen-erative or heredodegenerative. Insight into neuropsychological relation-ships is also enhanced by current biochemical findings.

The ultimate concern of the neuropsychologist in experimental neuropsychiatric findings is, of course, their relation to problems of perception and emotion. Interest in the chemical aspect of mentation was particularly aroused in 1949, when Mayer-Gross and Walker[24] reported their results: patients in hypoglycemic coma responded well to intravenous injections of glutamic acid, which accelerated return to consciousness. In hepatic coma, a disorder indicating a disturbance in oxidative metabolism, clearing of consciousness has also been obtained by the use of sodium glutamate. Just how this is accomplished is highly speculative at present. The consensus is that ammonium blood levels are changed temporarily by sodium glutamate, and this in turn affects the degree of conscious awareness. The action of glutamic acid upon brain metabolism seems to be even more complex, so that theories remain controversial. Glutamic acid and its derivatives have been used extensively during the past decade in the treatment of mental retardation, behavior disorders, general medical and psychiatric problems, and more recently in the organic conditions of the aged.[11, 18, 31] Following these trends the so-called tranquilizers and cerebral stimulants evoked even greater interest. Currently psychoses-producing drugs are being investigated, along with psychoses-relieving compounds.

While the literature on behavioral changes produced by chemotherapy is beyond the scope of this book, a summary of pertinent findings seems appropriate because organic mental syndromes are often involved. Evidence indicates that glutamic acid and its derivatives exert some metabolic influence on cortical centers affecting consciousness and perceptual processes. Tranquilizing drugs and cerebral stimulants, on the other hand, appear to alter cerebral metabolism by implicating the midbrain and brain stem. Similarities in behavior produced in monkeys by reserpine, hypothalamic lesions, and stimulation indicate that the hypothalamus is a most important control center for affective response. Modes of action of these chemical agents are still unknown.

Research with tranquilizing drugs and cerebral stimulants permits some general conclusions:

Affective and behavioral components, rather than ideational elements, are subject to alteration. Behavioral improvement has been striking, for example, in many cases where negligible change in intelligence quotient occurred following treatment.[32, 33, 34] Delusional ideation usually remains, but with a change in affect regarding the delusion, so that it is less bothersome. Such findings are compatible with neurological speculations as to cerebral centers affected by drug action, i.e., hypothalamic mechanisms rather than cortical reactors.

When behavioral changes occur, behavior is not so much altered as modified; the changes are quantitative rather than qualitative. Kovitz, Carter, and Addison[17] report that chlorpromazine and reserpine produce "essentially symptomatic improvement through less intensive and impulsive expression of emotion." Zimmerman and Burgemeister[33] use the term "emotional governor" in describing the ability of tranquilizers and stimulants to "bring the extremes of affect and behavior into more normal focus." "Chemical lobotomy" is the designation given by Delay, Deniker, and Harl.[6] Hoch[12] makes an important distinction between "chemical lobotomy" and surgical lobotomy, however, by noting that after chemotherapy patients do not develop an attitude of carelessness such as is frequently observed after surgical intervention.

BRAIN AND MIND: CHALLENGE TO NEUROPSYCHOLOGY

Evidence from localization studies, neuropathological research, and psychopharmacologic experimentation all points to the extreme complexity of neural organization. Consolidation of findings from many branches of science is essential to better understanding of neuropsychological mechanisms. Lashley[20] comments upon cerebral organization and behavior in this way:

As long as mind is thought of as a special kind of being, obeying an all-or-none law in its presence or absence, or as some special type of energy, such as Sherrington sought and failed to find, so long will its relation to the brain be incapable of investigation. Mind is a complex organization, held together by interaction of processes and by the time scales of memory, centered about the body image. It has no distinguishing features other than its organization. The mental phenomena must be subjected to an analysis as complete and detailed as that which is being made of neural activities. Only as progress is made in such an analysis, and as the picture of the brain's activities is completed, will it be possible to make significant correlations between the two organized systems. Meanwhile, there is no logical or empirical reason for denying the possibility that the correlation may eventually show a complete identity of the two organizations.

The future role of neuropsychology seems well depicted by Bishop,[2] when he says:

To me the difficulty seems to be that we as neurophysiologists are not good enough. We have been able to find some of the units, you might say, of neural activity—the nerve impulse, graded tissue response, four or five kinds of synapses, such modes of action as recruiting waves or recruiting systems and so on, pathways and nervous connections. But to put those together into functional patterns, when we get beyond a certain complexity, the trees are lost in the forest. It is impossible, by present methods—and I cannot imagine any that will work—to take apart the more complicated patterns, such as might correspond to mental behavior, and analyse them into the elements of nervous activity.

The question then arises, can psychology meet us halfway? Is there any way by which any psychological data or information can be either restated or looked at from a different angle, or broken down into smaller detail, until the psychologist, coming down toward neurophysiology, meets the physiologist going up? Since the neurophysiologist and psychologist both deal with functions of the same brain, can they arrive at a common degree of complexity which they can both understand?

How can psychology meet this challenge? Clearly the problem is part of the larger problem of the many unanswered questions which command the attention and cooperative research activity of both the neurologist and psychologist.

The first of these is one of definition. Inexactness of meaning is particularly impressive in such classifications as epilepsy, mental retardation, cerebral palsy, and geriatrics. Research in epilepsy, for example, has been hindered by the quest for a so-called "epileptic personality." Now it is recognized that various neural mechanisms have been grouped under the heading of convulsive phenomena. Neurologists and psychologists accept the need for further study of these neurological components and their expressions.

More precise terminology is also essential in categorizing mental deficiency. Deficiency has been shown to include heterogeneous neurological conditions such as amentia, brain injury, mongolism, cretinism, and others. Further delineation of brain-injured from the non-injured patient is indicated, together with consideration of differences in maturational rate, intellectual and personality makeup, and recoverability potentials.

Developmental anomalies and destructive processes are similarly grouped under the present definition of cerebral palsy. Information is lacking as to whether symptomatology may be similar or different when malformations are present, or when destructive processes intervene. A need for further knowledge applies equally to the definition of old-age processes, in the presence and absence of neurological disease.

Problems of etiology constitute another area of research for neurology and psychology, notably in epilepsy, mental retardation, cerebral palsy, and multiple sclerosis. Classifications of epilepsy, for example, may include idiopathic (unknown origin), symptomatic (seizures related to some illness), or traumatic (seizures which are the result of known injury or trauma).

Inasmuch as brain-injured children tend to perform less successfully on psychological test than those without known damage, etiological factors of mental deficiency should be explored more fully. The same recommendation applies to the study of children with cerebral palsy.

Assessment of the role of emotions in the etiology of and reaction to various neurological disease processes is one of the most challenging areas. What, for example, is the role of emotion in the pattern of epileptic seizures, in reaction to the presence of seizures, and in actually produc-

ing seizures in some instances? The interplay of psychogenic and neurological components in head trauma and postconcussive states requires
further investigation to estimate the possible role of pre-accident personality. The study of multiple sclerosis provides a particularly stimulating
opportunity because evidence suggests that premorbid (psychoneurotic)
personality may be an important factor in etiology of the disease itself.
Interrelationships among factors such as emotional lability, onset of
mental symptoms, and life expectancy await clarification. Other areas of
research include problems of geriatrics involving neurological conditions,
and also emotional origins of old-age processes themselves. Present
knowledge of norms with and without neuropathology is inadequate.
We need to know whether emotional factors are integral components
or independent aspects of such geriatric conditions as arteriosclerosis and
Parkinson's disease, and to what degree they affect prognosis and
eventual outcome of central-nervous-system disorders.

Psychological techniques now in use for probing these problems need
extension and revision. At best, they succeed in detecting the presence
of organicity in a high percentage of cases. Progress has been less
impressive in localizing neuropathology to precise areas of the brain, and
in highlighting attributes of thinking and behavior pathognomonic of
specific neurological disease entities. Revision of concepts of neural
organization and function provided by current neurophysiological findings should prove of inestimable value, such as hierarchically organized
representations and graded responses, in which noncortical systems play
a more active part.

Research will benefit from improvement in testing instruments, insist-
ence upon more homogeneous groups of clinical cases for study, more
adequate controls ranging from pathological to normal, greater concern
for accuracy in pre-illness baselines, more diligent assessment of intellectual abilities and personality, and identification of the influence of
emotions in the etiology and prognosis of central-nervous-system disorders. Research will be needed also to obtain further clarification of
emotional components as defense mechanisms against inroads of neurological disease processes in contrast to emotional aberrations of neurological conditions themselves. Further, future investigations will benefit
from more intensive study of behavioral patterns through observation,
and from greater resourcefulness in handling factors of socio-economic
and environmental pressures.

BIBLIOGRAPHY

1. BARD, P., and MOUNTCASTLE, V. B. Some forebrain mechanisms involved
   in expression of rage with special reference to suppression of angry
   behavior. *Res. Pub. A. Res. Nerv. & Ment. Dis.*, 27: 362–404, 1948.

2. Bishop, H. G. Discussion of Lashley's paper. In *The brain and human behavior. Res. Pub. A. Res. Nerv. & Ment.. Dis.*, 36: 18, 1958.

3. Bostroem, A. *Allgemeine und psychische Symptome bei Erkrankungen des Gross-hirns. Handbuch der Neurologie (Bumke-Foerster)*. Berlin: Springer: 1936.

4. Brock, S. *The Basis of Clinical Neurology*. Baltimore: Williams & Wilkins: 1953.

5. Chapman, L. F., Thetford, W. N., Berlin, L., Guthrie, T. C., and Wolff, H. G. Highest integrative functions in man during stress. *Res. Pub. A. Res. Nerv. & Ment. Dis.*, 36: 491–534, 1958.

6. Delay, J., Deniker, P., and Harl, T. M. Use in psychiatric therapy of a phenothiazine with selective central action (R.P. 4560). *Am. Med. Psychol.*, 110: 112, 1952.

7. Fulton, J. F. *Textbook of Physiology*, Ch. 15. Philadelphia: W. B. Saunders: 1955.

8. Goldstein, K. H. *Neurological Psychopathology*. New York: Grune & Stratton: 1936.

9. Halstead, W. C. *Brain and Intelligence*. Chicago: Chicago Univer. Press: 1947.

10. Hebb, D. O. *The Organization of Behavior*. New York: Wiley: 1949.

11. Himwich, H. E., Wolff, K., Hunsicker, A. L., and Himwich, W. A. Some behavioral effects associated with feeding sodium glutamate to patients with psychiatric disorders. *J. Nerv. Ment. Dis.*, 121: 40–49, 1955.

12. Hoch, P. Psychoses-producing and psychoses-relieving drugs. *Res. Pub. A. Res. Nerv. & Ment. Dis.*, 36: 335–346, 1958.

13. Jackson, J. H. *Selected Writings of John Hughlings Jackson*. Taylor, J. (Ed.) London: Hodder & Stoughton: 1931.

14. Jasper, H. H. Recent advances in our understanding of ascending activities in the reticular system. Henry Ford Hospital Symposium, *Reticular formation of the brain*: 319–332. Boston: Little, Brown: 1958.

15. Kluver, H., and Bucy, P. C. "Psychic Blindness" and other symptoms following bilateral temporal lobectomy in rhesus monkeys. *Am. J. Psychol.*, 49: 352–353, 1937.

16. Kohler, W. *Dynamics in Psychology*. New York, Liveright, 1940.

17. Kovitz, B., Carter, J. T., and Addison, W. P. A comparison of chlorpromazine and reserpine in chronic psychosis. *Arch. Neurol. & Psychiat.*, 74: 467–471, 1955.

18. Lapinsohn, L. I. Ritalin and serpasil in the treatment of Parkinson's disease. *Dis. Nerv. Syst.*, 17: 363–364, 1956.

19. Lashley, K. S. *Brain Mechanisms and Intelligence*. Chicago: Chicago Univer. Press: 1929.

20. Lashley, K. S. Cerebral organization and behavior. In *The brain and human behavior. Res. Pub. A. Res. Nerv. & Ment. Dis.*, 36: 1–18, 1958.

21. Lashley, K. S., Chow, K. L., and Semmes, J. An examination of the electrical field of cerebral integration. *Psychol. Rev.*, 58: 123–136, 1951.

22. Leeper, F. Review in *J. Abnorm. & Social Psychol.*, 45: 768–775, 1950.

23. Magoun, H. W. Non-specific brain mechanisms. In *Biological and Chemi-*

cal Bases of Behavior: 25–36. H. F. Harlow and C. N. Woolsey (Eds.). Madison: Univer. Wisc. Press: 1958.

24. MAYER-GROSS, W., and WALKER, J. M. The effect of (1)-glutamic acid on hypoglycaemia. *Biochem. J.,* 44: 92, 1949.

25. MERRITT, H. H. *A textbook of neurology.* Philadelphia: Lea & Febiger: 1955.

26. MONAKOW, VON C. *Gehirnpathologie.* Wien: Holder: 1905.

27. NIELSON, J. M. Cerebral localization and the psychoses. In *The brain and human behavior. Res. Pub. A. Res. Nerv. & Ment. Dis.,* 36: 467–477, 1958.

28. PENFIELD, W. Functional localization in temporal and deep sylvan areas. In *The brain and human behavior. Res. Pub. A. Res. Nerv. & Ment. Dis.,* 36: 210–226, 1958.

29. PENFIELD, W. Epileptic automatism and the centrencephalic integration system. *Res. Pub. A. Res. Nerv. & Ment. Dis.,* 30: 513–528, 1952.

30. PRIBAM, K. A review of theory in physiological psychology. *Ann. Rev. Psychol.,* 11: 1–40, 1960.

31. TOURLENTES, T. T., HIMWICH, H. E., and HUCKINS, D. A clinical evaluation of L-Glutavite in the treatment of elderly chronic deteriorated mental patients. *Illinois M. J.,* 112: 121–124, 1957.

32. ZIMMERMAN, F. T., and BURGEMEISTER, B. B. Preliminary report upon the effect of reserpine on epilepsy and behavior problems in children. *Ann. New York Acad. Sc.,* 61: 215–221, 1955.

33. ZIMMERMAN, F. T., and BURGEMEISTER, B. B. The effect of reserpine on the behavior problems of children. *New York State J. Med.,* 57: 3132–3139, 1957.

34. ZIMMERMAN, F. T., and BURGEMEISTER, B. B. Action of methyl-phenidyl-acetate (ritalin) and reserpine in behavior disorders in children and adults. *Amer. J. Psychiat.,* 115: 323–328, 1958.

ADDITIONAL REFERENCES

1. BRODAL, A. *The reticular formation of the brain stem: Anatomical aspects and functional correlates.* Springfield, Ill.: Charles C Thomas: 1958.

2. The central nervous system and behavior. *Transactions of the first and second conference,* Feb. 22–25, 1958, 1959. New York: Josiah Macy, Jr. Foundation: 1959, 1960.

3. KOHLER, W. The present situation in brain physiology. *Amer. Psychologist,* 13: 150, 1958.

4. MacLEAN, P. D. Contrasting functions of limbic and neocortical systems of the brain and their relevance to psychophysiological aspects of medicine. *Amer. J. Med.,* 4: 611–626, 1958.

5. MATARAZZO, R. G., MATARAZZO, J. D., SASLOW, G., and PHILLIPS, J. Psychological test and organismic correlates of interview interaction patterns. *J. Abnorm. & Social Psychol.,* 56: 329–338, 1958.

6. MILLER, N. E. Liberalization of basic S-R concepts: Extensions to conflict behavior, motivation, and social learning. In *Psychology: A study of a Science.* New York: McGraw-Hill: 1959.

⮞⮞

II

Neuropsychological Behavior

Although neuropsychological behavior is the end product of complicated biochemical, neurophysiological, and psychological components, relationships among the factors are more than haphazard. Bonds formed show a substantial degree of patterning, insuring consistency and continuity of behavioral expression within the individual. Prediction of behavior is possible within limits because of the integrative capacity of the nervous system. *The task of neuropsychology is to detect disturbances in this integration.*

In addition to the neurologist's examination and laboratory tests, procedures for assessing disturbances in integration are: 1) clinical observations of behavior in speech, locomotion, and mentation and 2) application of psychological test batteries.

An awareness of psychoneurological integration is what makes so many neurologists specialize in psychiatry, practicing as neuropsychiatrists. They have become keenly alert to disguises which various neural mechanisms may assume, with organic diseases parading as neuroses or psychoses, and vice versa. Subterfuges are emphasized in a recent report of Prout and Epple,[13] who advocate early recognition of neurological conditions in a psychiatric hospital. According to their findings, about 5 per cent of 3,500 cases admitted to New York Hospital's Westchester Division over a ten-year period presented some existing basic or associated neurological condition. Neurological manifestations included a wide range of symptoms, without consistent correlation with the psychiatric picture. Ocko[12] has also called attention to diagnostic perplexities in three patients who presented unusual psychiatric manifestations of neurological disease.

CLINICAL OBSERVATION

Breadth of view greatly enhances diagnostic ability and treatment planning. A middle-aged patient referred to a neuropsychiatrist with a diagnosis of schizophrenia turned his head very slowly and arose as if dazed when approached in the waiting room. The neuropsychiatrist immediately thought of Parkinsonism, which examination and laboratory tests later confirmed. Such clinical acumen in observing facial expression and motor reaction should be developed more fully by clinical psychologists as a supplement to formal testing.

Expression of central-nervous-system disorders has many facets: 1) neurological manifestations may appear as behavioral deviations with little or no confirmation on formal test; 2) disturbances may be elicited by test materials in the absence of overt behavioral change; 3) pathology may be evident in test performance and behavior; or 4) symptoms may not be detectable either by psychological techniques or observation. Since the nature and degree of neuropsychological changes are varied and highly individualized, every bit of available information must be analyzed.

Except for pioneers like Goldstein[4, 5, 6] few investigators have stressed observation or paid sufficient attention to behavioral aspects of organic disorders. Quantitative rather than qualitative approaches have to date been emphasized among clinicians.

One factor preventing widespread use of empirical data by clinical psychologists appears to be a dread of being unscientific. This anxiety seems to originate in criticism from the medical profession of the psychologist's frequent inability to provide convincing rationale for interpretations made. "Subjective" and "intuitive" are terms reflecting this skepticism on the part of neuropsychiatrists.

Fortunately, it is now becoming clear that clinical intuition is not synonymous with mere "hunches" or with mysticism. It is attributable to a clinician who carefully discerns and accurately interprets details of behavior often overlooked by the less resourceful. In the writer's experience, psychologists have shown considerable zeal in their desire to make diagnoses consistent with neurological findings and pathognomonic of some special disease process. They seem hindered, however, by misconceptions about possibilities of observational material, i.e., what information in a psychological test report may be of help to the neurologist, neurosurgeon, or neuropsychiatrist.

For example, it is sometimes assumed that detecting organicity will be of great help to the physician. Often such a finding is of only academic interest as, for instance, where a pre-operative brain tumor has been well defined by the neurosurgeon. If, however, descriptions of behavior are included that suggest the types of functioning affected, these may help to confirm the tumor's location, or its possible infiltration into other brain areas.

Observations of behavior often add weight to psychological test findings themselves. For example, a Rorschach interpretation of hysteria is convincing if it includes the note that a patient used his "paralyzed" right hand unwittingly to check a sneeze. To bridge the gap between neurological function and expression of disorder, clinical data in support of test findings are of great importance.

Sometimes patients are uninterested and apathetic during formal testing, and complain of fatigue, memory loss, or inability to concentrate, and generally poor performance. As soon as questions concerning their illnesses are introduced, however, their facial expressions often brighten up, speech becomes more fluent, and interest more readily aroused. These reactions can supply additional clues to basic potentiality for response and variability of affective tone.

Behavioral manifestations as essential supplements to formal testing are revealed prominently in head-injury cases involving financial compensation, because here formal testing usually constitutes a genuine threat to financial security. Hence patients often exaggerate symptoms or invent them. Accurate test results may be impossible; at best, minimal ratings may magnify any actual disability.

An illustration of attempted evasion of formal psychological testing was the behavior of a foreign-born patient who insisted he could not understand English when verbal intelligence test material was presented. As soon as items were repeated in his native Spanish, he claimed he could not hear, although no hearing loss had been reported to the neuropsychiatrist. Then picture completion and picture arrangement from the Wechsler-Bellevue Scale were given, whereupon the patient remarked that he needed glasses and could not see the materials. Formal testing was terminated. The patient's wife was then asked for details of his accident. As she attempted to give them, the patient interrupted, speaking very good English, and complained she was not being accurate; he proceeded to describe the circumstances himself and answered questions in English without hesitation. Deliberate attempts to conceal information were evident in his observable behavior.

Occasionally so simple an act as putting on a coat may be significant clinically. A middle-aged woman complained of an arm injury preventing free use of "arm muscles," producing "headaches" and "stiffness and weakness from the neck down" on the right side. During the entire psychological test session, she leaned on the desk to "prevent fatigue," and manipulated objects with difficulty. Reaction time was consistently slow. As she was conversing before leaving, the patient lifted her coat from the hanger easily, quickly raised both arms well above her head, placed both hands on the collar, and flexed both elbows as she did so. Certainly her facility tended to negate the degree of disability simulated during testing procedures.

BEHAVIORAL "SIGNS" OF ORGANIC IMPAIRMENT

Because expressions of aberration are unpredictable in the individual case, some classification system for recording organic features is desirable. Efforts of neurologists to systematize behavioral observations are reflected in a publication of Thomas[18] on organic mental syndromes. Thomas "signs" are well formulated and comprehensive. The present writer has paraphrased them below and recommends them to psychologists as a guide to clinical observations.

Thomas classifies mental symptoms as "reductive and productive"— the minuses and pluses of the disorder, or what the patient does not do, and that of which he does too much. Broad aspects of behavior are considered; observations were based upon ward cases.

According to Thomas, important categories of organic mental syndromes include a wide variety of components, among them the following:

	Reductions	*Productions*
Perception	In reaction time, acuity, and range, e.g., figure-ground relationships, meaning of materials	Illusions, hallucinations, e.g., complaints about persistent dreamy feelings
Attention	In range and maintenance, e.g., cannot pay attention to two things at once, such as eating while someone is talking to him	Distractibilities, rambling conversation, discontinuity of thought
Consciousness and thought processes	Lethargy, coma, difficulty in shifting from one idea to another, motivation poor, e.g., complains of listlessness	Hyperactivity and agitated stupor, delusions, hypochondriacal tendencies
Orientation	In recognition of present and sequence of past events, e.g., patient becomes confused as to whereabouts and how he got where he is	Incorrect and shifting orientations, e.g., keeps changing inaccurate statements about his surroundings
Memory	Especially in immediate, or recent recall, e.g., doesn't remember his new address, or who the President of the United States is	Falsifications, retrospective distortions, e.g., boasting of accomplishments, how hard he worked, etc., contrary to facts
Judgment	Impairment of insight and foresight, e.g., may overestimate strength and endurance; may live beyond means	Impulsive and self-defeating behavior, e.g., may cross street against moving traffic; take unnecessary chances; become inconsiderate, or asocial, disregarding consequences[3]

	Reductions	*Productions*
Affect	Weakening in all aspects, e.g., less patience, less control	Increased irritability, explosiveness, e.g., insulting people, starting arguments
Behavior		
immediate	Range and dynamic quality impaired, e.g., may become repetitive and talk only about himself; may show no interest in materials	May become negativistic or apologetic in a stylized manner, depressed, or uncooperative
long-term	May give up former habit patterns of eating, dressing, etc., e.g., may become careless about grooming, bathing	May play with food, masturbate monotonously

In summarizing his remarks, Thomas calls attention to the irreversible nature of symptoms generally. The toxic-infectious-exhaustive psychoses are illustrative of slow changes which are characterized by disorders of perception, orientation, attention, and awareness. Intracranial tumors and presenile deteriorating processes often produce general loss of functioning ability, the latter also revealing considerable memory impairment. In contrast, senile behavioral patterns often reflect individuality and character maintenance, according to Thomas, even though memory and behavior show deterioration. Paresis, alcoholism, and drug psychoses reflect a wide variety of aberrations.

Because reductive symptoms are more specific than productive signs, Thomas advocates always looking for the reductions. He likewise emphasizes the fact that a multitude of psychoneurotic and psychotic manifestations "may be the precursors" of an organic mental syndrome, pointing out a need to consider underlying psychodynamics. Awareness of limitation may, for example, produce feelings of inferiority and worthlessness, while confusion and memory losses may ameliorate depressive tendencies. Productive symptoms, in turn, may alter the direction and intensity of reductions themselves, attesting to the complexity of observable phenomena.

TEST AND BEHAVIORAL CRITERIA OF ORGANICITY

Baker,[1] a clinical psychologist, has recently set up criteria for predicting what we may expect in the test material and behavior of a patient. Although Baker does not categorize aberrations as minuses and pluses of behavior, all of her predictions could be handled in this way, making the similarity to those of Thomas striking. Both Thomas's and Baker's results unequivocally favor the use of observation as an aid to diagnosis and interpretation.

Intensification of defenses, especially of ego function, is postulated by Baker—e.g., increased constriction and hypo-mania. Signs of anxiety, inadequacy, perplexity, impotence, repetition, perseveration, hostility, impulsiveness, projection, regression, hypochondriacal and neurasthenic symptoms are among those listed.[2, 7, 14, 15, 16, 17] Memory disturbances, "agreed on by everyone," sensory disturbances, faulty judgment, and difficulties in abstract thinking with a tendency toward concrete behavior, may also appear. If sensible concreteness[4] is combined with faulty judgment and crudeness, without evidence of more generalized disturbance, suspicion of frontal lobe involvement is aroused, according to Baker.

Disturbances in perception of Gestalten[8, 9] may occur. If signs of visual disturbance are present, unaccompanied by motor impairment or crudeness and poor judgment, the probability of a parieto-occipital lesion is believed to be strengthened.[8, 9, 11, 15] If both visual and motor difficulties exist, extensive cortical or subcortical damage may be indicated.

The presence of strong hysterical reaction is considered controversial, pointing to possible brain damage or to multiple sclerosis.[10, 16]

Heterogeneity of test signs in general and appearance of only a few signs in each patient is the rule.

Clearly, organic mental syndromes are broad and complex Gestalten. When they do appear, constriction or exaggeration of behavioral patterns may be anticipated, with large individual variation within any specific central-nervous-system disorder. Deviation from one disease process to the next is also characteristic. With a passage of time, further complexities may be added by defense mechanisms erected to combat the inroads of a limitation recognized by the patient.

BIBLIOGRAPHY

1. BAKER, G. Diagnosis of organic brain damage in the adult. In Klopfer, B., *Developments in the Rorschach Technique*, II: 318–428. Yonkers, N.Y.: World Book: 1956.
2. BYCHOWSKI, G. The ego of the brain wounded. *Psychoanalyt. Rev.*, 36: 333–343, 1949.
3. CLECKLEY, H. M. *The Mask of Sanity.* (3rd ed.) St. Louis: C. V. Mosby: 1955.
4. GOLDSTEIN, K. H. *After Effects of Brain Injuries in War.* (2nd ed.) New York: Grune & Stratton: 1948.
5. GOLDSTEIN, K. H. Mental changes due to frontal lobe damage. *J. Psychol.*, 17: 187–208, 1944.
6. GOLDSTEIN, K. H. *Language and Language Disturbances.* New York: Grune & Stratton: 1948.
7. GRINKER, R. R., and WEINBERG, J. Neuroses following head and brain injuries. In *Injuries of the Brain and Spinal Cord and Their Coverings:*

329–341. Brock, S. (Ed.). Baltimore: Williams & Wilkins: 1949.

8. HALSTEAD, W. C. *Brain and Intelligence*. Chicago: Univer. Chicago Press: 1947.

9. HARLOW, H. F. Functional organization of the brain in relation to mentation and behavior. In *The Biology of Mental Health and Disease:* 244–264. New York: Hoeber: 1952.

10. LANGWORTHY, O. R. Relation of personality problems to onset and progress of multiple sclerosis. *Arch. Neurol. & Psychiat.*, 59: 13–28, 1948.

11. NIELSEN, J. M. *Agnosia, apraxia, aphasia. Their Value in Cerebral Localization.* (2nd ed.) New York: Hoeber: 1946.

12. OCKO, F. H. Unusual psychiatric manifestations of neurological disease. *Bull. New York Acad. Med.*, 35: 4: 269–271, 1959.

13. PROUT, C. T., and EPPLE, K. H. Early recognition of neurological conditions in a psychiatric hospital. *Bull. New York Acad. Med.*, 35: 3: 162–166, 1959.

14. RUESCH, J., HARRIS, R. E., and BOWMAN, K. M. Pre- and post-traumatic personality in head injuries. In *Trauma of the central nervous system. Res. Pub. A. Res. Nerv. & Ment. Dis.*, 24: 507–544, 1945.

15. RYLANDER, G. Mental changes after excision of cerebral tissue. A clinical study of 16 cases of resections in the parietal, temporal and occipital lobes. *Acta psychiat. et neurol.*, Suppl. 25–27, 5–8, 1943.

16. SCHILDER, P. Neuroses following head and brain injuries. In *Injuries of the Brain and Spinal Cord and Their Coverings:* 298–328. Brock, S. (Ed.). Baltimore: Williams & Wilkins: 1949.

17. STRAUSS, I., and SAVITSKY, N. Head injuries. Neurologic and psychiatric aspects. *Arch. Neurol. & Psychiat.*, 31: 893–955, 1934.

18. THOMAS, S. G. The organic mental syndromes. Elementary considerations. *Bull. New York Acad. Med.*, 33: 7: 487–492, 1957.

>>>

III

Tools of the Psychologist

Detection of disturbances in higher neural integrative processes is the common denominator of all clinical techniques and psychological testing procedures. Evaluation of neuropsychological behavior by testing procedures is an attempt to measure disturbances in integration by methods more specific than observation.

THE RATIONALE OF PSYCHOLOGICAL TESTING

Tests rest upon a more highly structured foundation than observation, i.e., on the foundation of controlled stimuli. In a test situation an individual confronts a series of prearranged stimuli which limit his choice and range of response. Whether simple or complex, the problems put to him are definite, requiring certain types of reaction. Possibilities for appropriate response are curtailed in this way. Yet because measurement of perceptual and integrative aberrations involves complex neuropsychological processes, a given stimulus often fails to disclose dysfunction. Sometimes deviations can be elicited by changing the nature of response demanded. Or, given a specific type of response, dysfunction may be revealed at other times by altering the stimulus provoking the response. A battery of test items covering a wide range of receptive and reactive capacities is therefore essential. Since a linear relationship does not exist between neurological and psychological components, the presence of neuropathology cannot always be confirmed by existing psychological techniques.

Psychologists' instruments have the common feature of estimating discrepancies between optimal and functional levels, which approximate each other in the normal individual who is without organic impairment. Standards of comparison are the individual's previous performance and group norms. The degree of success of psychological devices in detecting failures and abnormalities of integration is best understood by consideration of individual techniques themselves, in this chapter and the next.

In the language of the psychologist, disturbances in integration are described as interferences with functioning, i.e., as deviations from optimal or expected performance. Yet because neurological involvement in thinking and behavior is not a single entity, expressions of disorder take many forms.

Immediate memory is particularly susceptible to the presence of central-nervous-system pathology. Perception, visual-motor organization, abstract thinking, and judgment are also prone to show alterations consistent with cerebral malfunction. Beyond these generalizations, expressive patterning becomes highly individual, and proper measurement requires a multidimensional approach.

Laboratory criteria of the twelve highest integrative functions recently suggested by Chapman, Thetford, Berlin, Guthrie, and Wolff[9] are typical of those in general use: 1) higher aspects of perception; 2) motor skill and speed; 3) learning, conditionability; 4) memory; 5) time sense; 6) categorization, generalization, analysis, and synthesis; 7) adaptability, flexibility, plasticity, ease of shift; 8) extrapolation and planning; 9) association and fantasy; 10) communicability; 11) affective expression; 12) resistance to disorganization.

Practical test batteries assessing neuropsychological behavior must cover this wide range.

Techniques which lend themselves to the task are of three kinds: 1) intelligence tests, 2) instruments measuring specific deficiencies, many of which involve visual-motor syndromes, and 3) projective techniques.

INTELLIGENCE TESTS

Interference with intellectual functioning is best elicited by instruments which accentuate discrepancies of response levels. Such techniques deliberately attempt to compare the mechanisms relatively resistant to change with those more readily affected by disease processes. We know that remote learning is less sensitive to the presence of organicity than new learning, a fact used in applying intelligence-test material to clinical problems.

Three widely used batteries are the *Wechsler-Bellevue Scale for Adolescents and Adults*,[40] the *Wechsler Intelligence Scale for Children* (WISC),[42] *and the Wechsler Adult Intelligence Scale* (WAIS),[41] consisting of a verbal and a performance section.

WECHSLER-BELLEVUE TEST BATTERY

Verbal Scale

INFORMATION. A series of 25 oral questions graded in difficulty, calling for "the sort of knowledge that an average individual with average opportunity may be able to acquire for himself" (Wechsler), e.g., the number of weeks in a year, geographical locations, author identification.

COMPREHENSION. Ten oral questions involving common-sense answers and an understanding of social situations, such as usefulness of materials, or reactions to emergencies.

DIGIT SPAN. Repetition of groups of digits presented orally (groups of from 3–9 in given order and 3–8 in reversed order). Two trials are allowed for each group using different digits.

ARITHMETIC. Simple oral arithmetic problems graded in difficulty, such as making change and handling fractions. (Timed test.)

SIMILARITIES. A series of twelve items requiring recognition of similarity between two concepts. Materials are familiar, being fruits, articles of clothing, objects of art, etc.

VOCABULARY. Not scored. Definitions of 42 words, ranging from commonplace to rare.

Performance Scale

PICTURE ARRANGEMENT. Six sets of unordered pictures ranging from three to six in a series to be rearranged into meaningful sequence. Subject matter is mundane: a holdup, a fishing trip, etc. (Timed test.)

PICTURE COMPLETION. Discernment of missing details required in a series of 15 pictures presented one at a time for 15 seconds. Items are commonplace: facial features, household objects. (Timed test.)

BLOCK DESIGN. Reproduction within time limits of seven small designs of graded difficulty, with Kohs blocks larger than the patterns. Blocks are one-inch colored cubes with one side blue, one side yellow, one white, and one with a combination of yellow and blue, or red and white. When two colors are combined on one side, they are divided diagonally across the surface of the block. Patterns to be constructed use only red, white, or red-white combination sides. Four patterns require the use of four blocks, two patterns nine blocks, and one pattern sixteen blocks. (Timed test.)

OBJECT ASSEMBLY. Construction with wooden pieces of manikin, profile and hand. (Timed test.)

DIGIT-SYMBOL. Nine geometric symbols to be associated with nine numbers from samples provided. Paper-and-pencil test with score total number of symbols copied correctly within 90 seconds. (Timed test.)

Raw scores for each subtest are converted into weighted, or standard scores. By means of this conversion procedure, it is possible to compare ratings among various subtests and to detect variations in performance, i.e., between different types of functioning, which may be of clinical value. By totaling weighted subtest ratings, separate intelligence quotients may be obtained for the Verbal and Performance Scale. A combined, or Full Scale Quotient measures general intelligence. Estimation of organicity is based upon the assumption that results of certain subtests —i.e., digit span, arithmetic, block design, digit symbol—are more adversely affected than results of others—i.e., information, vocabulary, picture completion, object assembly—by neurological impairment of thinking. Tests with results most affected are termed the "don't hold" group, the others the "hold" group. Analysis of requirements for the successful completion of these various subtests reveals interesting differences:

Test	Requirements for success
"Don't hold" group:	
Digit span	Immediate memory for numbers in order and reversed. New learning, attention, considerable flexibility of thought, particularly for reversed repetition.
Arithmetic	Immediate memory, association of thought, reaction time, new learning.
Block design	Highly abstract thinking, analysis and synthesis, concept formation, plus speed of reaction.
Digit symbol	New learning, facility in forming new associations, ready ability to shift, concept formation, abstract thinking.
"Hold" group:	
Information	Recall of information known many years, remote learning.
Vocabulary	Perception, remote recall.
Picture completion:	Discernment of missing details in familiar subject matter.
Object assembly:	Concept formation, essential. Familiar materials—a manikin, profile, and hand—are used. Task more concrete than others, requiring little abstract thinking.

The tests most indicative of neurological involvement are precisely the ones most seriously affected by the aging process. The age factor must be considered in estimating the degree of intellectual impairment.

Wechsler considered age in his "deterioration quotient," where a distinction is made between expected loss due to age and excessive loss due to pathology. The deterioration quotient is obtained by subtracting the sum of the "don't hold" test ratings from the sum of the "hold," dividing this figure by the sum of the "hold" tests, and subtracting a correction for age. Wechsler considers a loss greater than 10 per cent over that allowed for age a sign of possible deterioration. With a loss higher than 20 per cent, the chances that true deterioration is present are greatly increased.

Materials on the Wechsler Adult Intelligence Scale and on the Wechsler Intelligence Scale for Children have similarly been adapted for clinical purposes, with subtest patterns available. Interpretation of results always rests upon comparison with group norms as well with the individual intertest variation.

SPECIAL TESTS

Some tests for the detection of neuropsychological disorder rely on qualities more specific than general intelligence. Items have been extracted from intelligence scales and used to determine loss of functioning ability. Vocabulary, one of the most reliable indices of optimal functioning ability, is a criterion accepted as a baseline from which to establish degree of interference with thinking.

One of the earliest in this "special" category was the Babcock test,[2, 3, 4] designed to measure intellectual impairment in individuals suffering from mental and organic disorders. Here vocabulary score was compared with results on other functions, such as immediate memory, new learning, motor skills, and information questions. Estimation of degree of impairment is expressed by Babcock and Levy in the "efficiency index," by converting the score on the Terman Vocabulary Test[37] into a vocabulary age. Expected average level of performance in the subtests is calculated from data on a normal population, and the obtained group scores averaged as an efficiency score. Subtracting the expected average from the obtained efficiency score gives the efficiency index. Degree of intellectual impairment is indicated by a negative efficiency index.

The Shipley-Hartford Scale[36] is likewise based upon the Babcock principle. It consists of forty multiple-choice vocabulary items and twenty problems that require abstract thinking and concept formation, graded in difficulty and timed. A conceptual quotient is derived by multiplying the abstract score by two and dividing the result by the vocabulary score. Conceptual quotients are expected to approximate 100 if no interference is present, and may be higher. Those below 70 are interpreted as revealing loss of functioning ability in a pathological degree. Age however, is not considered, and whether a loss has a neurological or purely functional origin cannot be determined.

The Hunt Minnesota Test for measuring deterioration of an irreversible nature[26] relies upon vocabulary as an indicator of remote learning capacity. Here age is considered, and the well-standardized Stanford-Binet vocabulary list is used.[37] The scale consists of three groups of tests: 1) those resistant to loss; 2) items sensitive to impairment; and 3) a series of interpolated tests of concentration and attention used for validation purposes.

The Hunt Minnesota Test is given in the sequence shown below (tests marked with * show deterioration; all others except Item 5 are interpolated):

*1. Exposure and first recall of ten pairs of designs.
*2. Second recall of design pairs.
*3. Presentation and first recall of ten pairs of words.
*4. Second recall of word pairs.
 5. 1937 Stanford-Binet Vocabulary Test.
 6. Information.
 7. Saying months of the year.
 8. Counting 1 to 20.
 9. Counting from 3 to 30 by 3's.
10. Attention test.
11. Counting backward from 25 to 1.
12. Reversed digits.
13. Saying months backward.
14. Serial subtraction of 3's from 79.
*15. Third recall of word pairs.
*16. Third recall of design pairs.

Comparison of vocabulary test score with those of the deterioration tests forms the basis for determining impairment in functioning.

Halstead[19] has developed one of the most elaborate batteries yielding an impairment score. It consists of ten subtests:

1. Categories. Abstraction is called for, as well as a variety of organizing principles, such as color, size, shape. Pictures are presented on a screen.

2. Flicker rate. A 631-B type General Radio Strobotac is used to measure low-level illumination critical flicker frequency (CFF) of a subject. Ten trials are given, with the subject making his own settings.

3. Flicker deviation. The average deviation of the last five settings made by the subject is recorded.

4. Formboard time. A modification of the Seguin-Goddard formboard test is employed, requiring geometric shapes to be fitted into grooves in a board while subject is blindfolded. Three timed trials are given, with the dominant hand, with the non-dominant hand, and with both hands. Score is the total time needed.

5. Formboard memory. After Test 4 the subject draws an outline of the board from memory, i.e., the shapes of blocks and their positions. Score is the number of shapes accurately drawn.

6. Formboard location. The number of figures out of ten accurately drawn in location is scored.

7. Rhythm. The Rhythm Test is from the Seashore Tests of Musical Ability. The subject decides whether two rhythms played on a tape recorder are the same or different.

8. Speech discrimination. Nonsense-syllable variants of the "EE" digraph are played back from a tape recording. Subject selects the spoken word from among several printed on an answer sheet.

9. Tapping rate. Finger oscillation rate is determined. Score is an average of five 10-second trials in which a mechanical counter is tapped as rapidly as possible with the extended finger of the dominant hand.

10. Time sense. Subject starts an electric clock with a sweep second hand by depressing a lever, watches the hand indicate 10 seconds and releases the lever, stopping the clock. After ten trials the face of the clock is turned away and the subject depresses the lever for the same period without watching the clock. The score is based on deviations of the subject's setting from 10 seconds.

A raw impairment score for the battery of Halstead's tests may be obtained by adding percentile scores for each of the ten components. The Halstead approach is interesting because of inherent psychophysiological aspects of functioning.

One of the best-known tests for eliciting distortions in the perception of spatial relationships is the Bender Visual-Motor Gestalt Test.[5] Here a subject copies figures presented on a card, taken from Wertheimer's series. Interpretation depends upon movement, characteristics such as degree of accuracy, integration of parts of Gestalten, and type of line used, all of which Bender claims have differential value for different clinical groups. Norms are not available.

Other tests of visual organization in which organic interference may be revealed are Benton's Multiple-Choice Retention Test[6] the Memory-for-Designs test of Graham and Kendall,[15] and Hooper's Visual Organization Test.[24]

In the Benton procedure, a test card bearing a design is shown to the subject for ten seconds. The card is removed and the subject shown another card with four more or less similar designs, one of them being the first design shown. He must then point out, or name, which of the four patterns is the original design. A series of such multiple choices is presented. In the Memory-for-Designs Test simple geometric designs are exposed for five seconds each. Reproduction follows each exposure with ratings on a four point scale.

In Hooper's Test the patient is confronted with a picture of a familiar object cut into several parts. This must be identified by constructing it on paper. According to Hooper, in detecting the presence of impairment by this technique, neither motor skill nor verbalization is decisive. Norms are not available for patients with neurological disorders.

Block-design material such as is incorporated on the Wechsler Scales has been used extensively for the detection of neuropsychological disorders. (Armitage,[1] Boyd,[7] Goldstein and Scheerer,[12] Grassi,[16] Lidz, Gay and Tietze,[27] Tooth[38]). Ability to form concepts, shift readily, think abstractly, analyze, synthesize, and react quickly are integral parts of response to block designs. Although most investigators have emphasized quantitative performances in these visual-motor Gestalten, Goldstein and Scheerer have called attention to qualitative features, including difficulty in organizing ability, impotence, and perplexity, which may be discerned by careful observation. Goldstein and Scheerer have avoided norms, insisting that there is a greater differential between qualitative indicators of difficulty than between quantitative estimations of interference. Goldstein's contention has also been that loss in ability to think abstractly is the outstanding characteristic of patients with brain damage. Upon this hypothesis, Goldstein and Scheerer developed their tests of concrete and abstract behavior:[12]

Cube Test. All except one of twelve block designs to be reproduced is taken from the original Kohs block series. The same cubes are presented as on the Wechsler Scales but designs use blue, yellow, and blue-yellow combinations as well as red, white, and red-white patterns. Designs require only four blocks.

Emphasis is placed upon observation of behavior, i.e., whether a patient uses a concrete approach or thinks abstractly is determined by degree of perplexity displayed, impotence, anxiety, and frustration, and by degrees of assistance rendered by the examiner. Success at the abstract level is credited if the patient makes patterns correctly without the assistance of certain modified designs which the examiner is permitted to introduce. Modification of designs is allowed only when failure is encountered. Three levels of abstraction and concreteness are established in this way:

1. Enlargement of the model to actual block size pattern.
2. Inclusion of lines dividing pattern areas of blocks.
3. Use of an actual block model.

No quantitative scoring criteria are provided, degrees of impairment being determined according to amounts of assistance needed, or complete failure to reproduce designs, along with general behavior.

Color Sorting Test. The object is to determine whether an individual can form an abstract color concept. The four parts comprising the test are:

1. Skeins of wool different in color and brightness are presented at random. The subject selects one and is requested to pick out all other skeins which belong with the first one.

2. Three skeins are presented, two of which are of the same hue but different in saturation and brightness. The third skein is of a different hue from the first two, but has the same brightness as one of them. The subject must abstract "belong together" on a basis of color or brightness.

3. Six samples of the same color are presented, varying from light to dark. A second series of six is given, having different hues but equal brightness values. A common quality in each series must be ascertained.

4. Skeins all of one color, such as all reds or all greens, must be selected, with reasons given for particular choices. Abstractness or concreteness is determined according to ease in selecting skeins on a concept basis, i.e., whether a subject picks them at random, suggesting some principle such as redness or greenness (abstract), or whether he uses a "matching" technique (concrete), which reflects weakness of concept formation.

Scoring is not provided; performance is judged qualitatively.

Object Sorting Test. After the subject selects any ordinary object from 30 on a table, he is asked to pick out all other objects which he thinks could be grouped with it. From this grouping the examiner selects some objects one at a time to which the subject must add others of his own choosing. He must then group all 30 objects into categories and name the categories.

Reasons for selection and adequacy of the selection itself constitute degree of abstraction or concreteness present.

Color Form Sorting Test. Twelve geometric blocks are used (triangle, square, circle), in four colors (red, blue, yellow, green), with reverse side of each block white. Subject is asked to make groupings, which may be done according to color or shape. Failure to shift to a different grouping as suggested by the examiner is used as basis for an estimation of impairment in concept formation.

Stick Test. Thirty-four printed figures are to be copied with sticks. Patterns are graded in difficulty. Qualitative analysis of behavior is made and degree of abstract thinking evaluated by noting distortions of figures reproduced.

Recognizing the value of the Goldstein-Scheerer criteria for abstract and concrete thinking, Rapaport, Gill, and Schafer[33] attempted to quantify scoring for the Object Sorting Test in terms of looseness or narrowness of concept formation. Ratings were awarded on a basis of conceptual level of verbalizations and of the comprehensiveness of groupings. Zaslow[43] also used the loose or rigid type of solution in a similar test. Zaslow's test consists of an ordered series of geometric figures ranging in contour from triangle to circle. These figures are placed in one row before the subject and he is required to state where the triangle ends and the circle begins. An attempt at quantification consists of counting the number of figures left in the middle grouping between triangle and circle.

The Hanfmann-Kasanin Test[20] had its roots in the work of Vigotsky,[39] who observed schizophrenic patients. It is similar to the Goldstein-Scheerer Color Form Sorting Test.

In the Hanfmann-Kasanin Test twenty-two forms of five different colors, six shapes, two heights, and two widths, are employed. These must be sorted into four categories according to the volume principle. Each of the four categories is labelled with a nonsense syllable hidden on one side of every block: tall-wide, flat-wide, tall-narrow, and flat-narrow. The examiner selects one block and asks the subject to add all similar blocks to it. It is expected that blocks will be sorted according to color, shape, height, or width. When this is done, blocks tend to fall into four categories. If errors occur, the subject is shown the hidden nonsense-syllable side of each block one at a time, until he can classify all blocks correctly. The principle used in sorting must also be stated.

Performance is evaluated according to approach, amount of help necessary, success in sorting, and adequacy of verbalization. Accent is upon qualitative factors underlying abstraction, although some basis for quantitative scoring exists in the construction of the test itself.

PROJECTIVE TECHNIQUES

The term projective is limited here to its narrowest connotation; the more creative aspects of response are elicited in projective techniques, and material is less stimulus-bound than in other tests. Of necessity, this is an arbitrary classification. Tests such as the Bender Visual-Motor Gestalt Test, and concept-formation techniques involving expressive reaction, might equally well be placed under the projective classification. Yet in all of these instruments, instructions or models limit the range of appropriate response for successful solution and emphasize the perceptual aspects of reaction. Techniques called projective under the present classification, on the other hand, allow maximum latitude for interpretation, and also consider personality structure to a greater extent. Hence interpretations embrace more comprehensive and complex Gestalten for discerning interference.

The Goodenough Draw-A-Man Test[13, 14] and its modifications such as the House-Tree-Person Test of Buck,[8] require a subject to draw without models, and to answer questions concerning his productions. Machover[29] developed a complete system of scoring and interpretation for the human-figure technique, based upon type of line used, organization, and verbalizations of the subject. Disturbances in perception and disorders of affect, as well as distortions related to body image, are particularly discriminating of neuropsychological difficulty.

Although the Lowenfeld Mosaic Test[28] has materials analogous to those in other tests measuring abstract and concrete behavior, a subject is not asked to construct patterns or form groups according to any designated rules. Instructions on the contrary allow him to construct anything he cares to make. Materials for the test consist of 465 small wooden forms of six colors: black, white, red, blue, green, and yellow. Five different shapes are utilized: squares, diamonds, and triangles (right, isosceles, and scalene). As he works, a subject may be questioned about his constructions, and a record is kept of each design produced.

Using this material, Diamond and Schmale[10] and Himmelweit and Eysenck[23] have noted even broader behavioral aspects of patients.

Most work with projective techniques has been done using the Rorschach Test.[34] The Rorschach Test consists of a series of ten inkblots presented one at a time to a subject, who is to tell what they look like, or might be. He may turn the card in any direction he wishes, and no time limit is set. Time of initial response to each card is recorded, however, as well as total response time for every card in the series, and position of the card for each response.

After the subject has responded to all ten cards, each one is presented again. He is questioned about the nature and location of response, and characteristics of the blot that suggested responses, a procedure known as the *Inquiry*. Sometimes it is necessary to test the limits following this, if the subject has not used determinants usually reported by others. Reluctance or inability to see concepts after they have been suggested, or to find similar ones, may thus be determined. Location, determinants, content, and popularity vs. originality of content are factors in scoring. Qualitative aspects of behavior are also weighed as parts of intricate Gestalten conforming to, or differing from, known personality and clinical syndromes.

In clinical use of the Rorschach, the "sign" approach has characterized attempts to discover psychoneurological disturbances. Piotrowski's signs[31] of organicity are typical of early efforts:

1. Total number of responses less than fifteen.
2. Response time more than one minute.
3. Only one human movement response.
4. At least one color naming response.
5. Percentage of good form less than 75 per cent.
6. Number of popular responses less than 25 per cent.
7. Repetition of responses
8. Impotence
9. Perplexity   all go together.
10. Automatic phrases

At first Piotrowski relied upon quantitative interpretation, and believed that at least five signs must be present to warrant a diagnosis of brain damage. Later he modified his view so as to include qualitative interpretation rather than any specific number of deviations.[32]

After examining pre- and postoperative brain-tumor cases, Harrower-Erickson[21] reported a constricted personality structure exhibiting poorer range of psychic reaction and greater uniformity than are found among normal individuals. These were expressed in Rorschach terms as vague whole responses, poor output, low number of human-movement responses (M) and color responses (FC, CF, C), and absence of shading responses in the forms of diffusion or vista (K and FK).

Following Piotrowski's lead, Hughes[25] developed signs which differentiate between organic, psychoneurotic, and psychotic patients. According to results of his study, Hughes' list is as follows:

1. Total number of main responses less than fifteen (organic).
2. Total number of main responses less than twenty-five (psychoneurotic).
3. Average time per response greater than one minute (organic).
4. Not more than one human-movement response (organic, psychoneurotic, and schizophrenic).
5. Less than 25 per cent popular response (organic and schizophrenic).
6. One or more color naming responses (organic and schizophrenic).
7. Animal movement (FM) greater than human movement (M) (psychoneurotic).
8. Rejection or refusal of a card (psychoneurotic and schizophrenic).
9. More than 50 per cent of responses determined by form only (psychoneurotic).
10. More than 50 per cent of responses animal movement (FM) (psychoneurotic).
11. Not more than one main form-color response (psychoneurotic).
12. Good form less than 70 per cent (organic and schizophrenic).
13. Perseveration (organic and schizophrenic).

14. Impotence (giving response despite recognition of inadequacy) (organic).

15. Perplexity (organic).

16. Automatic phrases (organic).

17. Color shock (psychoneurotic).

18. Shading shock (psychoneurotic).

19. Confused succession (schizophrenic).

20. Contamination (schizophrenic).

21. Position responses (schizophrenic).

22. Weighted sum of color response greater than number of human movement (M) (schizophrenic).

Still later, Ross and Ross[35] calculated a disability ratio in which a patient could be given a rating on both neurotic and organic features. Sign categories included:

1. Those signs common to neurotic and organic patients.

2. Neurotic differential signs.

3. Organic differential signs.

4. Organic excluding signs.

The procedure for obtaining a disability ratio is to add common scores and organic differential scores and then to subtract neurotic differential and organic excluding scores.

Common Signs	Score	Neurotic Signs	Score
Total number of responses less than 12	3	Failure on Card VI or IX (each)	6
Between 12 and 25	2	Failure on Card VII or X (each)	4
No human movement (M)	2	Delay or deviation on Card VI or IX (each)	3
No animal movement (FM)	2	Delay on Card II	2
No texture (Fc)	2	Deviation on Card X	2
No depth shading (K, k, or FK)	2	Anatomical responses greater than 30 per cent	3
No form-color (FC)	2	Anatomical responses between 20–30 per cent	2
No color (C, CF or FC)	2	Animal plus anatomical responses greater than 60 per cent	2
Form per cent greater than 60 per cent	2		
Form and animal movement greater than 70 per cent (F + FM)	2	Organic Signs	
Animal per cent greater than 60 per cent (FM)	2	Poor form (F −) greater than 30 per cent	3
Failure on cards other than VI, VII, IX or X (each)	2	Poor form (F −) between 20 and 30 per cent	2
Absence of popular response on both Cards IV and VI	2	Abstraction	3
Absence of popular response on Card III	1	Perseveration	3
or on Card X	1	Popular percentage (Piotrowski)	2
Delay on Card VII	1	Impotence	2
Deviation on Card VII	1	Perplexity	2
		Holding cards one way up	1

Organic Signs	*Score*	*Organic Signs*	*Score*
Absence of popular response on		Greater than 75 per cent whole	
Card II	2	(W) responses	1
or on Card VIII	2		
on Card I	1		
Color naming	1	*Organic Excluding Signs*	
Automatic phrasing	1	Animal movement greater than	
No movement (M + FM)	2	human movement (FM > M)	3
No more than 1 response on any		Color-form greater than form-	
card	2	color (CF > FC)	3

A list of signs which are not likely to appear on tests of persons with organic involvement was contributed by Dorken and Kral.[11] According to their studies of patients with organic brain lesions, the absence of seven signs increases accuracy of negative diagnosis by the Rorschach technique. These deficits are in the following:

1. number of human-movement responses plus the number of inanimate responses greater than two (M + m > 2).

2. presence of any diffuse shading responses (k + K + FK > 0).

3. number of texture-shading responses plus number of form-color responses greater than two (Fc + FC > 2).

4. total number of responses greater than twenty.

5. presence of space responses (S) greater than 0, with the exception of the inside S as anatomy in Card VIII, central position, top one-third.

6. total form level of all responses given greater than plus twenty.

7. proportion of good original responses greater than 15 per cent of total responses.

All such lists of signs have much in common and show considerable overlapping between the neurotic and organic categories. The neurotic signs formulated by Miale and Harrower-Erickson[30] illustrate this point:

1. total number of responses not greater than twenty-five.

2. number of human-movement responses (M) not greater than 1.

3. number of animal-movement responses (FM) greater than number of human-movement responses (M).

4. presence of color shock.

5. presence of shading shock.

6. complete refusal to respond.

7. pure form content greater than 50 per cent.

8. animal figures greater than 50 per cent.

9. form-color responses (FC) not > 1.

Where speech difficulties interfere, the graphic Rorschach developed by Grassi and Levine[18] is sometimes helpful. Here the subject is required to draw, not to name what he sees. Intellectual rather than emotional evaluation is favored in interpretation by this method.

Other personality tests have not been validated as instruments for the detection of organicity in studies to date. The Minnesota Multiphasic Personality Inventory[22] is in the experimental stage as a direct measure of organic disturbance, but conclusive results have not yet been published.

Present studies tend to combine quantitative and qualitative approaches more than earlier work did, and to show greater insight into the part emotional factors may play. Pre-morbid personality is now recognized as an essential baseline in determining degree and nature of loss. Assets and limitations of psychological techniques in assessing organicity are discussed in Chapter IV.

BIBLIOGRAPHY

1. ARMITAGE, S. G. An analysis of certain psychological tests used for the evaluation of brain injury. *Psychol. Monogr.*, 60: 1, 1946.
2. BABCOCK, H. An experiment in the measurement of mental deterioration. *Arch. Psychol.*, 117, 1930.
3. BABCOCK, H. The level-efficiency theory of intelligence. *J. Psychol.*, 11: 261–270, 1941.
4. BABCOCK, H., and LEVY, L. *The Revised Examination For The Measurement Of Mental Functioning.* Chicago: Stoelting: 1942.
5. BENDER, L. A visual motor Gestalt test and its clinical use. *Amer. Orthopsychiat. Ass. Monogr.*, 3, 1938.
6. BENTON, A. L. A multiple choice type of the visual retention test. *Arch. Neurol. & Psychiat.*, 64: 699–707, 1950.
7. BOYD, F. A provisional quantitative scoring with preliminary norms for the Goldstein-Scheerer cube test. *J. Clin. Psychol.*, 5: 148–153, 1949.
8. BUCK, J. N. The H-T-P technique; a qualitative and quantitative scoring manual. *J. Clin. Psychol. Monogr.*, Suppl. 4, 317–396, 1948.
9. CHAPMAN, L. F., THETFORD, W. N., BERLIN, L., GUTHRIE, T. C., and WOLFF, H. G. Highest integrative functions in man during stress. *Res. Pub. A. Res. Nerv. & Ment. Dis.*, 36: 491–534, 1958.
10. DIAMOND, B. L., and SCHMALE, H. T. The Mosaic test; I. An evaluation of its clinical application. *Amer. J. Orthopsychiat.*, 14: 237–250, 1944.
11. DORKEN, H., and KRAL, V. A. The psychological differentiation of organic brain lesions and their localization by means of the Rorschach test. *Amer. J. Psychiat.*, 108: 764–770, 1952.
12. GOLDSTEIN, K. H., and SCHEERER, M. Abstract and concrete behavior. An experimental study with special tests. *Psychol. Monogr.*, 53: 2, 1941.
13. GOODENOUGH, F. L. *Measurement Of Intelligence By Drawings.* Yonkers N.Y.: World Book: 1926.
14. GOODENOUGH, F. L. *Mental Testing*, New York: Rinehart: 1949.
15. GRAHAM, F. K., and KENDALL, B. S. Memory-for-designs test; revised general manual. *Percept. Mot. Skills*, 11: 147–190, 1960.

16. GRASSI, J. R. The Fairfield Block Substitution Test for measuring intellectual impairment. *Psychiatric Quart.*, 21: 474–489, 1947.

17. GRASSI, J. R. Contrasting schizophrenic patterns in the Graphic Rorschach. *Psychiatric Quart.*, 16: 646–659, 1942.

18. GRASSI, J. R., and LEVINE, K. N. The Graphic Rorschach manual. *Psychiatric Quart.*, 17: 258–281, 1943.

19. HALSTEAD, W. D. *Brain and Intelligence.* Chicago: Univer. Chicago Press: 1947.

20. HANFMANN, E., and KASANIN, J. Conceptual thinking in schizophrenia. *Nerv. & Ment. Dis. Monogr.*, Ser. No. 67, 1942.

21. HARROWER-ERICKSON, M. R. I. Rorschach studies of patients with cerebral tumors. *Arch. Neurol. & Psychiat.*, 43: 859–890, 1940.

22. HATHAWAY, S. R., and McKINLEY, J. C. A Multiphasic Personality schedule (Minnesota). *J. Psychol.*, 10: 249–254, 1940.

23. HIMMELWEIT, H. T., and EYSENCK, H. J. An experimental analysis of the Mosaic Projection Test. *Brit. J. M. Psychol.*, 20: 283–294, 1945.

24. HOOPER, H. E. Use of the Hooper Visual Organization Test in the differentiation of organic brain pathology from normal, psychoneurotic, and schizophrenic reactions. *Amer. Psychologist*, 7: 350, 1952.

25. HUGHES, R. M. A factor analysis of Rorschach diagnostic signs. *J. Gen. Psychol.*, 43: 85–103, 1950.

26. HUNT, H. F. A practical clinical test for organic brain damage. *J. Appl. Psychol.*, 27: 375–386, 1943.

27. LIDZ, T., GAY, J. R., and TIETZE, C. Intelligence in cerebral deficit states and schizophrenia measured by Kohs Block Test. *Arch. Neurol. & Psychiat.*, 48: 568–582, 1942.

28. LOWENFELD, M. A new approach to the problem of psychoneurosis in childhood. *Brit. J. M. Psychol.*, 11: 194–227, 1931.

29. MACHOVER, K. *Personality Projection in the Drawing of the Human Figure.* Springfield, Ill.: Charles C Thomas: 1948.

30. MIALE, F. R., and HARROWER-ERICKSON, M. R. Personality structure in the psychoneuroses. *Ror. Res. Exch.* 4: 71–74, 1940.

31. PIOTROWSKI, Z. The Rorschach inkblot method in organic disturbances of the central nervous system. *J. Nerv. & Ment. Dis.*, 86: 525–537, 1937.

32. PIOTROWSKI, Z. Positive and negative Rorschach organic reactions. *Ror. Res. Exch.*, 4: 147–151, 1940.

33. RAPAPORT, D., GILL, M., and SCHAFER, R. *Diagnostic psychological testing.* Chicago: Year Book Publishers: I, 1945; II, 1946.

34. RORSCHACH, H. *Psychodiagnostik.* Berne: Hans Huber Verlag: 1932.

35. ROSS, W. D., and ROSS, S. Some Rorschach ratings of clinical value. *Ror. Res. Exch.*, 8: 1–9, 1944.

36. SHIPLEY, W. C. A self-administering scale for measuring intellectual impairment and deterioration. *J. Psychol.*, 9: 371–377, 1940.

37. TERMAN, L. M., and MERRILL, M. A. *Measuring Intelligence.* Boston: Houghton Mifflin: 1937.

38. TOOTH, G. On the use of mental tests for the measurement of disability after head injury. With a comparison between the results of these tests in

patients with head injury and psychoses. *J. Neurol., Neurosurg. &
Psychiat.*, 10: 1–11, 1947.

39. VIGOTSKY, I. S. Thought in schizophrenia. *Arch. Neurol. & Psychiat.*, 31:
    1063–1077, 1934.

40. WECHSLER, D. *The Measurement of Adult Intelligence.* Baltimore: Williams & Wilkins: 1956.

41. WECHSLER, D. *Adult Intelligence Scale.* New York: Psychol. Corp. (Rev.
    Ed. 1955).

42. WECHSLER, D. *Wechsler Intelligence Scale for Children.* New York:
    Psychol. Corp. (Rev. Ed. 1949).

43. ZASLOW, R. W. A new approach to the problem of conceptual thinking in
    schizophrenia. *J. Consult. Psychol.*, 14: 335–339, 1950.

IV

>>>

Assets and Limitations of
Psychological Techniques

Batteries have proved preferable to any single test instrument for detection of disturbances in neuropsychological integration. Because in most cases the use of only three or four formal testing instruments is practicable, those chosen should be as comprehensive as possible.

CLINICAL TECHNIQUES

Clinicians use combinations of techniques which will enable them to arrive at some estimate of intellectual capacity, special skills, and affective response. These have been found to provide the broadest and hence best frameworks for differentiating highly individual and unpredictable organic syndromes.

Techniques may be classified according to the specific functions they test:

Intellectual Impairment

Babcock-Levy Mental Efficiency Test
Halstead's Test Battery
Hunt-Minnesota Test
Shipley-Hartford Scale
Wechsler-Bellevue Scale
Wechsler Adult Intelligence Scale (WAIS)
Wechsler Intelligence Scale for Children (WISC)

Personality

Rorschach "signs"
  Baker-Klopfer
  Dorken and Kral
  Harrower-Erickson
  Hughes
  Piotrowski
  Ross and Ross

Conceptual Thinking

Goldstein-Scheerer Tests of Abstract and Concrete Behavior
Hanfmann-Kasanin Test
Kohs Block Designs and Modifications
Lowenfeld Mosaic Test
Zaslow Test

Visual-Motor Perception

Bender Visual-Motor Gestalt Test
Benton Multiple Choice Retention Test
Goodenough Draw-A-Man Test
Graham-Kendall Memory-for-Designs Test
House-Tree-Person Test (H-T-P)
Hooper Visual Organization Test

INTELLIGENCE TESTS

Intelligence test scales, notably the Wechsler-Bellevue Scale for Adolescents and Adults,[50] basis of the Wechsler Intelligence Scale for Children (WISC),[52] and the Wechsler Adult Intelligence Scale (WAIS),[51] are established techniques of genuine assistance to the neuropsychologist because they activate thought processes differing in degree of susceptibility to alteration. Considerable information on the relationships of optimal and functional intellectual levels is obtained in this way by quantitative comparison of psychological variables.

Wechsler's basic logic for clinical adaptation of these batteries is universally accepted as correct. His "hold" and "don't hold" test dichotomy is considered sound for estimating interference with intellectual functioning by analysis of subtest patterning. Subtest scores such as the following illustrate this point.

"Hold" Test Weighted Scores		*"Don't Hold" Test Weighted Scores*	
Information	15	Digit span	5
Vocabulary	14	Arithmetic	6
Picture completion	13	Block design	5
Object assembly	14	Digit symbol	4

Here the wide discrepancy definitely evidences interference with thinking and lowering of functioning level. One may speculate that organic factors are probably accountable, because of the nature of subtests affected and the uniformity of performance in general. Usually, however, interference is not apparent in such striking degree, and further scrutiny of subtest patterning becomes necessary.

Sometimes patients emotionally disturbed do just as poorly on tests requiring attention, concentration, or abstraction as those with mild or severe degrees of neurological involvement, and subtest scores in themselves are not discriminative. Clues must be pursued rather in an analysis of performance on certain test-items and in qualitative aspects of functioning. One prevalent tendency among emotionally disturbed persons is to fail easy problems, while readily handling the more complex. Greater uniformity of response is usually apparent in patients with neurological disorders, among whom consistently poorer work appears as the complexity of tasks increases.

So far as the writer has observed, many organic patients experience difficulty in reproducing within time limits the last two complicated block designs on the Wechsler-Bellevue Scale for Adolescents and Adults (Nos. 6 and 7). This finding however, receives no support from Baker,[8] who states, "The fifth [sic] design is often found easier by organics because, once the idea of making the stripe is grasped, there is less necessity to follow the pattern." Baker probably refers to the sixth design, which is the striped pattern. The present author has found this one to be the most troublesome for a majority of patients, with and without neurological disorders; but confusion seems especially prominent in the patient with organic involvement. Ability to "grasp" how to make the stripe is one of the nuances tending to rule out organic interpretation (in persons of at least average intelligence).

The total score for digit span is often lowered in cases of neurological disturbance, but emotional disorders may lower it also. A distinction can sometimes be made on this test between organic and nonorganic patients by contrasting performance on forward and reversed digit repetition. Ordinarily, and as expected, a patient having an organic disorder will remember more digits in forward order than in reverse, since the former task demands less concentration and sustained effort. When the number of digits to be repeated in reversed order exceeds the number repeated in forward order, emotional interference is likely.

An erratic inter-item and inter-test pattern, with a wide scatter of successes and failures, is more characteristic of emotional instability than of neurological pathology. Often, it reveals greater flexibility of conceptual thinking and keener insight than the organic case displays, alternating with inappropriately poor reaction, or complete failure.

Generalizations, nevertheless, should be viewed with caution, and these suggestions used only as hints possibly applicable to individual diagnosis.

Specific items of the Stanford-Binet Intelligence Test[48] (Forms L and M) sometimes prove to have differential value. Similarities, pictorial likenesses and differences, digit repetition, memory for sentences and stories, and drawing tests often reveal more than the usual amount of confusion among organic patients. Interpretation is usually enhanced by noting wide discrepancies between tests on the Stanford-Binet verbal intelligence scale and those of motor skill on the Merrill-Palmer,[47] Pintner-Paterson,[41] and Arthur[5] performance scales. In the author's experience, undue slowness of reaction time and marked difficulty on accuracy-scored tests such as formboards, mazes, and block designs favor an organic interpretation. Differential diagnosis is most valid, under these conditions, when findings are considered qualitatively as well as quantitatively, and in conjunction with results of other tests.

Efforts to combine subtest scores on the Wechsler-Bellevue, WAIS, and WISC scales into a single ratio or quotient measuring organicity have met with some success in the individual case, but more often failed of validation in group studies. Analysis of individual test items is now agreed to be of greater assistance in diagnosis than combination scores encompassing a wide range of psychological functions. The logic of this may be understood by considering two subtests such as digit repetition (immediate memory for numbers) and block design (abstract thinking of greater complexity). It is extremely unlikely that thought disturbances in these areas would show sufficient overlapping to permit ratings to be added and a psychologically meaningful average obtained. The same is true of any measure which attempts to reduce organic interference to a single mathematical term and assumes a linear relationship between intricate variables.

A study demonstrating the typical unreliability of such measures is that of Gutman.[27] After testing thirty brain-damaged patients and using thirty normals as controls, Gutman reported the following percentages of correct and incorrect diagnoses utilizing the ratios of Levi, Oppenheim, and Wechsler,[35] of Reyell, and of Hewson.[30]

	Correct Diagnosis of Brain-damaged Per cent	Misclassification of Normals Per cent
Wechsler (D.I.)	43	33
Reyell	50	30
Hewson	60	17

Agreement among the three criteria was secured in only 33 per cent of the cases. Other studies in keeping with these results are those of Allen,[3] Rogers,[43] Kass,[34] Diers and Brown.[19]

SPECIAL TESTS

Techniques such as the Babcock,[6] Shipley-Hartford,[46] and Hunt-Minnesota[33] compare vocabulary rating (remote learning, or optimal intellectual level) with response to material involving abstract thought (functional ability). Vocabulary is a good index of general intelligence, has high retest reliability, and is a stable measure. In contrast, abstract thinking is susceptible to change in the presence of organicity, an attribute favoring this function as a differential indicator. Most clinicians, nevertheless, have found instruments using these variables of little discriminative value in evaluating nature and degree of interference with thinking.

Age, sex, and intelligence quotient were not considered in construction of the Shipley-Hartford Scale. It is therefore not surprising that several investigators report disappointing results from its clinical application. (Magaret and Simpson,[37] Garfield and Fey,[22] and Manson and Grayson[39].) Garfield and Fey present evidence that the conceptual quotient (ratio between abstract-thinking score and vocabularly rating) declines sharply on a basis of age alone. Significantly, Crown,[18] Yacorzynski,[53] and Capps[17] show vocabularly itself to be less resistant to change than had formerly been supposed.

Considerable overlapping among groups and too many false positives among persons of high vocabularly score have been recorded in the adaptation of the Hunt-Minnesota Test. (Aita, Armitage, Reitan and Rabinowitz,[2] Canter,[16] Malamud,[38] Meehl and Jeffery.[40]) Validity of the Hunt-Minnesota as a measure of organicity is therefore open to question. A fallacy seriously limiting usefulness of all tests of this type is the concept of organicity as a unitary entity, expressed consistently in one kind of function.

Halstead's test battery[28] has been reported valuable in discriminating between normals and patients with lesions of the frontal lobes, but less successful in differentiating organic patients from psychoneurotics or psychotics (Yates[54]). If it is established beforehand that a patient is neither neurotic nor psychotic, Halstead's impairment score provides a reliable localizing sign of a frontal-lobe lesion. His approach is comprehensive enough to include physiological aspects of functioning. This advantage is present also in the thorough perceptual studies of Bender and Teuber.[10, 11]

Tests such as the Bender Visual-Motor Gestalt[9] have in isolated instances related perceptual disturbances to organicity. Because validation rests essentially upon case history data, convincing validation studies have to date been lacking, as Billingslea[13] and others point out. In the present author's experience, the technique's greatest usefulness is in revealing severe pathology; but it is distinctly limited for routine use because of false positives without neurological confirmation.

Benton's Visual Retention Test,[12] Graham and Kendall's Memory-for-Designs Test,[25] and Hooper's Visual Organization Test[31] likewise require further corroboration, and appear to suffer from over simplification. Benton's claim that his test differentiates parieto-occipital lesions from those of frontal origin offers an interesting possibility for further investigation. Overlapping between severely-deteriorated schizophrenic patients and mildly-deteriorated organics has made individual diagnosis equivocal on the Memory-for-Designs Test,[25] although large group differences have been recorded.

Improved standardization procedures are needed for all available visual-motor organization techniques, as well as for use with nonpathological control subjects. Although frequently revealing, visual-motor tests, like those of concept formation, generally afford too narrow a basis of measurement to be used without supplementation.

The Hanfmann-Kasanin test,[29] Zaslow approach,[55] and Goldstein-Scheerer batteries of concrete and abstract behavior[23] are often very helpful in evaluating difficulties that manifest as abstract-thinking losses. Most investigators agree, however, that excellent descriptions of test behavior of patients with moderate and severe frontal-lobe damage constitute the outstanding contribution of Goldstein and Scheerer. The observational method of diagnosing organic disorders is stressed in their studies.

Examples of success with a qualitative approach are innumerable. When, for instance, a patient is able to complete all block designs within time limits, no impairment may show if performance scored compares favorably with work on other subtests of the Wechsler scales. Yet his approach may be characterized by perplexity as to how to proceed and remarks that the particular task is hard. Impotence may be revealed in comments about slowness or inadequacy of response.

In some cases, confusion about patterning lowers ratings only slightly. If most scorable reactions still fall within time limits, quantitative comparison of subtest scores becomes worthless. Suspicion of interference is augmented greatly, on the other hand, by any slow, methodical, consistent tendency to match blocks one by one with models or cards. Observations may then be corroborated by using materials of different levels of concreteness or abstraction, i.e., by having the size of designs approach, or differ from, actual block size.

Again, in such tests as the wool sorting series, the number of skeins sorted correctly has little clinical meaning without a description of behavior. If a patient is asked to select all red skeins, he may do so by different methods. He may grasp any skein from pale pink to dark red in unordered or random fashion. Such behavior suggests a conception, or abstraction, of redness. Or he may begin by grasping the palest pink skein and comparing each succeeding skein (matching it as nearly as possible in color) with the preceding one. With this stimulus-bound technique, the same number of skeins may be selected, so that the end-product is identical; nevertheless, the second approach reveals concreteness rather than abstractness—a lack of conceptual ability. Here observation may adduce valuable information about integrative mechanisms that might prove resistant to quantitative analysis.

Concern with different levels of concreteness and abstractness underlies Grassi's Block Substitution Test.[26] His technique follows customary block-design procedure closely, except that modification requires a reproduction of patterns from block models rather than colored drawings on cards.

Boyd[14] varied the approach by giving different weights to steps outlined by Goldstein in an attempt to set up norms. Although unsuccessful quantitatively, Boyd's work calls attention to the important fact that higher intelligence usually goes with higher scores on the block design test. Although the number of cases reported was small, indications that intellectual level may have a significant influence on block-design scores warrants further corroboration. Findings that psychotic patients tend to do worse than the brain-damaged on this material are also provocative.

The block-design rotation test (Shapiro[45]) was developed because some patients are so prone to rotate patterns unwittingly. Shapiro investigated this tendency and believes that rotation forms a basis for differentiating perceptual anomalies related to thinking disorders. Further research must determine the discriminative claims for rotation among various clinical groups, especially as the phenomenon is often observed in the behavior of schizophrenic patients.

Lidz, Gay, and Tietze[36] found that the Kohs block-design test successfully separated a group of twenty-one organics with deterioration from fifteen nondeteriorated schizophrenics, with a mis-classification of only two in thirty-six. Unfortunately, age was not controlled in their study.

An interesting approach is the analysis by Armitage[4] of block-design material according to time, number of correct placements, number of incorrect moves, and order of placing blocks. Significant differences were not obtained, however, between a group of normals and one of neurological patients. Tooth[49] was also unsuccessful in screening one hundred cooperative Navy officers with a history of head injury or post-concussive state from fifty normal control subjects. The color-form sorting and block-design tests were used.

Examples cited are characteristic of research in general. The conflicting results reported suggest a need for both elaboration and refinement of method.

PROJECTIVE TECHNIQUES

Diagnostic findings of the Goodenough Draw-A-Man Test,[24] and modifications such as the House-Tree-Person (HTP) test,[15] are inclusive of disturbances in body image, perceptual anomalies, and coordination difficulties. Rigidity in thinking may be reflected in a stiff, robot-like reproduction of a man, perplexity and confusion in poor quality of work. Subjective feelings related to organic interference may be expressed in a variety of ways, such as overemphasis upon detail, or by omission of important features, in marked concern for the maintenance of symmetry, and by a few primitive features in an otherwise acceptable reproduction. Heavy lines are often used by patients with organic disorders. Joining of lines at crucial points may be poor. A tendency toward fragmentation is sometimes seen in inability to connect limbs to the body of a human figure, or to attach branches to the trunk of a tree.

Feelings of intellectual inadequacy are often thought to be reflected in preoccupation with the head in drawing a person, as well as in making the head disproportionately large. Limpness of arms and legs, hanging branches, dangling roots of trees, and sagging figures may convey feelings of helplessness and awareness of limitation. In the drawing of a house, undue emphasis on symmetry of windows and doors may point to conflict and concern for balance. Perseveration may reflect "stickiness" and inability to shift readily. Such features are typical of those encountered in the interpretation of organicity; but because many of them also appear in the drawings of individuals without neurological disorders, extreme caution must be used in attempting diagnosis by reliance on drawing techniques. The writer believes that interpretation of drawing techniques should be made only in conjunction with other formal test results and with observational material.

Considering the fact that Piotrowski had an extremely small number of non-homogeneous patients in his initial group, remarkably good results have been obtained using his Rorschach signs of organicity.[42] They have also served as a basis for considerable investigation and refinement by other clinicians.

Hughes claims 82 per cent accuracy in identifying organic, brain-damaged patients from normals, manic depressives, and schizophrenics, as against 20 per cent correct when the Piotrowski set of signs was used.[32] Dorken and Kral[21] report 92.9 per cent correct diagnosis among their cases as compared to 50 per cent correctly diagnosed by Piotrowski's method, and 75 per cent using the Ross and Ross disability ratio.[44] This high percentage of accuracy was secured by considering signs not likely to appear in persons with organic involvement.

An important conclusion on neuropsychological disturbances was reached by Aita, Reitan, and Ruth,[1] in treating Piotrowski's signs statistically. They found that the appearance of any sign may be a function of extent and kind of organic damage. Another important finding from Diers and Brown[20] is a correlation between low intellectual level and signs of organicity, showing need for intellectual considerations when interpreting organic features.

Although the preceding signs are Rorschach signs, careful study reveals that they transcend the bounds of test materials and have a great deal in common with general behavior. This is apparent in Baker's review of Rorschach literature, in which a list is given of Rorschach indicators that hold up well.[8] Baker's conclusions embrace reports of other investigators as well as her own experience. In line with these conclusions it is the writer's considered opinion that the following signs are of greatest value in differentiating organic damage from other types of disturbance:

1. Among persons of high intelligence, Piotrowski's repetition (Rpt) sign is generally significant. In mental retardation, disregard of form in at least three responses per record is not uncommon, thereby invalidating this sign as a differential.

2. Piotrowski's perplexity (Plx) sign appears to arise from feelings of inadequacy and is reflected in a subject's distrust of his performance, together with a need for constant approval and reassurance. Baker includes interest in the "correct" response as reliable for all degrees of damage, but in the writer's experience, correctness is also a concern frequent among patients with hysterical tendencies who believe there is a "right" answer to each card.

3. Piotrowski's impotence (Imp) sign denoting inability to improve response even after recognition of its inadequacy or inappropriateness; disparaging remarks are often a clue. This sign seems particularly discriminative of moderate and severe damage.

4. Piotrowski's automatic phrasing (Ap) is a good differential sign when it appears, but is less frequently encountered than some of the other signs.

5. Perseveration of content regardless of blot contour is a very reliable differential sign. Impressions of organicity are reinforced if the patient is unable to introduce new concepts when asked to do so. Baker

points out that when this sign is combined with "pickiness" there is almost certainty that a focal lesion is present. Accompanying seizures may be expected.

6. "Pickiness" indicates picking out very small details on most cards and referring to them as "sticking out," especially in unusual areas. The combination (perseveration and pickiness) is uncommon in clinical practice, but a very reliable sign when it does occur for detecting small focal lesions.

7. Threat to intactness of organism, i.e., disintegration of body image is a very reliable sign. Failure to accept human figures, for example, on Card III because "leg is falling off"; concern with decaying objects, deterioration of substances, etc. The writer also finds that human beings seen as animals in Card III where the usual arm is interpreted as a second leg, indicates regressive features.

8. Impairment of organization ability (analysis and synthesis) is a very reliable differential. Failure to disentangle two concepts, with resultant incongruous combinations; efforts to overcome perceptual difficulties by covering up one part of the card with the hand; inability to organize clearly seen details into meaningful wholes; disturbances in figure-ground relationships.

9. Personalization of response as support for concepts reported, is a reliable sign when it appears. Difficulty in abstract thinking is suggested when a patient introduces experiential material: e.g., "This reminds me of my sailboat. I just finished painting it, so I know."

10. Free use of color with passive content, especially in color-form (CF) responses, among patients with mild or recently acquired brain damage is a useful sign. Ordinarily form-color (FC) responses predominate in early organicity, but may become lowered in later stages of disease processes as affective control weakens.

Aita and co-workers,[1] and Baker[8] report a "catastrophic reaction," i.e., complete inability to handle blot material because of anxiety, as a reliable sign. It is rare, in the present writer's experience. Baker also lists the use of shading in the beginning of the record (Cards I and II) as one of her best signs. She recognizes, however, that patients who cannot accept their disabilities may deny shading or fail to use it. This sign is not often found among organic cases in the author's experience, but is a good one.

Sometimes additional light is thrown upon Rorschach signs when they are interpreted in conjunction with results of other tests. Baker calls attention to the combination of a poor Rorschach and superior Wechsler-Bellevue performance as suggesting mild organic damage, or multiple small lesions. The writer agrees with Baker that the presence of a passive Rorschach combined with very aggressive Thematic Apperception Test content, and a Wechsler-Bellevue performance showing signs of deterioration is sometimes reliable (although uncommon) among epileptics with grand mal seizures.

Thus in many cases the "sign" method is of inestimable value to the neuropsychologist in detecting organicity. Nevertheless, its usefulness may be limited by overlapping between so-called organic signs and psychoneurotic or psychotic manifestations. An illustration of the latter is an unusual pathological response to Card III of the Rorschach series, where the central portion (red) is interpreted as a second arm of the human figure. As a "sign" the response is not discriminative in itself, because it has appeared in schizophrenia and temporal lobe tumor (verified). It is significant, nevertheless, because it reveals a confusion in organization and in synthesis which is common to these two divergent clinical syndromes. By considering mutually exclusive features of Rorschach protocols in conjunction with such knowledge, an accurate diagnosis frequently may be reached.

Experience has demonstrated the wisdom not only of considering "signs" as parts of larger, interpretive Gestalten, but also of studying broader constellations of personality and behavior affected by brain damage.

At present, batteries of tests supplemented by observations of behavior are the techniques of choice for clinical usage. Many of the neuropsychological tests are still in a relatively embryonic state. More precise technical skills, a review of existing information, and expansion of both theory and application may contribute toward improved understanding of neuropsychological relationships.

Clearly, future research should be in two directions. One approach demands greater specification of function, while the other requires broader generalization. Such a function as the ability to shift readily illustrates this point. It is now recognized that failure to shift involves many components which need delineation, while at the same time shifting permeates numerous aspects of behavior. These are not limited to intellectual functioning, where emphasis has been placed to date, but include emotional components as well. Evaluation of emotional factors as they are related to, and affected by, organicity, is one of the more promising avenues open to future investigation.

BIBLIOGRAPHY

1. AITA, J. A., REITAN, R. M., and RUTH, J. M. Rorschach's test as a diagnostic aid in brain injury. Amer. J. Psychiat., 103: 770–779, 1947.
2. AITA, J. A., ARMITAGE, S. G., REITAN, R. M., and RABINOWITZ, A. The use of certain psychological tests in the evaluation of brain injury. J. Gen. Psychol., 37: 25–44, 1947.

3. ALLEN, R. M. A note on the use of the Wechsler-Bellevue Scale Mental Deterioration Index with brain-injured patients. *J. Clin. Psychol.,* 4: 88–89, 1948.

4. ARMITAGE, S. G. An analysis of certain psychological tests used for the evaluation of brain injury. *Psychol. Monogr.,* 60: 1, 1946.

5. ARTHUR, G. *A Point Scale of Performance Tests.* New York: Commonwealth Fund: 1930.

6. BABCOCK, H. An experiment in the measurement of mental deterioration. *Arch. Psychol.,* 117, 1930.

7. BABCOCK, H., and LEVY, L. *The Revised Examination for the Measurement of Efficiency in Mental Functioning.* Chicago: Stoelting: 1942.

8. BAKER, G. In Klopfer, B., *Developments in the Rorschach Technique,* II. Yonkers, N.Y.: World Book: 1956.

9. BENDER, L. A visual motor Gestalt test and its clinical use. *Amer. Orthopsychiat. Ass. Monogr.,* 3, 1938.

10. BENDER, M. D., and TEUBER, H. L. Spatial organization of visual perception following injury to the brain. *Arch. Neurol. & Psychiat.,* 59: 39–62, 1948.

11. BENDER, M. D., and TEUBER, H. L. Disturbances in visual perception following cerebral lesions. *J. Psychol.,* 28: 223–233, 1949.

12. BENTON, A. L. A multiple choice type of the visual retention test. *Arch. Neurol. & Psychiat.,* 64: 699–707, 1950.

13. BILLINGSLEA, F. Y. The Bender Gestalt. An objective scoring method and validating data. *J. Clin. Psychol.,* 4: 1–27, 1948.

14. BOYD, F. A provisional quantitative scoring with preliminary norms for the Goldstein-Scheerer cube test. *J. Clin. Psychol.,* 5: 148–153, 1949.

15. BUCK, J. N. The H-T-P technique: a qualitative and quantitative scoring manual. *J. Clin. Psychol. Monogr.,* Suppl. 4, 317–396, 1948.

16. CANTER, A. H. Direct and indirect measures of psychological deficit in multiple sclerosis. *J. Gen. Psychol.,* 44: 3–50, 1951.

17. CAPPS, H. M. Vocabulary changes in mental deterioration. *Arch. Psychol.,* 242, 1939.

18. CROWN, S. Notes on an experimental study of intellectual deterioration. *Brit. M. J.,* 2: 684–685, 1949.

19. DIERS, W. C., and BROWN, C. C. Psychometric patterns associated with multiple sclerosis. I. Wechsler-Bellevue patterns. *Arch. Neurol. & Psychiat.,* 63: 760–765, 1950.

20. DIERS, W. C., and BROWN, C. C. The Rorschach "organic" signs and intelligence level. *J. Consult. Psychol.,* 15: 343–345, 1951.

21. DORKEN, H., and KRAL, V. A. The psychological differentiation of organic brain lesions and their localization by means of the Rorschach test. *Amer. J. Psychiat.,* 108:764–770, 1952.

22. GARFIELD, S. L., and FEY, W. F. A comparison of the Wechsler-Bellevue and Shipley-Hartford Scales as measures of mental impairment. *J. Consult. Psychol.,* 12: 259–264, 1948.

23. GOLDSTEIN, K. H., and SCHEERER, M. Abstract and concrete behavior; an experimental study with special tests. *Psychol. Monogr.,* 53: 3, 1941.

24. GOODENOUGH, F. L. *Measurement of Intelligence by Drawings*. Yonkers, N.Y.: World Book: 1926.

25. GRAHAM, F. K., and KENDALL, B. S. Memory-for-designs test: revised general manual. *Percept Mot. Skills*, 11: 147–190, 1960.

26. GRASSI, J. R. *The Grassi Block Substitution Test for Measuring Organic Brain Damage*. Springfield, Ill.: Charles C Thomas: 1953.

27. GUTMAN, B. The application of the Wechsler-Bellevue Scale in the diagnosis of organic brain disorders. *J. Clin. Psychol.*, 6: 195–198, 1950.

28. HALSTEAD, W. C. *Brain and Intelligence*. Chicago: Chicago Univer. Press: 1947.

29. HANFMANN, E., and KASANIN, J. Conceptual thinking in schizophrenia. *Nerv. & Ment. Dis. Monogr.*, Ser. 67, 1942.

30. HEWSON, L. The Wechsler-Bellevue Scale and the Substitution Test as aids in neuropsychiatric diagnosis. *J. Nerv. & Ment. Dis.*, 109: 158–183; 246–266, 1949.

31. Hooper, H. E. Use of the Hooper Visual Organization Test in the differentiation of organic brain pathology from normal, psychoneurotic, and schizophrenic reactions. *Amer. Psychologist*, 7: 350, 1952.

32. HUGHES, R. M. A factor analysis of Rorschach diagnostic signs. *J. Gen. Psychol.*, 43: 85–103, 1950.

33. HUNT, H. F. A practical clinical test for organic brain damage. *J. Appl. Psychol.*, 27: 375–386, 1943.

34. KASS, W. Wechsler's Mental Deterioration Index in the diagnosis of organic brain disease. *Trans. Kansas Acad. Sc.*, 52: 66–70, 1949.

35. LEVI, J., OPPENHEIM, S., and WECHSLER, D. Clinical use of the Mental Deterioration Index of the Bellevue-Wechsler Scale. *J. Abnorm. & Social Psychol.*, 40: 405–407, 1945.

36. LIDZ, T., GAY, J. R., and TIETZE, C. Intelligence in cerebral deficit states and schizophrenia measured by Kohs Block Test. *Arch. Neurol. & Psychiat.*, 48: 568–582, 1942.

37. MAGARET, A., and SIMPSON, M. M. A comparison of two measures of deterioration in psychotic patients. *J. Consult. Psychol.*, 12: 265–269, 1948.

38. MALAMUD, R. F. Validity of the Hunt-Minnesota Test for organic brain damage. *J. Appl. Psychol.*, 30: 271–275, 1946.

39. MANSON, M. P., and GRAYSON, H. M. The Shipley-Hartford Retreat Scale as a measure of intellectual impairment for military prisoners. *J. Appl. Psychol.*, 31: 67–81, 1947.

40. MEEHL, P. E., and JEFFERY, M. The Hunt-Minnesota Test for organic brain damage in cases of functional depression. *J. Appl. Psychol.*, 30: 276–287, 1946.

41. PINTNER, R., and PATERSON, D. G. *Pintner-Paterson Performance Test Series*. Chicago: Stoelting: 1917.

42. PIOTROWSKI, Z. The Rorschach inkblot method in organic disturbances of the central nervous system. *J. Nerv. & Ment. Dis.*, 86: 525–537, 1937.

43. ROGERS, L. S. A comparative evaluation of the Wechsler-Bellevue Deterioration Index for various adult groups. *J. Clin. Psychol.*, 6: 199–202, 1950.

44. Ross, W. D., and Ross, S. Some Rorschach ratings of a clinical value. *Ror. Res. Exch.*, 8: 1–9, 1944.

45. Shapiro, M. B. Experimental studies of a perceptual anomaly. *J. Ment. Sci.*, 97: 90–110, 1951.

46. Shipley, W. C. A self-administering scale for measuring intellectual impairment and deterioration. *J. Psychol.*, 9: 371–377, 1940.

47. Stutsman, R. *Mental Measurement of Pre-school Children.* Yonkers, N.Y.: World Book: 1931.

48. Terman, L. M., and Merrill, M. A. *Measuring Intelligence.* Boston: Houghton Mifflin: 1937.

49. Tooth, G. On the use of mental tests for the measurement of disability after head injury. With a comparison between the results of these tests in patients with head injury and psychoses. *J. Neurol., Neurosurg. & Psychiat.*, 10: 1–11, 1947.

50. Wechsler, D. *The Measurement of Adult Intelligence.* Baltimore: Williams & Wilkins: 1956.

51. Wechsler, D. *Adult Intelligence Scale.* New York: Psychol. Corp.: 1955.

52. Wechsler, D. *Wechsler Intelligence Scale for Children.* New York: Psychol. Corp.: 1949.

53. Yacorzynski, G. K. An evaluation of the postulate underlying the Babcock deterioration test. *Psychol. Rev.*, 48: 261–267, 1941.

54. Yates, A. The validity of some psychological tests of brain damage. *Psychol. Bull.*, 51: 359–379, 1954.

55. Zaslow, R. W. A new approach to the problem of conceptual thinking in schizophrenia. *J. Consult. Psychol.*, 14: 335–339, 1950.

ADDITIONAL REFERENCES

1. Beck, H. A., and Lain, R. L. Use of the WISC in predicting organicity. *J. Clin. Psychol.*, 11 (2): 154–158, 1955.

2. Fisher, J., Gonda, T. A., and Little, K. B. The Rorschach and central nervous system pathology; a cross-validation study. *Amer. J. Psychiat.*, 111: 487–492, 1955.

3. Hertz, M. R., and Loehrke, L. M. An evaluation of the Rorschach method for the study of brain injury. *J. Proj. Tech.*, 19: 416–430, 1955.

4. Manson, M. P. Relationships of intelligence, mental efficiency, mental deterioration and disease. *Arch. Neurol. & Psychiat.*, 70: 587–597, 1953.

5. Michael-Smith, H. The identification of pathological cerebral function through the H-T-P technique. *J. Clin. Psychol.*, 9: 292–295, 1953.

6. Small, L., and Bellak, L. Projective methods. In Spiegel, E. A., *Progress in Neurology and Psychiatry.* New York: Grune & Stratton: 1955.

V

>>

Neuropsychological
Examination and Report

Problems presented to most clinical psychologists are straightforward and well defined. School psychologists, for example, may be asked to estimate the intellectual ability of a child, ascertainable by means of standard intelligence test. Those concerned with commitment of mental defectives to state institutions, or with determining disability status under the Social Security Act, do similar testing; results fall into a predetermined dichotomy. Primary emphasis is upon current intellectual functioning.

When behavioral and psychiatric referrals are made, application of an intelligence test plus one or two projective tests in most instances makes possible an adequate personality evaluation. Preoccupation likewise is with immediate performance.

Neuropsychological examination, on the other hand, differs from other types of clinical testing in purpose and direction as well as in complexity. It is designed to determine the presence or absence of organicity; avenues of expression and extent of impairment in psychological functioning vary, however, with the individual, and involve longitudinal considerations as well.

Certain requirements are unique to neuropsychological testing. These include (1) more extensive use of behavioral observation as an adjunct to formal testing, (2) greater individual choice in selecting a test battery, (3) heightened vigilance in interpreting reaction as testing proceeds, and (4) greater tact and resourcefulness in dealing with patients.

BEHAVIORAL OBSERVATIONS

Special attention must be paid to a patient's responsiveness and to qualitative aspects of his behavior. Knowledge of the patient's behavior is often of great assistance to the neurologist; he should be given an account of it with accuracy of interpretation and with emphasis upon factual description. This observational aspect of the neuropsychological examination begins as soon as the patient enters the door. It should not end until he has gone.

If light is to be shed upon the inroads of organicity on the personality, many questions need to be answered. Does the patient appear apprehensive or resentful when first approached? If so, are these tendencies noticeably modified by conversation and assurance before formal testing begins? Is he receptive to suggestions such as hanging up his coat? What is his attitude toward others who may accompany him? How quickly does he move? Does he show any signs of ataxia or imbalance? Does he appear clumsy? Is he able to follow simple requests like sitting in a designated chair, or pulling it up to the desk?

Is he talkative, and do conversations ramble? Are remarks apologetic? Does egocentricity or an hypochondriacal preoccupation characterize remarks? Are comments repetitive? Is he quiet, speaking only when spoken to? Is he evasive?

Under stress of formal testing, are tension and uneasiness much more apparent? Are signs of sensory disturbances present (e.g., vision, color vision, hearing, aphasia)? Is hand coordination good, fair, or poor? Is hand preference well established, i.e., does he use the same hand in writing, drawing, and in the manipulation of objects? Does switching from one hand to the other frequently occur? Is this patterned?

What is his reaction to difficult materials? Can he follow complicated instructions? Does he constantly ask to have questions or instructions repeated? Does concentration show impairment? Is interest sustained? Is he persistent? Does he give up too quickly? What is his reaction to failures? Is he oblivious of them? Does he become argumentative, or embarrassed?

Is he restless and fidgety? Is his approach slow and methodical, or impulsive and careless? Does he alternate between the two? Do special types of materials, or questions, produce a faster or slower reaction?

Does he fatigue easily? Are changes in affect prominent? Which particular areas of performance suffer, and in what way?

Is lack of foresight prominent, such as making drawings too large for the paper? Is judgment poor in general? Is confusion apparent? Is the patient aware of this? Are comments made during testing consistent with the case history (usually taken later)? Does a tendency prevail to exaggerate or to minimize educational background and training? Does he show embarrassment regarding limited education? Does he seem fairly well satisfied with progress in his job? Does he report a pleasant home life? Are any special grievances expressed? Is he noticeably depressed?

What is the patient's reaction to his symptomatology? Does he brighten up and seem eager to discuss difficulties? Do signs of discouragement and depression characterize his response to questions about his condition?

Does he appear greatly relieved when the testing period terminates? Does he ask how well he has done? Does he seem satisfied? Does he defend poor performance by claiming ambiguous questions were asked? Does he minimize difficulty of materials and boast of prowess? Does he report accurately to relatives waiting for him? Is his response to companions the same as to the examiner?

These illustrations indicate the kinds of information to be gleaned from observation. There are many more, all to be interpreted qualitatively.

FORMAL TESTING

Although standard intelligence test materials and projective techniques ordinarily form the nucleus of neuropsychological examination, the criteria governing selection of a particular battery are at the same time more tentative and more specific than for other testing. This is true because there is no way of pre-determining whether impairment will be expressed in intellectual, affective, and/or behavioral areas. Problems referred by the neurologist range from those with "suspicion of pathology" to those with clearcut evidence of neurological impairment and inroads made by disease processes, as well as those accompanied by exaggerated emotional lability and resistance to testing.

Where application of a standard test battery is feasible, the rule is to proceed from the general to the specific, inasmuch as initial findings may give further clues to directions to be taken. If intellectual impairment is reflected on intelligence test, weak areas noted may be investigated further. Difficulty on block designs suggests possible impairment in ability to shift and in abstract thinking. Having established suspicion by some limited evidence of impairment, the neuropsychologist uses more specialized techniques such as the Goldstein-Scheerer tests to fix more accurately the conditions under which difficulty occurs. With no lines drawn on the sample cards, a patient may be able to complete only the first few block designs, and yet do very well if outlines are shown. Having size of designs and blocks identical is often helpful to patients who have trouble with less concrete types of materials, such as those on intelligence test scales. If results on similarities test indicate deficiencies in categorization, the sorting tests may assist in obtaining clearer proof of the nature of damage.

Sometimes marked emotional overlay masks ability. The ability may be elicited later by different tests. The writer has found it possible on certain tests to get adequate performance by the introduction of similar materials after failure has occurred. This is especially true when patients become frustrated and upset by awareness of failing. One instance is that of a patient who could repeat only three digits in forward order and two in reverse on the Wechsler-Bellevue Scale for Adults. After finishing the battery, she was told that a much easier series would be given (from the WISC). Under the new conditions, she repeated seven digits in forward order and six in reversed order.

If difficulties in handling figure-ground relationships appear on drawing tests such as the Bender Gestalt, or Rorschach Test, such alternatives as the graphic Rorschach, or retention tests requiring drawing may prove profitable. Special problems like aphasias usually require performance or non-language tests as more adequate measures of ability. Where speech and motor handicaps are observed in the same patient, modification of techniques is the rule, i.e., subtests from various batteries are used and methods introduced that demand a minimum of verbalization and movement. Usually only a rough estimate of ability and degree of organicity is then possible.

Impairment of body-ego concept, when frequently noted on Draw-A-Man Test may be verified by Rorschach findings or other drawing techniques such as the House-Tree-Person Test. Sometimes the Thematic Apperception Test throws additional light upon the nature of an observed aberration.

Thus, the selection of neuropsychological test materials requires alertness of a high degree. Skill must be developed in weighing evidence as the examination proceeds, not later. This is particularly necessary for ambulatory patients where only one session may be possible. Therefore, within the limits of strain on the patient, too many confirmatory data are to be sought in preference to too few.

Important as the selection of test criteria is to proper diagnosis, successful examination of individuals with neurological disorders depends heavily, too, upon skill in establishing and in maintaining rapport. Nowhere are insight and patience more essential. Patients showing anxiety and insecurity must constantly be reassured; those reluctant to perform must be encouraged without being pushed beyond their capacity for response. Unless negativistic or argumentative individuals are handled with tact and resourcefulness, poor cooperation and refusal to continue may even make testing impossible. Because fatigue is so common among people with central-nervous-system disorders, examiners must be on the alert for signs of it well in advance of actual complaint. Long drawn out testing should be avoided.

Methods for obtaining maximal results will vary with each person and situation. Each clinician must work out his own devices, since there is no substitute for experience. The examiner can, on the other hand, avoid some glaring technical faults inimical to rapport. One of the errors most disturbing to neurological patients (or to any others for that matter), is a tendency on the part of some examiners to depend upon books and papers for one or more items in the test battery. Scales like the Wechsler or Stanford-Binet should be learned verbatim in their entirety, so as to avoid hunting around for a certain page, or for a paper with arithmetic problems written out. Fumbling with boxes or performance materials also makes a poor impression. Time lost in this way may drag out a test session beyond the endurance of the neurological patient. To put the patient at ease, the clinician himself must have complete command of his tools.

Another undesirable tendency is rigidity of presentation, i.e., always giving subtests or presenting items in identical order. A much wiser course is to vary them according to the needs of the individual patient. The writer, for instance, finds it harder to reach older adults quickly if the information test of the Wechsler Scales is introduced first. Embarrassment about limited training or years elapsed since school poses an unneccessary threat to some. If simpler questions, such as those of comprehension, are given initially, the patient may be more at ease by the time informational questions that rely upon educational background are presented.

When awareness of limitation creates a problem, time limits may well be disregarded, except for purposes of scoring. Sometimes individuals have to be encouraged even to try. They may need constant reassurance as to the acceptability of their performance. For instance, if they have completed all but two or three blocks in the harder patterns when time limits are up, calling attention to time may disrupt their performance. It is much less frustrating if they are allowed to complete patterns, not knowing that they have exceeded the allotted time. To give a patient insight into failures he can do nothing about is certain to destroy his confidence. Such dejection may be particularly important if mental deterioration is present, and hence should be avoided whenever possible.

Aside from the possible effects of a disease process which may have organic features, many persons become alarmed and overly sensitive at the suggestion that anything is "wrong with their head." On this account they are more fearful of psychological testing than of other forms of examination. Frequently patients are heard to exclaim, "Anywhere but my head. I'm afraid I'm going to die, or maybe I'll go crazy or something." Thus any technique or procedure which alleviates anxiety and tension, builds up a patient's ego and makes neuropsychological examination as relaxed as possible, is invaluable. Smooth and efficient testing in a sympathetic atmosphere does much to insure optimal functioning and cooperation.

THE NEUROPSYCHOLOGICAL REPORT

After routine details of name, address, date of birth, chronological age, education, and date of examination, the neuropsychological report should contain a paragraph or two on impressions of observed behavior. In these, two tendencies must be avoided. One is giving a mere description of appearance and conduct without interpretation, conveying little information to the neurologist.

An illustration of this tendency is seen in the following extract from an externe's report: "The patient was a good-looking man with blue eyes. He came in, sat down, and asked what the test was for." Such uninformative comments not only detract from the quality of a report, but make it so lengthy that neurologists frequently turn immediately to the summary at the end and never read the rest.

A tendency toward interpretation without supporting evidence is equally to be shunned. If a patient is reported "slow in responding," the neurologist will want to know grounds for impressions of slowness, such as manifest fear of failure, stalling for time, or inability to hurry even though he tried. If a patient is described as negativistic and resistant, a personal bias of the examiner may be suspected unless reasons are given. Remarks such as "I don't see the value of testing," or "The questions are childish;" refusals of materials; completion of easiest tasks only, are samples of behavior supporting subjective opinion. Behavioral illustrations of qualities attributed to an individual, or of conclusions reached, make a good check on the examiner's objectivity.

A brief summary of pertinent facts from the life history should be included. Some of the usual items are educational background, age of leaving school, specialized training, past and present employment, and marital status.

To obtain a statement from the patient on presenting symptoms and reason for referral is routine procedure unless contraindicated by special request from the referring physician. Often complaints stated differ from those reported to the neurologist or psychiatrist, giving him cause to check further on the patient's condition or credibility.

The body of the report is, of course, concerned with test results. A verbal and performance quotient should be reported from intelligence tests, with figures accompanied by supplemental information as to level implied—e.g., I.Q. 102, Average intelligence, or 74, Borderline. Many neurologists are not familiar with I.Q. ranges within the categories.

If scores are minimal, the fact should be stated, with reasons as far as may be judged for the discrepancy between functional and potential levels. An optimal level should always be estimated, since it helps the neurologist determine extent of damage, or deterioration. A statement regarding possible organicity is extremely important, whether or not any is found. Psychologists may be evasive when findings are negative and omit reference to organic features because they did not uncover any. The omission renders the report unreliable because the neurologist cannot be sure that the psychologist examined for this feature.

Variation in degree of certainty about test results should also be admitted. If memory losses are recorded, new learning is impaired, and an intelligence-test pattern points directly to organic origin, we may state that "definite evidence exists for organic interference with functioning on these types of tests." To credit such certainty to all aspects of testing is not only misleading but also illogical, and fails in most cases to fit the neurological picture. As an example, Rorschach signs may show a large overlap between neurotic and organic features. In central-nervous-system disorders neurologists do not dwell upon attempts to isolate either feature, recognizing that they are usually interacting and integrative. There are, of course, cases such as those involving accident compensation where the physician may be asked to evaluate the influence of various factors in the individual's total adjustment because financial remuneration is at stake. Discrete elements such as malingering, psychoneurosis, psychosis, or organic brain damage must sometimes be disentangled in order to assign weights to them, although such a request is an exception.

Finally, a summary brief paragraph should end the report. For the neurologist, its most valuable feature is the interpretation, or impression, of findings as a whole. If positive results show the presence of organic features, he will know the psychologist elicited them by neuropsychological techniques. If results are negative, he will most appreciate the acknowledgement that "organicity did not appear during testing on these types of materials."

Examiners must be aware that because of their nature, or because of lack of refinement in psychological techniques, central-nervous-system disorders may indeed exist without revealing themselves on psychological test. Hence all examiners must recognize that their data may in some cases not coincide with those obtained from other types of neurological examination. If positive findings are obtained in the absence of neurological or clinical confirmation, on the other hand, one should not become unduly distrustful of clinicians' tools but wait to see whether the passage of time may reveal symptomatology.

Succeeding chapters treat the applications of psychological techniques in specific neurological disorders, with case histories. They illustrate the present status of testing procedures in neuropsychology.

VI

▸▸

Epilepsy

The psychological investigation of epilepsy has been hindered by the quest for a so-called "epileptic personality," assumed to differ from normal in a variety of ways. Early publications contain dogmatic statements about this personality, although evidence for it is controversial, highly subjective, and lacking sufficient basis in controls. With the development of projective techniques, recent investigators have recognized that findings based upon this premise are questionable. However, the term still occurs in the literature.

The presence of convulsive phenomena is the only factor common to such classification. Once it is accepted, symptomatology must be defended as reflecting a central-nervous-system disturbance specific enough to produce uniform alterations of ideation, affect, and behavior which are pathognomonic of epilepsy. Neurological, anatomical, and physiological evidence opposes the concept of one "epileptic personality," and shows that errors in attempting to maintain this position have clearly been those of oversimplification.

Difficulties of the psychologist in evaluating individuals with convulsive disorders are best understood by considering some of the neurological findings to date, along with current problems for the neurologist.

DEFINITION AND ETIOLOGY

The first problem is one of definition, long a subject of controversy. Jackson,[9] in commenting upon the nature of epilepsy, remarked that very little was known regarding numerous permanent and transient states of nerve tissue which may cause, or prevent, failure or loss of function. Much more recently epilepsy has been described by the Gibbses and

Lennox[6] as a "paroxysmal cerebral dysrhythmia," and by Penfield and Erickson[12] as "the tendency to recurring epileptic seizures." Neither definition is acceptable to Walter,[15] who believes the first inaccurate because epilepsy need "not always be paroxysmal, cerebral, or dysrhythmic," and the second of little value. Many neurologists feel that factors in addition to paroxysmal discharge are needed to explain convulsive disorders.

Two current but divergent views on nomenclature are reported by Walter:[15] 1) that the term should be limited to those cases with verified major convulsions and/or minor seizures showing gross disturbances or loss of consciousness, and 2) that it should include transient impairment of voluntary motor power, sensation, or consciousness. Both extremes are considered untenable, because the first classification fails to cover a large number of patients and the second includes a number of conditions encountered in other disease entities.

Whether a narrow or broad basis is chosen for defining epilepsy, agreement has emerged on one important point: an awareness that a sound concept must describe a number of neurological, physiological, and psychological processes, both interacting and integrative.

Problems of etiology of epilepsy fall into two categories: 1) origins of the convulsive process, and 2) more immediate factors which precipitate attacks from time to time. The latter often differ from the former.

Clark[3] and others tried to explain the appearance of convulsive attacks in psychoanalytic terms, as expressions of the death wish, regression to prenatal security, or unconscious desire for the unconscious. Recently Bellak[1] introduced a more plausible explanation in psychoanalytic terms by postulating a positive correlation between general integration of the cerebrum and integrative ego function. Under this theory, organic brain damage recorded on test may be produced by diffuse lesions or very marked dysrhythmia. If the general cerebral disturbance is not severe enough to produce "organic" signs because ego impairment is relatively mild, the observed impulsive, obsessive-compulsive traits may still appear as ego defenses. Bellak does not claim, of course, that these personality variables are pathognomonic diagnostic signs of epilepsy and recognizes the need for corroborating data.

Current findings, especially those of the electroencephalographers[5, 15] have done much to undermine psychogenic or functional arguments. Distinct electroencephalographic patterns related to symptomatology can be demonstrated in many cases, in some instances related to a particular focus, indicating a neuroanatomical basis of origin. In neurological terms epilepsy is currently thought of as a disturbance of the central nervous system involving failure to maintain delicate metabolic balance or equilibrium of nerve cell. Threshold alterations which account for the appearance of convulsive discharges are still poorly understood.

Frank convulsive attacks are usually classified according to symptomatology and etiology. Common categories are based upon clinical observation of attack:

Petit mal. Momentary interruptions of consciousness with or without minor movements (often consist of momentary staring into space as if thinking, the patient being able to continue what he was doing in some instances after a few seconds). Sometimes questions asked immediately preceding the attack have to be repeated. Petit mal is often mistaken by the layman for a behavior disorder originating from inattention. Nodding of the head or jerking of the limbs is not uncommon.

Grand mal. Seizure with loss of consciousness lasting a few minutes or longer and usually followed by drowsiness. Sometimes the seizure is preceded by an aura, and falling; tongue biting and incontinence may or may not accompany it. Convulsive passing into unconsciousness is generally distinguished from fainting by occurrence of some form of clonic or tonic movement.

Psychomotor. An attack involving disorders of the psyche as well as automatic and involuntary movements. Behavioral manifestations are common, as is amnesia for the attack. The form of epilepsy in which psychological factors contribute most clearly to the pattern of an attack.

Petit mal, grand mal, and psychomotor attacks may occur alone or simultaneously in the same patient. They may also appear successively, and it is not unusual to observe a change from one category to another, as, for example, a grand mal pattern emerging after several years' reduction in frequency of petit mal attacks. The reason for this shift is unknown, but in terms of psychological readjustment, it is of greatest importance.

Incidence statistics reveal that by far the greatest number of patients suffer from grand mal seizures. In number of attacks reported within the individual, petit mal takes the lead. Petit mal is sometimes referred to as a child's disease because it usually appears in childhood, although exceptions occasionally occur. The appearance of convulsive seizures for the first time in adults over thirty-five or forty years of age is viewed with suspicion by neurologists as more probably symptomatic of some condition other than epilepsy, such as intracranial neoplasm or arteriosclerosis.

Various medications are prescribed for different kinds of attacks. Occasionally a drug effective in one type will aggravate another. After years of treatment, it is not uncommon for patients to maintain complete control of convulsive attacks without further medication. Spontaneous remissions sometimes occur.

Psychological tests have established that mean intelligence quotients for random samples of epileptic populations tend to fall within the average range (90–109), although some investigators report averages which are below 100, the mean of the average interval (Yacorzynski and Arieff,[16] Zimmerman, Burgemeister, and Putnam[17]).

Efforts to relate degree of intellectual impairment to type, severity, frequency, or duration of convulsive seizures have produced varying results. The bulk of evidence to date indicates a positive correlation between degree of organicity present and unfavorable influence on intelligence test. As in other disorders, however, exact measurement of organic interferences usually presents a problem. Where focal brain injuries exist (traumatic epilepsy), where the onset of attacks has been associated with some inflammatory brain process (symptomatic epilepsy), or where a so-called organic basis for the attacks is hypothesized, interference with thinking and behavior is often easier to detect. Initial reports, as a matter of fact, used the nonorganic-organic dichotomy to describe deviations found. Later evidence shows such classification to be of little value in the individual case, since overlapping is prevalent. Location and extent of brain damage are important factors influencing test results, as are intellectual capacity and emotional stability, all of which operate simultaneously.

Heredity appears to have been overemphasized in early reports, since later figures reduce the probability factor in original statistics. In the nineteenth century Gowers[7] reported that inheritance seemed to account for 35 per cent of cases treated. Today this estimate would be considered too high and open to serious doubt. Recent statistics gathered by the Gibbses (Table 1) are more in keeping with current thought, which places greater emphasis upon "unknown" origins.

Table 1.[5] Incidence of Epileptic Seizures of Unknown Origin

Type of Attack	Number of Patients	Per Cent— Cause Unknown
Grand mal	4,458	79.5
Petit mal	335	85.4
Petit mal and grand mal	551	78.2
Psychomotor	517	76.3
Psychomotor and grand mal	1,323	73.2
Anterior temporal focus	1,237	73.9
Jacksonian	237	41.0
Focal	230	48.0

Percentages in Table 1 show that except in a minority of cases, a causal relationship between any one factor and the appearance of convulsive discharges cannot be validated. It is also of interest that in the Gibbses' data, known or presumed etiological factors are more common in cases with Jacksonian or focal epilepsy than in those without cortical focus. The authors point out further that birth injury seems to contribute particularly to causation of parietal, midtemporal, and occipital EEG foci. Prematurity is more common in cases with occipital epileptic foci than in any other of their groups, indicating a possible causal role in this type of localized disorder.

The approximately equal incidence of positive histories in patients with Jacksonian and focal epilepsy as compared with other types suggests to the Gibbses a constitutional factor. This, they believe, takes the form of a special vulnerability, either localized or diffuse. This susceptibility or proneness to convulsive disturbance has been noted by a number of authorities. It is supported by the higher incidence of abnormal EEG's among relatives of known epileptics than among normals, and the fact that familial epilepsy usually shows itself within the first few years of life. On the basis of findings to date, therefore, constitutional factors seem to provide barriers ranging from strong to weak, and thresholds from high to low, for resisting alterations of balance.

LOCALIZATION

Immediate and precipitating factors accounting for convulsive disturbances—including experimentally produced convulsions of the grand mal type—have been studied extensively among both humans and animals. This research shows that such seizure discharges do not depend upon a particular type of stimulation. The brain responds to electrical, mechanical, chemical, or thermal stimulation, provided it is of sufficient strength. The indication is that deviations from normal reaction relate to intensity and duration of stimulation rather than to differences in kind. Of interest in this connection is the fact that when seizures are produced experimentally, patterns consistent with grand mal epilepsy can be shown in electroencephalographic recording, but so far it has not been possible to duplicate spike-and-wave patterns suggestive of petit mal. Such a finding lends support to the clinical assumption that different types of attacks have different underlying cerebral origins.

It is currently recognized that a seizure discharge may develop in, and spread to, any part of the brain, no one area showing greater susceptibility than any other.

Convulsive disorders are generally classified as diffuse (generalized) or focal (involving one limb or one side of the body), depending upon the observed symptoms. Jackson[9] hypothesized that a site of origin in the brain was indicated in the pattern of a seizure, an assumption confirmed by later work. Jasper,[10] Penfield and Erickson,[12] and others have conducted elaborate research directed to the site of origin of seizures.

Penfield and Rasmussen[13] report that the highest-level seizure originates in the diencephalon, starting with petit mal, or loss of consciousness without lateralization. Unconscious adversive seizure starts with loss of consciousness and turning to the opposite side, while conscious adversive starts without sensory aura or loss of consciousness but with turning. Jacksonian, or motor seizures start with somatic movement; autonomic seizures arise in the diencephalon, although abdominal (gastrointestinal) aura originates in the island of Reil. These authors bring out numerous expressions of focal convulsive attacks classified by site of origin.

Only elementary forms of motion or sensation are produced when seizures originate in one of the integral specialized areas such as the somatic motor and sensory, or the visual and auditory areas. Penfield-Rasmussen findings indicate that discharge spreads from one ganglionic cluster to adjacent ones in a manner which is analogous to a fire spreading from one inflammable bundle of branches to the next. In this way sensations involving diverse end organs such as the fingers and toes are accounted for, not on a functional synaptic relationship basis, but rather on one of randomly juxtaposed nerve-cell involvement. When epileptic discharges do occur along acquired neural synapses, especially in the temporal cortex, they may produce illusions, hallucinations, dreams, and memories.

Disturbances in nerve-cell metabolism, on which convulsive phenomena appear to depend, are obviously complex neurophysiological and psychological processes, embracing areas of structure and function having far-reaching effects. It should therefore not be hard to understand why psychological measurement of the epileptic patient requires still more careful study.

PSYCHOLOGICAL EVALUATION

Intelligence retest results over periods of time generally vary up or down by only a few points. Except in institutional cases of long duration, or in isolated noninstitutional patients, little evidence has been presented so far for mental deterioration among epileptic patients.

A word of caution is appropriate here regarding use of the term "deteriorated" to describe retest quotients of individuals with epilepsy where a marked lowering in functioning level has been recorded and where organic components seem of prime importance. Often emotional instability, drug toxicity, inadequate baseline, or some other factor is later found to be responsible for a poor rating on test. The term "deteriorated" is wisely reserved for use with patients who have been examined over a period of years and who have tested progressively lower without exception, while showing a clinical picture increasingly less favorable. The majority of persons with convulsive disorders do not fall into this category.

In attempting to diagnose and treat patients with epilepsy, three psychological aspects command the attention of the neurologist, as Caveness[2] points out:

1. emotional problems that arise as a reaction to seizures.
2. those that act as a precipitant to individual seizures.
3. those that contribute to the pattern of seizures.

These factors are of equal importance to the psychologist, particularly since most epileptics are tested following onset of attacks. Very little is known so far about the preconvulsive personality of individuals with epilepsy and a postconvulsive baseline for psychometrics is the rule.

Individual differences in reaction to the presence of convulsive attacks are striking, and indicate varying degrees of maladjustment. Factors that act as precipitants to seizure take numerous forms. Emotional problems of many kinds contribute also to the pattern of seizures. Most of the latter are limited, however, to the psychomotor type of attack.

The Gibbses[5] remark that the so-called "epileptic personality" is common to individuals having psychomotor epilepsy, but uncommon among those with grand mal and petit mal. A wide range of psychiatric symptoms is characteristic of persons with psychomotor epilepsy, e.g., neurosis, depression, hysteria, paranoia, schizophrenia and the like, especially when convulsions are not prominent clinically. Oftentimes diagnosis is incorrectly made because psychological factors mask symptoms of organic involvement.

It has also been demonstrated that different psychiatric symptoms may be associated with anterior temporal lobe foci which appear identical.[5] In many instances medication may reduce seizures and change the EEG to normal, but will aggravate psychiatric disorders. The Gibbses believe this suggests a relative independence of ictal symptoms of psychomotor epilepsy and nonictal psychological disorders, i.e., of physiological and psychological elements as expressed in behavior.

Personality measurement of individuals with convulsive disorders becomes a problem of estimating the interrelation of anatomical, physiological, and emotional factors in a constitution where a low threshold for brain-cell metabolic instability is assumed. Projective techniques for measuring diffuse and focal organic disturbances are applicable here, and to date the test found most valuable is the Rorschach.

Following the lead of Guirdham[8] over twenty years ago, the "sign" approach has been most widely used to detect organicity and translate epileptic symptoms at the behavioral level. Piotrowski[14] supplemented his original organic signs with others more specific to epilepsy. Several investigators including Minkowska[11] have used this technique.

A recent elaborate study of Delay, Pichot, Lempériere, and Perse[4] is interesting because it combines the "sign" approach with what is called a variable of "experience-balance." The latter seems to vary as a function of etiology and location, and is related to the degree of adaptation of the subject. In studying the variable, the investigators have attacked the heart of the controversy as to whether the pattern of over-responsiveness, heightened affect, irritability, etc., empirically attributed to persons with convulsive disorders, has any basis in test results of a more objective nature. Their attempt likewise constitutes a step toward a more global approach to the problem of epilepsy.

The Delay study followed the record of fifty ambulatory epileptic patients in whom diagnosis had been confirmed both clinically and by electroencephalogram. The age range was wide, from fifteen to sixty years, although thirty-nine of the subjects were under forty.

Findings of Delay and co-workers indicate that the Rorschach records of epileptics of average intelligence revealed some deviation from normal, falling in general between a typically neurotic response and an organic pattern. They report, nevertheless, that evidence is insufficient regarding the roles of heredity, constitution, predisposition, or reaction to the disorder as causal factors. Their results tend to favor organic origins for personality deviations, abnormalities falling into a bipolar pattern. This consists of either a coarted, constricted, retarded and undifferentiated personality syndrome, or one which is expansive, dilated, and "extratensive," with many color and shading responses. They believe the coarted type has achieved more adaptiveness in social adjustment than the dilated type, which is felt to have a less favorable prognosis at the psychological level.

At best, such findings are suggestive rather than definite. A survey of neurological and psychological research shows very little of differential value reported, even in delineating the patient with epilepsy from the one with organic involvement. For any group of epileptics, psychological generalization is all but impossible because of wide differences in intellectual level, personality structure, reaction to environmental pressures, and defenses developed to handle the disease process. These problems, combined with those of poorly understood neurological variables, such as nerve-cell equilibrium, make it clear that much is yet to be learned. Some progress has been made, however, in the field of neuropsychological testing, as the following case histories indicate. To the neurologist their greatest value is in the insights they provide into the interaction of organic and emotional factors underlying the individual's adjustment to his environment. Adequate psychological evaluation is often a great asset in treatment, because the neurologist or neuropsychiatrist approaches therapy with improved adjustment of the individual as his goal, rather than symptomatic improvement.

CASE HISTORIES

Case I   Mild organic impairment in a thirteen-year old girl with petit mal and grand mal epilepsy

THE CLINICAL PICTURE

A Negro girl with normal birth and developmental history prior to appearance of petit mal attacks and grand mal seizures at age six. Petit mal attacks were reduced over seven years from twenty-five to thirty per week, to five to six per week. Grand mal seizures appeared erratically, on an average of one every one to six weeks. The day before psychological testing a grand mal seizure was reported. Seizures lasted for three or four minutes, followed by a period of drowsiness lasting for at least one-half hour, sometimes longer.

EEG tracing at the time of psychological evaluation was diffusely abnormal, with convulsive features consistent with grand mal seizures. Neurological examination was negative.

During the psychological test session the girl was selfconscious, awkward, reserved, apologetic, and compulsive in her efforts to cooperate. An eight-grade school placement was reported with good grades except in arithmetic. Resentment toward her stepmother and sibling rivalry with two stepsisters were reported, and the patient felt that her father was more permissive with the siblings than with her.

WECHSLER-BELLEVUE SCALE RESULTS

Information	9	Picture arrangement	8
Comprehension	10	Picture completion	7
Digit span	10	Block design	7
Arithmetic	6	Object assembly	10
Similarities	8	Digit symbol	6

Verbal scale quotient	101	
Performance scale quotient	91	
Full scale quotient	96	Average

On the verbal section the low arithmetic rating was in keeping with the reported school difficulty. Digit symbol score was the lowest on the performance section because reaction time was slow. Response to the block designs also showed unusual difficulty, with the fourth pattern taking 3′ 25″ instead of the required 75″. Confusion was particularly acute where diagonal lines were involved, as on designs Numbers 4 and 6. After time limits had expired the following pattern was produced for Number 6: see Figure 1.

FIG. 1. Attempted reproduction (left) of block design (right) by a 13-year-old girl with petit mal and grand mal epilepsy.

Poor work on block designs and the digit symbol test accounted for most of the discrepancy between verbal and performance quotients, reaction definitely favoring verbal scores. Although all of the quotients secured fell within the average range, blocking on an emotional basis was apparent, and ratings were considered minimal ones. Potential ability at the high-average level of intelligence appeared probable.

DRAWING OF A PERSON

About twenty minutes was consumed in drawing a very ornate figure of a woman. A great deal of care was taken to achieve accuracy of detail, and numerous remarks were included about the inadequacy of her performance. A need to explain details was also expressed in such comments as, "This is a piece of fur, a shawl," and "This is a hat." When she had finished, the girl apologized for the drawing, saying, "I know it's not very good."

The figure itself was fairly well proportioned, although hands and feet were unduly small, and the left arm had much less detail than the rest of the drawing. Because a large hat and fur piece were included, the figure had a rather top-heavy appearance.

Questioning revealed that the drawing was intended to portray an unmarried woman about twenty-seven years old who worked as a secretary and who was "a pretty good person." When asked what was the best thing the woman did, the girl replied, "She has pretty good manners." Her worst fault was reported as, "She drinks, she uses a lot of heavy beverages."

RORSCHACH RECORD

Performance	Scoring and Inquiry
Card I*	
12″ 1. Looks like a bat to me or else . . .	W F A P The whole thing looks like a bat to me. (?) Just because he has spreading wings and a body.

* Card held in upright position unless otherwise indicated.

Performance	Scoring and Inquiry

2. Looks like parts of it could be mountains.

    de   mF   Rocks
Looks like rocks are falling. (?) Off the mountains.

3. Looks like a man with two heads and an arm sticking out—not a human being.

    D   M   F   (H)
He's probably angry, he wouldn't raise his hands that way unless he was angry, or he's a caveman. No, he's angry, I guess.

4. Two sets of eyes.

    S   F   Ad
These spaces look like eyes. (?) animal eyes.

62"
Card II
10" 1. Looks like a building way up there. Looks like a building that's caught on fire. That's all I see.

    d→W   Fm   CF   Arch
                  C'F
                  FK
A building covered by smoke. Looks like it's on fire. The red is the flame and the black the smoke.

36"
Card III
15" 1. Looks like two men here— they look like butlers—and further back it . . .

    W   M   FC'   H   P
           Fc
They have a white collar. (?) They look the way men are built with legs and a head, not much hair. I didn't notice it before, they're fixing something, a pot of stew or something. They have a beard, too.

2. Looks like a hallway, and then . . .

    D   FK   Arch
This is a hallway or an entrance to something. (?) I can tell by the shape.

3. The sides look like two women.

    dr   M   Fc   H   O
I can see their head, part of the nose, a collar. They're sitting in a rocking chair.

48"
Card IV*
8" Can you turn it?
23" 1. ∨∧ Looks like feet.

    D   F   Hd
The shape of it looks like a boot and . . .

---

* Symbols after numeral denote position of card being held: apex ∧∨><
corresponds to top of card as presented to subject.

Performance   Scoring and Inquiry

2. V   Upside down it looks   W   FM   A
       like a horse, a horse   A flying horse like the gasoline ad-
       that has wings and his   vertisement.
       legs doubled up.

41"
Card V
4" 1. V This looks just like a bat   W   F→FM   A   P
         although the head doesn't The wings in particular make this
         look like it—just looks like look like a bat. (?) A bat getting
         two arms sticking up—but ready to fly.
         the wings are right.
    2.   Looks like a donkey, sort   D→W   F   Fc   (A)
         of, I don't know whether Here are the ears, hind legs, head—
         you'd call it wings or not. maybe two wings—maybe made up
                                   for a masquerade. (?) With a cos-
                                   tume on.

49"
Card VI
40" V∧ I have no idea.   dd   F   Obj
                                   This looks like the point of a spear—
                                   has a point sticking out. Nothing else
                                   I'm familiar with.

47"
Card VII
16" 1. These look like two dogs.   D   F   (A)
                                   Looks like they are in a cartoon. (?)
                                   They look exaggerated—not a good
                                   shape. (?) No special kind of dog.
     2. Then it looks like further   d   FK   C'F   Arch
        down a hallway—like a   A small picture and probably in the
        building—a small church— winter. The white down there is
        that's all.   probably snow. (?) Looks like it's in
                                   the distance—a winter scene.

58"
Card VIII
17" 1. V Looks like a sundae—ice   W   CF   cF   Ice Cream
         cream—the colors do.   Peach—strawberry   maybe—mixed—
                                   pistachio. (?) Looks soft.
     2. This way it looks like two   DF→FM   A   P
         animals, prairie dogs on The shape of them looks like prairie
         each side.   dogs. (?) They might be climbing or
                                   walking.

Performance   Scoring and Inquiry

40"

Card IX

15"   1. ∨∧ Looks like two men and   D   M   H
              it appears as if they're   Looks like they're on top of a bal-
              fixing something.   cony. (?) They seem to be standing
                                            on something.

      2. ∨   Upside down looks like   D   M   FK   H
              there's a lady in be-   Fc
              tween all these colors—   KF
              you can see just part of   Looks more like an old lady because
              the balcony in the back-   of the hat and shawl. There is the
              ground.   balcony. There seems to be a light
                                            back there.

68"

Card X

12"   1. ∨   These look like crabs, and   D   F   A   P
              there's . . .   Shape of crabs. (?) Dead looking.
      2. ∨   Another animal.   D   F   A
                                            Also looks like a crab. Looks more
                                            like a crab than the other one.

      3. >   Two things look like but-   D   F   A
              terflies—either one. No,   Shape. (?) That's all.
              looks more like two little
              puppies.
      4.   Then something that has   D   F   Obj
              eyes—I don't know what   Looks like when you have gas and
              you call it.   put it over your face—may be a gas
                                            mask.
      5.   There's two things that   D   F   A
              look like they're lady   Just the shape.
              bugs.

84"

INTERPRETATION

Organic signs indicated on intelligence-test material are the discrepancy between verbal and performance quotients, and favoring the former;
low arithmetic, block-design, and digit-symbol test scores, and the exceptional confusion in reproducing the block-design patterns. Such
inadequacies were in keeping with behavior, manifesting feelings of
uncertainty and insecurity. The drawing of a person is not typically
organic, with no gross distortions in body image, but it is of interest that
the left arm is poor in comparison with the rest of the figure. Numerous
erasures, compulsiveness, and apologies would be consistent with anxiety

often seen in individuals with organic pathology, if considered in the light of total findings.

Rorschach responses reflect higher intellectual capacity than the intelligence test, and a lowering in present functioning level. Other features consistent with the presence of an organic disorder would be: the extreme variation in the use of color (from "fire" to "ice cream"); dissatisfaction with concepts but inability to improve upon them such as the response "this looks just like a bat though the head doesn't look like it—just the two arms sticking up, but the wings are right;" attraction to blackness in the cards; difficulty in disentangling details with disturbance in figure-ground relationships such as "a lady in between all these colors."

In assessing degree of organic interference, which here is relatively mild, it is well to remember that responsibility for all of the impotence and perplexity should not be placed unequivocally upon the disorder. Exaggeration of limitation is aggravated in this case by personal and social factors only remotely related to the epileptic process, namely: 1) difficulties of adjustment to a step-mother and step-sisters, and 2) problems of social acceptance because of racial prejudice.

Only after these factors had been alleviated or controlled could the degree of interference with functioning due to her epileptic condition be measured. The interaction of such variables is extremely complex, and at present no adequate tools exist for estimating their influences exactly.

Case II   Test and retest of a thirty-year-old epileptic woman showing mild organic impairment, exaggerated by drug toxicity

THE CLINICAL PICTURE

Petit mal attacks and grand mal seizures since the age of seven. Convulsive phenomena followed influenza with very high fever and were diagnosed as "symptomatic" epilepsy. Petit mal attacks occurred on an average of several per week; grand mal seizures ranged from one every three or four weeks to several in one week. Seizures lasted ten minutes, followed by drowsiness for one hour.

EEG tracing at the time of psychological test was diffusely abnormal and included dysrhythmia and slowing consistent with a convulsive disorder. Neurological examination was negative, except that a combination of drugs used to control grand mal seizures had produced a toxic state.

The patient arrived fifteen minutes late for her appointment and apologized but offered no excuse. As testing began, she talked incessantly, with many irrelevancies and facetious remarks. Seemingly in an effort to impress the examiner, she spoke pedantically and with conviction. Obviously testing was a great threat to her.

Attention and concentration were poor and reaction time much slower than expected, especially since she reported an excellent cultural background which included a college education. When the examiner suggested to her that talking about one thing and concentrating upon another is very difficult, she agreed and said, "All my life I've been told to shut my trap." Following this remark, performance improved, but not for long. The next time she was reminded, she laughed and replied, "You should have my husband doing these things. They're not for me."

Interestingly, when a hard task was introduced, she complained that she was "having a long petit mal attack" (not visible) and "just blacking out." She also stated, "I'm going to have a grand mal attack later today, so I really can't solve this now." Resistance was apparent, but under pressure, she completed many tests which she originally had denied being able to do. Near the end of the test session, she indulged in disparaging remarks about her "slowness," "stupidity," and "lack of intelligence," in contrast to her rather aloof manner at first, suggesting her awareness of her inability to cope adequately with some of the materials and a gradual reduction in the need to hide this deficiency.

WECHSLER-BELLEVUE SCALE RESULTS I

On the Wechsler-Bellevue Scale the verbal-scale quotient was only 91, performance quotient 87, and full-scale quotient 88, the latter falling within the low average range. Subtest scores were as follows:

Information	13	Picture arrangement	9
Comprehension	11	Picture completion	10
Digit span	3	Block design	5
Arithmetic	3	Object assembly	7
Similarities	9	Digit symbol	4

A significantly erratic test pattern was obtained, making all scores minimal. Such items, for example, as who wrote *Faust* were correctly answered, while others such as repetition of three digits were incorrect. More than the usual amount of unpredictability was characteristic, and at times answers bordered on the irrational. As one illustration, the patient's response to the question why land in the city costs more than land in the country was "Because it's under so much concrete."

Block-design reproduction presented particular difficulty. Only Numbers 1 and 4 were completed within time limits and the last two most complicated patterns were done very slowly (4'05" and 5'15").

Judging from the patient's best work and her conversation and background, an estimate of superior intelligence was made, under optimal conditions.

BENDER GESTALT I

Degree of distortion was not commensurate with that found on intelligence test, but two figures were rotated and lines were substituted for dots in another. Too many dots in a series of 12 suggested perseveration on this particular test.

DRAWING OF A PERSON

An exceptionally well-drawn head of an angel complete with halo was obtained from the patient. It definitely revealed training and artistic talent and was far superior to the rest of her work. Because she kept redrawing this figure and used it in place of a signature on her letters, it is omitted as possibly identifying.

RORSCHACH RECORD I

Performance	Scoring and Inquiry

Card I

9″ 1. A Hallowe'en mask.

W   S   F   Mask
It has eyes and a mouth. (?) They folded it and here are the holes.

12″

Card II

8″ 1. They just spilled ink twice in a row. It comes out the same on two sides and different colors also.

D   CF   Ink
Just ink, that's all. (?) It doesn't look like anything to me.

14″

Card III

5″ 1. A couple of people. Not much else, it looks like so much ink. They were careless with the red ink.

W   M   Fc   H   P
Butlers, I think, carrying something. (?) They have uniforms on.

15″

Card IV

16″ 1. They made an effort to make it look like something, but I can't tell what it is, just a great big blurb.

W   F   Sex
From the delicacy of it you'd look for a sexual reaction, but I haven't the slightest idea what.

32″

Card V

20″ 1. It doesn't look like much, it's inartistic, almost the same on both sides.

—   —   —   —
I can't accept this.
(Turns card over)

29″

Card VI

16″ They spilled ink—a picture of ink.

W   CF   Ink
It's just a mess, that's all—nothing more.

Performance	Scoring and Inquiry

32"

Card VII

6" Same for that. No use whatso-   W   CF   Ink
ever.   Just another mess.

15"

Card VIII

11" 1. There are more colors and   W   Fm   Obj
they all resemble a child   D   FM   A   P
folding napkins. The two Well, now animals are to be seen.
sides are the same. They look like bears climbing up
something. Don't ask me what.

34"

Card IX

32"   Nothing.   Still nothing—ink.

Card X

7" 1. More ink—somebody's worked   W   CF   Ink
harder to make it look like More ink.
something, but it doesn't.

16"

INTERPRETATION I

Although the difference was very slight between verbal and performance quotients on the Wechsler material, this was apparently the result
of a general lowering in functioning level in all parts of the scale. The
high information score suggested above average intellectual ability under
optimal conditions, especially since quality of the best responses reached
the superior level. Items requiring new learning fared badly.

Response to the Rorschach was very much less productive than expected. This seemed largely the result of fatigue and lack of effort,
although clearly the cards posed a threat to the patient and she was too
confused to exert much creative ability. Significantly, nevertheless, out
of such an impoverished protocol, human movement, animal movement,
and texture were obtained. Marked concern with symmetry is the outstanding characteristic of the meagre record, along with extreme helplessness in the use of color.

After this first psychological test session, medication for epilepsy was
adjusted, and the same battery of psychological measures was repeated
nine days later.

After the patient's initial remark that she did not "see the sense of
repeating these things again," cooperation was better during the second
test session. Talking was excessive, but better rapport with her was
possible. At one point she remarked, "I've been accused by the doctor of
giving you a hard time before. I'll be good today."

WECHSLER-BELLEVUE SCALE RESULTS II

Improvement in intelligence test ratings was marked, with the verbal-scale quotient raised 23 points to 114 and the performance

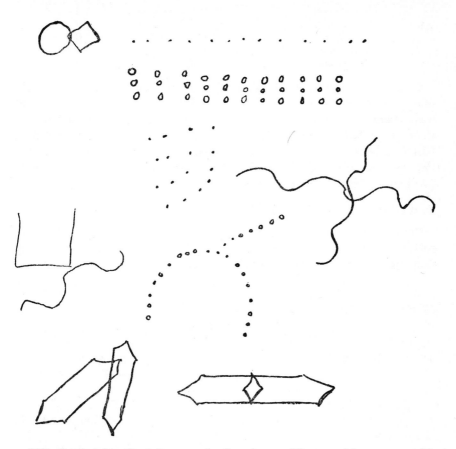

FIG. 2. Bender Gestalt reproduction by a 30-year-old woman with "symptomatic" epilepsy.

quotient 15 points to 101. These scores placed the second full-scale quotient near the upper end of the average range, or 108. Subtest scores on retest appear below:

Information	13	Picture arrangement	12
Comprehension	14	Picture completion	12
Digit span	10	Block design	8
Arithmetic	7	Object assembly	7
Similarities	14	Digit symbol	7

Comparison with ratings on the previous series gave positive point changes on all but two tests:

Point Increases on Retest after Nine Days

Information	0	Picture arrangement	3
Comprehension	3	Picture completion	2
Digit span	7	Block design	3
Arithmetic	4	Object assembly	0
Similarities	5	Digit symbol	3

Greatest change showed upon digit span; concentration was definitely better on retest. Similarities and arithmetic came next, with least change on information and object assembly. Since the latter two tests are relatively insensitive to interference, the contrast between best and least improvement has an organic tinge, but not nearly in the degree noted formerly. Verbal material was still favored, with much overlapping between first and second test patterns.

BENDER GESTALT TEST II

Better organization on second test could be noted (Fig. 2), but rotation of the plane was again apparent, and significantly, too many dots again appeared. Some of the figures still seemed slightly off balance, although improved, and cooperation was obviously better.

RORSCHACH RECORD II

Performance	Scoring and Inquiry

Card I

4″   1. A butterfly.

                                     W   F   A   P
                        The general shape of it, the head and wings.

     2. An elephant.

                                         D   F   A
                        The shape, his head and long trunk.

     3. Boats

                                         S   FC′   Obj
                        Sailboats. They have white sails.

     4. Two ducks

                                         D   F   A
                        Shape, the head and wings.

     5. Two people raising hands.

                                         D   M   H
                        On the top it looks like two people but only one on the bottom; it must be a two-headed person. No, I guess there are two of them.

74″
Card II

6″   1. A hip bone.

                                     W   F   At
                        The whole thing looks like a skeleton. (?) It has the shape of the hips.

Performance

2. Two rabbits or two dogs.

3. The White House dome.

84"
Card III
2" **1.** Two butlers.

2. Two dogs.

3. A dog.

4. Two little boys.

5. A woman's head.

6. A fish.

98"
Card IV
5" **1.** This also looks like a large butterfly.

2. A bearskin rug.

51"
Card V
4" **1.** They all look like butterflies.

Scoring and Inquiry

DF→FM   A   P

It looks like the shape of some animal, probably dogs. (?) It looks like they have their noses rubbing together.

S   FC'   Obj

The shape of it looks like the White House dome and it's white (confusion with the Capitol dome).

W   M   Fc   H   P

They're carrying something. I guess it's a bucket. (?) Their uniforms look like butlers. (?) Fancy.

D   F→FM   A

Fox terriers because they are small and shaped right. They seem to have something on their head. They're balancing something, I don't know what.

d   Fc   Ad

He has a large head and a bow around his neck. (?) He's some kind of a fuzzy dog, probably a poodle.

W   M   H   P

They're sticking out their bellies.

dr   F→M   Hd

Her face is looking down with her head lowered.

D   F→FM   A

It looks like a flying fish. It's flying.

W   F   A

The whole thing looks like a butterfly, the shape of it with wings and a head.

D   Fc   Aobj

The head and the body spread out make it look like a bearskin rug. (?) I'm looking at the fur side.

W   F   A   P

The general shape, the whole thing. (?) Just the shape.

Performance	Scoring and Inquiry
2. A fan dancer.	D→W M Fc H

She has a bandana on and her skirt spread out as if she were dancing.

| 3. A rabbit's head. | d F Ad |

The shape of it looks like a rabbit.

49"
Card VI

| 5" 1. An open peach | W Fm Food |

This part is just the shape of an open peach, as if you'd cut it open down the middle and opened it up. Here are the two pieces.

| 2. A preacher or cherub at the top. | dd F (H) |

You can see the back of someone's head and the wings. (?) A cherub, I guess. Looks like it's mounted on something.

| 3. A man's face. | D F Hd |

The shape of a man's face.

| 4. A swallow. | W F A |

The whole thing looks like a bird. Here is the head and here are the wings.

76"
Card VII

| 8" 1. Two women. | D M Fc H |

They are two women talking. They're leaning over on a fence, I guess. (?) The hairdo looks like women.

| 2. Two headless girls. | D M Fc Hd |

They're dancing. Here are their arms and legs and skirt.

56"
Card VIII

| 8" 1. I'm ashamed. Two beavers. | D FM A P |

They're climbing on something. (?) Being ashamed. (?) I called them bears or something else before. I should have said beavers.

| 2. A spider. | D F A |

This is the shape of a spider.

45"
Card IX

| 4" 1. Clowns. | D M Fc (H) |

These look like clowns. They're blowing horns and they have padded bellies.

2. Donkeys.

           D F Ad

Just the head of the donkey. It's a pretty good shape.

3. A baby.

           D FC Fc H

It's pink and wrapped up. You can see the head and the body.

57"

Card X

5" 1. This looks like the Zoo. Crabs.

           D FM A P

These look like crabs. They seem to be eating something. (?) They have a lot of legs.

2. Shells.

           D CF Obj

They are coiled and colorful like shells.

3. A mouse.

           D FC A

It's a brown mouse. The color and shape suggest it.

4. A wishbone.

           D F Obj

It's a pretty good shape of one.

52"

INTERPRETATION II

The second Rorschach protocol confirms the clinical estimate of superior intelligence and agrees in showing a lowering in present functioning level, even with a remarkable improvement over the first protocol. Organic features are much harder to enumerate here, although some seem indicated. Reduction in variety of content, very mild repetition "They all look like butterflies," use of FC', much more interest in color than is demonstrated in concepts using this determinant. On the whole, however, only mild organicity seems revealed, emotional components being much more prominent.

Case III   Severe organic damage in a twenty-four-year-old woman with petit mal, grand mal, and psychomotor epilepsy

THE CLINICAL PICTURE

Age twenty-four and one-half years at the time of psychological test. Birth and development normal. Walking and talking at the expected times. Progress uneventful with a seventh-grade placement in school before the appearance of petit mal, grand mal, and psychomotor attacks at age eleven years. Considered idiopathic. Frequency of petit mal, several a day; grand mal, one every eight to ten days; psychomotor, one every two weeks. Grand mal seizures typical of generalized convulsions, lasting about ten minutes. Always tired afterward. One precipitating factor causing attacks was overeating. Psychomotor attacks consisted of sudden running around with purpose of getting out of room or house. Behavior reported as very difficult, with periods of irritability unrelated to seizure occurrence, and wide mood swings often noted. Also said to be forgetful and to exercise poor judgment.

Neurological examination was negative at time of psychological testing. EEG was abnormal with convulsive features. No focal signs.

Behavior during the psychological test session was very good, and the patient was friendly and cooperative. Failure disturbed her badly. Insecurity was clear in the many remarks she made showing recognition of deficiencies and in her hesitant approach to harder problems.

STANFORD-BINET TEST RESULTS

On the Stanford-Binet test (Form L) a mental age of ten years, four months, I.Q. 69 (borderline) was earned, using a sixteen-year-old norm. A basal age was established at Year VII, with all tests except memory for sentences creditable at year VIII and all except paper cutting and memory for designs acceptable at Year IX. Failures at Year X included memory for reading, word naming, and repetition of digits. At Year XI all tests were passed except memory for designs and memory for sentences. All items except the Minkus completion test were creditable at Year XII. Her highest successes were the plan of search at Year XIII, vocabulary and abstract words at Year XIV, and vocabulary at the Average Adult I level, where a vocabulary score of twenty-two words was achieved.

Approximately the same degree of interference was recorded on performance test (Arthur Revision Form II). There a performance score of ten years, three months, was recorded. All test ratings fell near the ten-year norm; no outstanding features were seen except slowness in reaction time. Form perception seemed relatively good. Borderline performance ability was recorded.

DRAWING OF A PERSON

Three attempts were made at drawing a man, all of which fell far short of the usual figure. As she worked, the patient became very much embarrassed and stated that drawing had always been her "worst subject" in school. Even though dissatisfaction with her efforts was expressed, the examiner felt that she was not aware of the degree of limitation apparent. The patient seemed to want assurance, but once this was given, did not appear to recognize almost complete failure. (Fig. 3.)

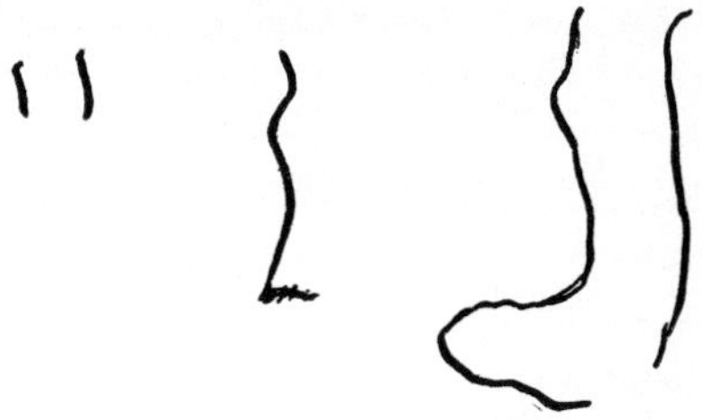

FIG. 3. Figure of a man drawn by a 24-year-old woman with petit mal, grand mal, and psychomotor epilepsy.

RORSCHACH RECORD

Performance	Scoring and Inquiry

Card I

5″ 1. Could be an animal.

W F→FM A P
It's somewhat of an eagle. It looks like it's going to spread its wings but then again by the little things up here it looks like a moosehead. Yes, here are the wings and neck. I say it's a moosehead.

21″

Card II

13″ 1. This looks like two bears.

D FM A P
D CF Blood
It looks like they're rubbing noses or else they're in a fight. (?) I guess they're in a fight. This might be the blood.

28″

Card III

7″ Good Lord, I don't know.

26″ 1. It looks like regular people picking up a bowling ball or something, human beings.

W M Fm H P
It looks like men bowling. Here is the head, the neck, the hand, and the leg. The leg should be joined here. It looks like it's falling off.

2. A bow tie in between here.

D F Obj P
It looks like a bow tie. (?) The shape of it.

47″

Card IV

8″ 1. A giant standing on his head.

W M (H)
He's big and ugly like a giant. His feet are up over his head.

2. Would you like me to say it's some animal?

D F A
I don't know what kind of animal this is. I can see his back and feet,

Performance	Scoring and Inquiry

but I can't see his head. Ooh, he looks crawly.

3. It could even be a tree growing.

        D Fm Pl
This is not so good. It just looks like roots and branches.

54"
Card V
3" 1. A bat.

        W FM A P
Looks like he's flying. His wings are all spread out. His head is here and these look like feelers.

14"
Card VI
14" 1. One of those flies getting ready to sting you, or else

        W FM A
At first I thought it looks like a fly— the whole thing—head and body, then

2. It could be another small insect with a long body.

        W FM A
I saw this small insect up top with a long body and wings. (?) He's flying, too.

36"
Card VII
14" 1. This looks like a map but in between

        W F Geo
Looks like a geography map. It reminds me of those in school.

2. If that's not an insect that's a boat stuck in between mountains and cliffs. How you mistake things if you haven't binoculars!

        dd FM Obj
And I guess this is a boat, yes, looks like a very small boat that got caught in between the cliffs in a storm. (?) I don't know if it will ever get out. I hope so. They will.

67"
Card VIII
23" 1.   Some kind of a flower. No. (Rejected)

        D FM A P

2.   An insect, too.

Looks like a rat now—two rats climbing over the ground.

3. > Part of a butterfly, isn't it?

        D F Ad
It's shaped something like it, not too much. (?) Just the shape.

4. ∨ This way it looks like a flower, like the leaves falling off here.

        W CF mF Pl
I don't know what kind of a flower this is but it's got pretty colors and it looks like leaves falling off here.

Performance	Scoring and Inquiry

58"

Card IX

25" 1. Looks like a snowball but they usually grow on a bush, so it has to be some other kind of plant—but it's a plant.

D→W   CF   C'F   Pl

The white thing makes it look like a snowball that turns colors, but the rest of it looks like a plant. It's not the right shape plant for a snowball plant, but I don't know what kind of plant it is. Anyway here are the green leaves.

48"

Card X

15" 1. ∨∧ This looks like some kind of an insect, but this looks like they take them to the laboratory and feed them.

D   FC→FM   A

Looks like some kind of a little brown bug.

2. This part is the pipe they feed the flowers, and the insects have gotten on it.

D   CF   Pl

The flower is pink and green. I don't know what kind it is. Here are the brown insects and the yellow part could be leaves.

D   FC   FM   A

It could be a butterfly, too. It looks like a yellow butterfly flying.

71"

INTERPRETATION

The outstanding feature of the Stanford-Binet material is the difficulty with memory tests as opposed to a vocabulary score at the adult level. Failures in reproducing designs from memory and in completing the paper-cutting test (Year IX) also point toward trouble with perception of spatial relationships. This hypothesis is borne out dramatically in the attempted figure of a man, where interference reaching pathological proportions is striking. After three attempts, and efforts to portray the figure in profile position, which indicates maturity, the most primitive and regressive kind of drawing resulted.

The Rorschach record reveals a great need to intellectualize anxiety and feelings of inadequacy, apparent in attempts at sophistication such as "map" responses, and references to "binoculars," and to "laboratory," suggesting a scientific background with which she is little familiar. "Stickiness" may be noted in the perseveration of insects, flowers, and plants, along with trouble in finding satisfactory form, an effort typical of organic patients, who usually succeed only partially in their attempts to maintain good form level consistently. Overreaching with an effort to take care of everything in the card is also reflected. Limitation in content is apparent, with emphasis predominantly upon simple concepts involving nature and animal life.

It is of interest that the content of the Rorschach is relatively free from very aggressive elements, although belligerent behavior was reported as typical at home. Also noteworthy is the fact that the lower part of Card VII suggests not a snug harbor but a "very small boat caught between cliffs in a storm," and trying to get out. A characteristic pattern of "getting out" is reported when the patient has a psychomotor attack.

All the work shows more interference with thinking than in Case I, or in Case II when toxicity did not intervene. One possible explanation lies in the fact that medication had been grossly inadequate over a period of twelve years before evaluation in an individual having to cope with three kinds of convulsive attacks.

DISCUSSION OF CASES

Clinical behavior and intelligence level differed considerably in three epileptic patients tested. In all cases evidence was obtained for organic interference with thinking and with adjustment. Block designs, digit-symbols, and arithmetic tests showed particular difficulty. All of these are considered sensitive to the presence of organicity. Intertest patterns, however, reflected a great deal of variability in the expression of these organic factors.

In all instances, projective techniques revealed a combination of organic and emotional features which prevented adequate adjustment. The relative weights of these factors are harder to assess. In one instance organic elements seemed to predominate, while in another neurotic components were more striking. Uncertainty, anxiety, attempts to intellectualize conflict, and obsessive-compulsive trends were some of the traits noted. Whether these are basic to a preconvulsive personality, or are defense mechanisms erected against the central-nervous-system disorder, or against the exigencies of everyday life, is not clear from available data.

EPILEPSY AND NEUROPSYCHOLOGY

Findings are essentially in keeping with those of other investigators. Of all psychological techniques applied to problems of epilepsy, intelligence testing has produced the most certain general findings. Average intellectual ability may now be assigned to epileptics as a group while, contrary to previous opinion, mental deterioration is relatively rare.

Individual personality evaluation has also met with success. Since the neurologist or neuropsychiatrist is treating an individual rather than a symptom, such a contribution is meaningful to prognosis and treatment. Maladjustment, common among epileptics, may interfere with long-range therapy more than neurological factors: i.e., even when attacks have been completely controlled by medication for long periods of time, fear of recurrence may keep the individual tense, anxious, withdrawn, or hypochondriacal. Hence the value of psychological evaluation is now recognized as a helpful adjunct to therapy.

The relative weights of emotional and organic elements in total adjustment are far more easily determined for a given epileptic than for epileptics as a group. Traits assignable to large numbers of epileptic patients are still controversial. Hence testing has done much to dispel the notion of the "epileptic personality," so prominent in earlier literature. Only in rare cases can "epileptic organicity" be differentiated from that produced by other central-nervous-system disorders. Overlapping is typical between organic and psychoneurotic features, especially in the explosive behavioral disorders of children. Still less is known about underlying mechanisms accounting for particular deviations. Recognition of these very problems, on the other hand, represents, with its shift toward more neurologically oriented thinking, genuine progress.

BIBLIOGRAPHY

1. BELLAK, L. In DELAY, J., PICHOT, P., LEMPÉRIÈRE, T., and PERSE, J. *The Rorschach and the Epileptic Personality*. Logos Press, 25–27, 1958.
2. CAVENESS, W. F. Emotional and psychological factors in epilepsy: general clinical and neurological considerations. *Amer. J. Psychiat.*, 112 (2): 190–193, 1955.
3. CLARK, L. P. A personality study of the epileptic constitution. *Amer. J. Med. Sc.*, 148: 729–738, 1914.
4. DELAY, J., PICHOT, P., LEMPÉRIÈRE, T., and PERSE, J. Le test de Rorschach dans l'epilepsie. I. La personnalité epileptique. *Encephale*, 43: 374–378, 1954.
5. GIBBS, F. A., and GIBBS, E. L. *Atlas of electroencephalography*. II. Cambridge, Mass.: Addison-Wesley Press: 1952.
6. GIBBS, F. A., GIBBS, E. L., and LENNOX, W. Epilepsy: a paroxysmal cerebral dysrhythmia. *Brain*, 60: 377–388, 1937.
7. GOWERS, W. R. *Epilepsy and Other Chronic Convulsive Diseases; Their Causes, Symptoms and Treatment*. New York: Wood & Co.; 1885.
8. GUIRDHAM, A. The Rorschach test in epileptics. *J. Ment. Sc.*, 81: 870–893, 1935.

9. JACKSON, J. H. *Selected Writings*. Taylor, J. (Ed.). New York: Basic Books, 1958.
10. JASPER, H. H. In PENFIELD, W. G., and ERICKSON, T. C. *Epilepsy and Cerebral Localization*, Ch. 14. Springfield, Ill.: Chas. C Thomas; 1941.
11. MINKOWSKA, F. Le test de Rorschach dans l'epilepsie essentielle. *Ann. Med. Psychol.*, 102: 545–558, 1944.
12. PENFIELD, W. A., and ERICKSON, T. C. *Epilepsy and Cerebral Localization*. Springfield, Ill.: Charles C Thomas; 1941.
13. PENFIELD, W. A., and RASMUSSEN, T. B. *The Cerebral Cortex of Man: A Clinical Study of Localization of Function*. New York: Macmillan: 1950.
14. PIOTROWSKI, Z. The personality of the epileptic. In *Epilepsy: Psychiatric Aspects of Convulsive Disorders*. Hoch, P., and Knight, R. (Eds.). New York: Grune & Stratton; 1947.
15. WALTER, W. G. Epilepsy: A symposium on its various aspects. In *Electroencephalography*. Hill, D., and Parr, G. (Eds.) London: MacDonald; 1950.
16. YACORZYNSKI, G. K., and ARIEFF, A. J. Absence of deterioration in patients with nonorganic epilepsy with especial reference to bromide therapy. *J. Nerv. & Ment. Dis.*, 95: 687–698, 1942.
17. ZIMMERMAN, F. T., BURGEMEISTER, B. B., and PUTNAM, T. J. Intellectual and emotional makeup of the epileptic. *Arch. Neurol. & Psychiat.*, 65: 545–556, 1951.

ADDITIONAL REFERENCES

1. BENTON, A. L. The Rorschach test in epilepsy. *Amer. J. Orthopsychiat.*, 26 (2): 420–426, 1956.
2. GOLDMAN, G. D. A comparison of the personality structure of patients with idiopathic epilepsy, hysterical convulsions and brain tumors. Paper read before Eastern Psychological Assoc., Atlantic City, 1952.
3. PRUYSER, P. W., and FOLSOM, A. T. The Rorschach experience balance in epileptics. *J. Consult. Psychol.*, 19: 112–116, 1955.
4. ROUMAJON, Y. Quelques aspects psychiques de l'epilepsie chez l'enfant. *Med. inf. Par.*, 65: 39–42, 1958.
5. WILLIAMS, D. The structure of emotions reflected in epileptic experience. *Brain*, 79 (1): 27–67, London, 1956.
6. ZIMMERMAN, F. T., and BURGEMEISTER, B. B. Explosive behavioral anomalies in children on a possible epileptic basis. *New York State J. Med.*, 56: 2537–2542, 1956.

VII

>>>

Mental Retardation

Measurement of organicity in individuals with limited intelligence requires an understanding of mental retardation in neurological terms. Simple or primary mental retardation is regarded as an amentia rather than a dementia, as a constitutional lag in development rather than a disease process. It is presumed to be a reflection of 1) an incomplete or arrested growth of certain brain cells, 2) a deficiency in associative or integrative neural mechanisms, or 3) a combination of these. Whether such an amentia is familial or idiopathic, in most instances explanation of this "unfinished" neuropsychological tendency is entirely lacking.

Neurologists use the term "secondary" mental retardation when organic rather than genetic factors seem to account for the deficiency or add to mental handicap already present. In many cases organic factors may be deemed the sole cause of arrested development. In others causes are difficult to isolate.

Mental retardation therefore may be idiopathic, familial, related to infections, birth injury and trauma, or the result of chronic degenerative disease processes. Clinical types may include patients with microcephaly, hydrocephaly, postencephalitic syndromes, mongolism, paralysis, epilepsy, cerebral palsy, sclerosis, meningitis, congenital syphilis, endocrine dysfunction and others. Some of these clinical syndromes are not uncommon in combination, as for instance, mental deficiency, epilepsy, and cerebral palsy in the same child.

Even when an accurate history is obtained, it is frequently difficult to be certain that one is dealing with a case of genuine mental deficiency, i.e., a hereditary or constitutional deficiency, and not with a case of pseudo-mental retardation. Differentiation between constitutional deficiency, with or without organic impairment, and pseudo-mental retardation on a functional or psychogenic basis is a task requiring time and study. Many psychotics act and function like mental defectives, while behavior problems are widespread among mentally retarded children. Behavioral conflicts are not inevitably inherent in mental deficiency per se, but arise in an environment constantly demanding more than the individual is capable of giving.

Sometimes confirmation of organic interferences with thinking in the mentally retarded is possible by neurological examination and laboratory techniques; sometimes it is not. To detect neuroanatomical pathology in the brain of a mental defective may or may not be possible, even if convolutional defects in brain structure or defective development of neurons exist. Relationships between structural defect and psychological functioning are not linear, and conclusions must be tentative.

The trend among clinical psychologists is to think of mental retardation and mental deficiency in broader terms than were used heretofore. Investigators have become increasingly aware in the last decade that arbitrary classification by intellectual level failed to give proper scope to the problem. A variety of factors—anatomical, neurological, psychological, psychiatric, socio-economic, cultural, and historical—must be scrutinized in the individual case. Emphasis is now upon the individual as a dynamic Gestalt rather than an intelligence-test statistic. Recently reported successes in psychotherapy such as Sarason and others have undertaken with mentally retarded children[13] stress this current tendency and point to a brighter outlook for the retarded child.

Adjusted to new awareness, intelligence tests have proved useful in measuring certain aspects of intellectual retardation and in setting limits on expectation that are especially meaningful to educators and vocational-guidance personnel. Such demarcations as low-average ability and borderline capacity help in indicating intellectual limitation for formal education and training. It is also generally accepted that anyone with an intelligence quotient below 65 (approximately), i.e., a quotient showing a lag in development of more than one-third of the person's expected rate, may justifiably be considered as having seriously limited intellectual capacity.

While all agree that intelligence quotients within the defective range reveal very severe intellectual handicap, a classification of "mental deficiency" implies a neuropsychological unity which is never present. Through widespread use of this wastebasket category in earlier work, fundamental problems of etiology were frequently neglected and individuals stereotyped as hopelessly handicapped.

For many years extensive research has been done on groups of children with endogenous and exogenous "feeblemindedness" in order to distinguish those with brain injury from those with no known neurological involvement beyond the original constitutional defect (Bensberg,[5] Bijou, and Werner,[6] Halpin[10]).

Experimental results, as a whole, show less favorable response from brain-damaged children on psychological test than from non-injured children, as might be anticipated. Conclusions are tentative, nevertheless, because often information on the exact nature of cases studied is lacking, heterogeneous types of brain-injured children are grouped, and controls are poor or absent. Several studies using one instrument in testing for organicity reveal a need for more extensive work using batteries of tests.

Disagreement among investigators using a single instrument for comparative purposes is revealed in the research of Bensberg[5] and that of Halpin[10] with the Bender Gestalt test. In comparing the performances of brain-injured and familial mental defectives on the Bender Gestalt, Bensberg included 322 subjects, one-half brain-injured and one-half with inherited or familial mental deficiency. The brain-injured group comprised cases with Little's disease, birth injury, postencephalitis, and congenital syphilis. These were equated for chronological age and mental age with the familial group, and the familial group was found significantly more accurate in its reproductions than the brain-injured group. Of eight characteristics treated by the Chi-square technique, three were significantly more frequent in the brain-injured children. These aberrations were reversals, repetition of parts, and use of lines instead of dots.

In Halpin's study of rotation errors made by brain-injured and familial defective children on two visual-motor tests (Bender Gestalt and Goldstein-Scheerer Stick Test), brain-injured cases were diagnosed by means of neurological examination and an abnormal electroencephalogram. They were matched by pairs with non-injured children. Under these conditions, only a chance relationship was apparent between number of rotations on the Bender and Goldstein-Scheerer tests. In keeping with the performance of organic patients in general, brain-injured children as a group made more errors on visual-motor integration tasks than the matched familials. Because few reversals were noted on the Bender Gestalt Test in contrast to the findings of Bensberg and others, Halpin concludes that "Rotation does not seem to have a single unequivocable referent in behavior," and therefore cannot be predicted from one visual-motor task to another.

Halpin's study was based upon fifteen cases, so that conclusions are difficult to corroborate. Without question, however, considerable overlapping exists between groups of brain-injured children and those with familial mental deficiency, no matter what test is used. Halpin and Patterson[11] stress this in their study using the Goldstein-Scheerer Tests. Although they found the Stick Test best for analyzing types of visual-motor disturbances observed in mentally retarded children (difficulties being more prevalent in the brain-injured children than in the familial defectives), they are in agreement with a majority of investigators reporting that, irrespective of diagnostic tool used, no one test in itself is adequate for detecting organic impairment in mental retardation.

Efforts to separate brain-injured cases from the non-injured reveal that little attention has been paid to underlying mechanisms and dynamics of behavior which account for observable differences. Bender[4] recognizes this when she speculates that higher-grade defectives (probably hereditary or constitutional defectives) show slowness or simplification of maturational processes and a more unified system in general, thereby producing a simple Gestalt such as is found in the normal younger child. However, a simple retardation throughout the motor Gestalt function does not appear indicated, motor control usually being better than in normal younger children. Bender states that among the group of high-grade hereditary defectives, small, energy-conserving figures are the rule. Less play is apparent and primitive loops are often used.

Curtailment of productiveness and many "organic" signs may frequently be seen on the Rorschach test, but these are also apparent in many cases of very low-grade defectives without known brain damage. Arbitman[1] reports a lower number of total responses, few large details and human-movement responses, together with higher animal-movement content among mental-defective subjects than among normal subjects having an average mental age of seven years, four months. Studies generally are in agreement with these findings, reflecting limitation of creative ability associated with curtailed intellectual endowment. Such a condition inevitably makes a diagnosis of organicity difficult in most cases. In the author's experience, a positive correlation exists between severity of mental retardation and similarity to organicity, especially on projective techniques.

To summarize evidence to date, differences found between brain-injured and non-brain-injured children are essentially those of degree rather than of kind. No one pattern of response is characteristic of the individual subject on intelligence or personality test. Findings which favor the presence of organic factors depend upon success in recognizing interference with previous functioning in a complicated Gestalt unique to the individual. Progress has been relatively slow because the broader aspect of these Gestalten have not yet been thoroughly investigated.

Suggestions for further study include the need for: 1) More descriptive material on the case history. 2) More homogeneous groups for comparative purposes. 3) More adequate controls, ranging from cases of suspected but unconfirmed brain damage to normal children. 4) Better control of variables such as learning-ability differences, previous responsiveness to training, socio-economic level, and special aptitudes.

TESTING BRAIN INJURY

In the actual test situation, the total intelligence quotient does not usually help one to differentiate between organic and non-organic cases, unless some deteriorating process is apparent, which is the exception rather than the rule. Brain-injured children tend to test with remarkable consistency over long periods of time, if the injury has made inroads some time before the initial test. In Table 2 are a series of examples of mental ages and intelligence quotients on the Stanford-Binet Intelligence Test (Form L) for a brain-injured and a non-brain-injured child.

Table 2. Comparison of Mental Ages and Intelligence Quotients of Brain-Injured and Non-Brain-Injured Children

Brain-Injured Child (Male)*			Non-Brain-Injured Child (Male)		
C.A.	M.A.	I.Q.	C.A.	M.A.	I.Q.
6-7	4-2	63	6-5	4-0	62
7-1	4-5	62	6-10	4-2	61
7-7	5-0	66	7-5	4-6	61
8-1	5-2	64	7-11	4-9	60
8-7	5-5	63	8-6	5-2	61
9-1	5-8	62	8-10	5-4	60

* Encephalitis three years prior to first test.

During the three years these two cases were studied, a total gain in mental age of eighteen months was credited to the brain-injured boy, while one of sixteen months was earned by the non-brain-injured child. Slightly more irregularity existed among retest quotients of the brain-injured boy, but the basic level of intelligence remained approximately the same as at the beginning of study. These samples are typical of children who are retarded, inasmuch as they indicate very reliable retests over extended periods of time, once a rate of mental growth has been well established. Predictions as to ultimate level are usually accurate, although exceptions do occur.

A word of caution is in order regarding the psychologist's conception of brain injury and its prognosis: the writer has often observed that very pessimistic limits have been set on possible development of the brain, and grave errors committed. Frequently parents are told that their child will never talk, walk, attend regular school, reach a mental age of five years, or the like, whereas later progress completely negates these predictions. Potentialities of the brain for change over long intervals are overlooked, especially in such conditions as postencephalitis and head

injury among very young children. Although attainment of average
mental development may not be indicated by presenting symptoms, it is
extremely dangerous and unscientific to make dogmatic predictions
without a number of long-range psychological tests. Differences in
maturational rates, potential recoverability, and responsiveness to medication are factors of great import. Since most patients cannot be followed
over a period of years, unwarranted predictions should be avoided.

The term "mental deterioration" has sometimes been used erroneously
to describe children who earn intelligence quotients upon retest which
are lower than a previous standard. Actually, this designation should be
limited to an irreversible, progressively poorer performance with neurological and clinical verification. From a psychological standpoint mental
deterioration in children must include a lowering in mental age, not
merely intelligence quotient. Even recording the same mental age on
subsequent tests is not evidence for deterioration but simply deceleration
in new learning rate. Disease processes which produce degenerative
mental symptoms are uncommon in childhood and are generally confirmed by medical findings or physical aberration.

Analysis of individual test patterns is usually more fruitful for detecting
organicity than consideration of total scores. Sometimes a hint is given
in wide variability of subtest patterns, with certain high spots suggestive
of greater potential than is borne out by performance as a whole. Here
results must be supplemented as much as possible by observations of
behavior, since confusion or perplexity may be detected beyond that
assignable to emotional disturbance. Such confusion is sometimes seen
on performance test rather than on verbal material such as the Stanford-
Binet. It tends to appear consistently on retest over a year or two, provided the organic condition does not improve, and even after a ceiling
effect has become apparent in areas involving new learning.

As in the non-injured child, intelligence retest quotients of brain-injured
children generally reflect a consolidation of material previously failed at
lower levels of a test, before the addition of new material at higher
levels initially. Whether this is due to maturational change, or a removal
of interference is not always clear. Significantly, however, mental defectives generally show insight into requirements if problems are simple
enough. Tests requiring abstraction and categorization may be consistently passed, up to and including Year VI of the Stanford-Binet (Form
L), and then just as consistently failed from Year VII upward, when the
same types of material become more complex. Categorization is, therefore, not an all or none affair, and one ought not to say that mental
defectives lack the ability to think abstractly, or make other such generalizations without definite qualification.

MONGOLISM

Mongolism is a discrete neurological entity which involves a degenerative disease process of the skeletal musculature, with defects in myelination of the spinal cord and peripheral nerves. Anatomical skeletal growth retardation may be discerned at an early age and poor motor coordination is typical because of cord pathology.

The etiology of mongolism has for some time constituted a perplexing problem. Benda[2] has defined it as "congenital acromicrio," on the theory that it resulted from hypofunctioning of the pituitary gland. Many neurologists have related mongolism to poor health of the mother during the early months of pregnancy (Benda,[3] Engler[9]). As a whole, the profession has favored a nonhereditary, or nongenetic interpretation.

Recent studies of Lejeune,[12] however, have presented some startling evidence indicating that failure of one somatic chromosome to disjoin accounts for mongoloid characteristics. If Lejeune's work receives further corroboration, it will be a tremendous step forward in understanding basic neuropsychological mechanisms.

Studies of Brousseau,[7] Benda,[2] Tennies,[14] and Wallin[15] show that the worst cases of mongolism fall within the defective range in intelligence, many of them within the very low-grade classification. Zimmerman, Burgemeister, and Putnam[16] have pointed out, nevertheless, that age is an important factor and that many mongoloid children have average or low-average development as infants. Before reaching adulthood very serious mental retardation is characteristic of mongoloid children generally.

Differences between non-mongoloid and mongoloid children usually become increasingly apparent on intelligence tests with the passage of time, mongoloid children showing a consistent drop in mental age along with a lowering of intelligence quotient. In contrast, non-mongoloid children attain quotients approximating their former rate of growth.

There are always exceptions to the rule; below is a case history of an adult mongoloid male who still rates close to low average on the Wechsler-Bellevue Adult Intelligence Scale. Cant, Gerrard, and Richards[8] also report one case of a girl with mongoloid appearance and normal intelligence (I.Q. 116). Differences in initial handicap and in deterioration rate must always be considered prognostically, a factor which points up the necessity for reporting individual scores rather than group averages. When a steady decline in intelligence and motor performance does occur, it often parallels regressive neurological changes which are irreversible.

Poor emotional control, explosive outbursts, extremes of affect, and behavioral deviations are often observed in mongolism. Yet many clinicians are under the impression that mongoloid children exhibit personality and behavioral patterns indicating more than the usual amount of "niceness" found among other defectives, or among children in general. Whether this "niceness" comes of special sampling is not known, but the writer is in agreement. Most mongoloid children tested have been agreeable and cooperative. They have also been willing to take larger doses of unpalatable medication than other defectives, possibly because their sensory equipment is less acute than most.

Mongoloid speech is invariably indistinct. Difficulties in perception are prominent on tasks requiring discrimination and visual-motor organization. A concrete rather than an abstract approach is outstanding, marked by deficient organizational and categorizing ability. Mongoloid children display typical pre-school traits such as inquisitiveness, talkativeness, hyperactive bursts and distractibility. A certain naïvete has been noted by numerous investigators, and Benda[2] has expressed the belief that of all mentally retarded children "the mongoloid represents the clearest example of infantilism."

Mongolism is of special interest to the psychologist since it comprises the developmental weaving and integration of patterns in the presence of an arresting process. Because this process has usually made great inroads before full development has been reached, provocative insights are afforded into neuropsychological dynamics of a very complicated nature. Mongolism also serves to illustrate that many facets of mental retardation need to be further explored.

CASE HISTORIES

Case I   Mental retardation in a fourteen-year-old girl following birth injury and encephalitis

THE CLINICAL PICTURE

History of instrument birth and birth injury. Roentgenogram of the skull revealed a decompression of the right temporal region. Progress was complicated by the presence of measles at age nine months, with subsequent high fever and postencephalitic symptoms. The patient sat up at eight months, walked at twenty-two months, and talked first at three-and-one-half years, showing very slow progress.

At the time of psychological test, neurological and EEG findings were negative. The patient had been attending a "low-I.Q." class in public school for several years, with little evidence of learning ability. Indifference and distractibility characterized her behavior during the test session.

INTELLIGENCE AND PERFORMANCE TEST RESULTS

The Stanford-Binet Test (Form L) revealed a mental age of 5 years, 3 months, intelligence quotient 38, well within the low-defective range, and indication of severe retardation. There was nothing remarkable about the pattern of responses: a basal age was established at Year IV and all tests were creditable at Year IV-6 except aesthetic comparisons. At Year V the copying-a-square and memory-for-sentences tests were failed. Her highest successes occurred at Year VI, where the vocabulary, bead stringing, and mutilated picture tests were passed.

On the Merrill-Palmer performance test a rating of 4 years, 11 months was obtained, closely approximating the verbal score. All successes fell between forty-two and sixty-five months, with poor form perception outstanding. A left-handed preference was shown throughout her work.

FIG. 4. Figure of a person drawn by a 14-year-old girl with mental retardation following birth injury and encephalitis.

When asked to draw a person, the reproduction shown in Figure 4 was made. The patient said, when questioned, that the figure was a "girl about six years old."

RORSCHACH RECORD

Performance	Scoring and Inquiry

Card I
4" 1. A bird.

W   F   A
de   F   A

Here it is (pushed hand in circular motion to cover whole card). It is a big bird with wings and it has three children here (points to center humps). They look like little birds.

Performance   Scoring and Inquiry

10"
Card II
7" 1. Fire.

D   C   Fire
D   CF   Blood

This red here and here are two little
bloods. (?) Because they're red.

14"
Card III
5" 1. Boy.

W   F   A←H

I don't see a boy. I see two little
ducks. Here's their body and here
their hands. (?) Here's their heads.

11"
Card IV
27" I don't know.

W   F   A

A big fish. That's all he looks like
(again pushed hand over entire card).

Card V
8" 1. A cushion.

W   F   Obj   O
D   FM   A   O

Here is a spider trying to get under
the cushion. (?) It's a cushion because it looks like one and he's trying
to get under it.

17"
Card VI
3" 1. A tree.

W   F   Pl

Here is the trunk and the branches.
It's a big tree, isn't it?

9"
Card VII
4" 1. Children.

D)_W   M   H
D)^W   F   Arch

They are fighting [*sic*] a home that's
not built (vague in pointing to bottom
—little house?). (?) They are a girl
and a boy (right and left) ? I don't
know why.

11"
Card VIII
2" 1. Blue mices.

D   FC   FM   A   P

They are blue (points to usual pink
bears). (?) They are taking a walk
somewheres.

Performance	Scoring and Inquiry

9"

Card IX

3" 1. A clistert [*sic*]? A thing.

W F A O
A big wolf. (?) All of it. (?) It is big and it looks like one.

12"

Card X

12" 1. A pleudet [*sic*]?

D FC FM A
Two little tiny mices. They are brown mices. They are eating something.

19"

INTERPRETATION

Mental deficiency is unmistakable in this girl's test pattern. Suspicion of organic interference with thinking also exists in view of the following.

On the intelligence test, vocabulary is one of the highest scores earned, while difficulty is shown in making a square at a lower level, and form perception generally is poor. These facts are not sufficient in themselves to make a diagnosis of organicity, but they point in this direction when combined with unevenness in quality of figure drawing, plus a Rorschach showing considerable variation in form level, poor whole responses, along with explosiveness and perplexity in the use of color on some cards and mild and controlled use on others.

The Rorschach protocol is also interesting in showing, even at this low level, ability to recover in the inquiry and to add substantially to the quality of the record, a tendency sometimes not recognized as possible in organic patients. The overall impression likewise is that the Rorschach shows slightly higher intellectual potential than a 38 intelligence quotient would indicate. The writer deems hazardous a generalization beyond this point, or any attempt to assign to birth injury or the encephalitic process the causes of this interference. The only hint given is the fact that the patient did not sit up until age eight months, indicating delayed progress before her encephalitic episode. This would favor a probability of considerable damage and retardation before, or at, birth.

Case II   Organic interference in a thirteen-year-old mentally retarded girl with a suspicion of birth injury

THE CLINICAL PICTURE

Forcep marks on the forehead at the time of birth. Labor of the mother reported as long and hard, necessitating the use of instruments. Development was marked by slowness and by extreme hyperactivity, restlessness, outbursts of irritability, and temper tantrums. The child was reported able to sit up at age six months, to walk at fifteen months, and to talk at two-and-one-half years.

Neurological examination was negative, as were roentgenogram and pneumoencephalogram. EEG showed a highly disorganized record with dysrhythmia, slowing, and high voltage activity, interpreted as abnormal.

During the psychological test session, the patient's behavior was characterized by tension, anxiety, dread of failure, and the need for constant reassurance as to the acceptability of her performance. She moved about constantly, jumping up on some pretext to look at everything in the room. On occasion she would blame her failure on the examiner, saying that a certain fact had not been included in a story, so that she could not know it, and stating, almost belligerently, "I never heard of that word." She was also suspicious, continually viewing test papers, inquiring what the examiner was writing down, and trying to pull the paper toward her in an effort to see for herself.

INTELLIGENCE AND PERFORMANCE TEST RESULTS

On the Stanford-Binet Test the patient earned a mental age of 9 years, 10 months, intelligence quotient 74, which falls within the borderline range. A very wide scatter of successes was recorded, from Year VII to Year XIV inclusive, suggesting interference with thinking and the probability of a low-average potential intellectual level. Much of this interference was believed to be emotional in nature; but this in itself is sometimes a reflection of organic brain damage. The erratic scatter of response to verbal material shows no definite area of deficiency, with vocabulary at Year XII, and two other tests passed here, as well as plan or search at Year XIII.

On the Arthur Performance Tests (Form II), a score of 8 years, 5 months was obtained, which gives a quotient of 63. This is definitely lower than the verbal quotient. The patient's functioning ability was recorded near the upper end of the defective range. Her performance revealed an unusual degree of awkwardness in the use of her hands, with form perception also poor. When drawing tests were required, the patient always became defensive, saying, "I'm no good at drawing." This was true, for she showed very poor reproductive skill on motor test. A range of scores from 5 to 15 years also indicated emotional interference with thinking on the performance type of test.

RORSCHACH RECORD

Performance	Scoring and Inquiry
Card I	
2″ 1. This looks like a butterfly.	W F→FM A
	These things up here look like the things butterflies fly with.

Performance	Scoring and Inquiry

12"

Card II

2" 1. This looks like a butterfly.

W FM A

This looks the same as the other one
—like a butterfly that flies. And this
looks like

D F A P

a dog. (?) That's how a dog looks.

9"

Card III

4" 1. A monkey.

W FM Fm A

You can tell by his tail that's broken.
Here are his feet, his head. He must
be climbing something.

11"

Card IV

3" 1. A butterfly—no—a butterfly.

W F Ad

This looks like a butterfly, but he
doesn't have any head.

W F Pl

It looks like a tree, too, up this way.

9"

Card V

5" 1. A bird that flies with his
wings.

W F A P

Or a butterfly—this should be cut off
and this should be his head.

12"

Card VI

4" 1. A tree.

W F Pl

It had a trunk and branches.

8"

Card VII

5" 1. A circle from some kind of
clouds.

W KF Clouds

They just look like clouds—all cloudy
like (touches surface with hand).

14"

Card VIII

4" 1. A rainbow.

W FC Rainbow

A rainbow with many different colors.

11"

Card IX

5" 1. A tree or

D→W F Pl

Here (midline) this looks like the
trunk of a tree.

2. A rainbow.

W FC Rainbow

This has the colors looking like a
rainbow.

Performance	Scoring and Inquiry

11"

Card X

2" 1. A rainbow or

                                   W   FC   Rainbow

                     Colors or

                     It is a tree and maybe it has leaves.

       2. A tree.   W   F   Pl

                     The stem and the branches.

14"

In testing the limits, the men in Card III were rejected because they have no arms but "two feet." Lobsters were seen in Card X in the lower green and grasshoppers in the upper green. Bears without a tail were found in Card VIII.

INTERPRETATION

Factors favoring the likelihood of organic interference with thinking are indicated in this girl's feelings of inadequacy combined with uneven development on verbal test and a higher potential suggested. Her poor motor coordination, difficulty with drawing tests, poor form perception, and the discrepancy noted between verbal and performance ability as a whole, would also be in keeping with this assumption. The marked poverty of responses to the Rorschach, perseveration, emphasis upon whole responses of very poor quality, repetition, automatic phrasing, rejection of human figures, and mention of "broken" parts fit into this concept, as do the general perplexity and lack of growth revealed. Her ineffective handling of color, along with efforts to use the form element at the expense of more spontaneous reaction, seems to reflect a weakness in organizational ability, in spite of attempts to conform.

Because the Rorschach is so poor, however, in the face of rather good intellectual ability as shown on test, compulsive-obsessional features must also be taken into consideration in interpreting the protocol, which may or may not be conditioned by the brain damage presumed to be present. The protocol is believed to represent an emotional maladjustment which may have exaggerated basic limitations. In the last analysis, the patient may be more handicapped by her defensive techniques than by the amount of brain damage per se.

The following two cases are included because they show much milder retardation on psychological test than is generally associated with mongolism and cretinism. (Cretinism is an endocrine disorder caused by hypofunction of the thyroid gland. Children with cretinism have many of the physical and psychological characteristics of mongoloid children.)

Case III   Relatively mild organic interference in a
mongoloid male twenty-one years of age

THE CLINICAL PICTURE

Birth and early development reported normal. The patient sat alone at age nine months (average progress), walked alone at seventeen months, (slightly slow), and spoke some words at one year (average). Sentences, however, were not heard until the boy was three years of age. Childhood diseases included measles, chicken pox, and scarlet fever, all of which were mild.

Neurological examination at the time of psychological test was negative, except that awkwardness was noted and the patient walked with a broad base. EEG revealed muscle tension and some slowing, but was interpreted as within normal limits.

During the psychological test session, cooperation was excellent and effort sustained. The patient's manner reflected a desire to be acceptable and friendly. He introduced conversation, responded well to praise, and was disturbed by failure. Lack of insight into the nature of failures was noticeable. Good social training seemed clear in his polite responsiveness. Speech was indistinct and typically mongoloid. Motor awkwardness was relatively mild in the presence of mongolism.

WECHSLER-BELLEVUE INTELLIGENCE SCALE RESULTS

Wechsler-Bellevue Intelligence Scale results were as follows:

Information	7	Picture arrangement	6
Comprehension	11	Picture completion	6
Digit span	3	Block design	7
Arithmetic	0	Object assembly	11
Similarities	10	Digit symbol	5

Verbal scale quotient	80	Low average
Performance-scale quotient	78	Borderline
Full-scale quotient	77	Borderline

Unevenness in performance is characteristic here, with comprehension involving common sense and an understanding of social situations giving him his highest subtest rating on the verbal scale. The rating on similarities is exceptionally good also, particularly in view of the fact that mongoloid individuals are prone to have a very concrete approach to problems in general, while this score is almost average. His most sophisticated response to the similarities material was the one in which he related a poem and a statue to art.

On the information section, knowledge of Shakespeare's *Hamlet*, and geographical locations of Rome, Tokyo, and South America suggest a pattern of maturity. Yet evidence supporting Benda's remark that "the mongoloid represents the clearest example of infantilism" may be found in the answer of "Santa Claus" to the question as to who discovered the North Pole. Observation of behavior was even more convincing: the patient not only laughed when he said this, as if an old friendship had been revived, but when questioned subsequently, explained, "There's no doubt about that answer. Everybody knows that one."

The patient's facility on the object-assembly material may be noted, with extra credit for speed on the last two more difficult tests. His block-design rating is also exceptionally good in view of his age and condition, and much better than his response to the digit-symbols test which requires speed in forming new associations.

H-P-T TEST

The patient drew a very large house using heavy lines, and including many windows, some of which were outside the outline of the building. The roof, on the other hand, was omitted. Proportioning was poor and a tendency to lean toward the left was observed. His figure of a man was a stick drawing, over-simplified to the point of omitting pupils of the eye, hands, and feet. Scored, it would be rated at pre-school level of intelligence, being very infantile in concept. The figure of a tree consisted of a huge trunk with lines for branches like a bundle of sticks, without appropriate attachment of limbs. As a whole, all reproductions seemed to reflect some distortion of spatial relationships and definite maturational lag.

RORSCHACH RECORD

Performance	Scoring and Inquiry

Card I
3″ This is a—let me concentrate—
15″ 1. It's a spider.

W F KF A
    mF

Here he is—you can see his shade but he's fair—his arms are up here and down here too. (?) The shade looks like smoke—he's in smoke—it looks like it's smoking.

22″
Card II
11″ 1. These are smoke skeletons.

W KF FC At
    C′F

The red up here and the brown down there makes it look like smoke —they look to me like skeletons. (?) They have red hoods on so they look like skeletons, but they shouldn't have

Performance

any white. (?) Witches—or spooks—
yes that's like it, too.

24"
Card III
4" 1. These are plain skeletons and

       W F Fc At
Well—they've got a hood and hands
and feet and they're spooky. Every
time I see a skeleton, I dash right
out.

    2. A butterfly in between them.
       D FC A P
Here it is. It's a pretty color.

29"
Card IV
5" 1. That is a bear rug.

       W Fc Aobj
Well, this keeps you warm because
it's fur. (?) This is the underneath
side because it's dark.

16"
Card V
4" 1. A bat.

       W FM A P
This looks like it's a bat flying.

11"
Card VI
18" 1. A sheep's skin.

       W Fc Aobj P
This looks like fur. (?) It's the underneath side. A bear has heavier wool
—and a sheep has light wool. I like a
sheep better.

29"
Card VII
14" 1. Two persons in smoke.

      D→W M KF H
             mF
             Fc
They are in flames. (?) They are girls
because their eyes are smaller and
they have hair—one is blonde and
one is brunette like my mother [True,
his mother has dark brown hair.].
They're standing in the flames . . .
they'd better get out.

23"
Card VIII
16" 1. Two rats climbing a colorful
      web.

      D)$_W$ FM A P
      D) CF Obj
They have one, two, three feet and
a tail and they're climbing up a very

Performance	Scoring and Inquiry
	pretty web. (?) The shape of it makes it look like a web and these things (inner lines).

34"
Card IX
2" 1. Fire.

        W CF KF Fire
                mF
This is smoke and flames are showing through. It looks like everything is on fire—burning.

10"
Card X
17" 1. The blue things are crabs.

        D F→FM A P
You can eat them—here they are—they're beautiful crabs (laughs). You get them on the beach. They look as if they're trying to get away. (?) Maybe they know they will be cooked.

63" I'm thinking.
80" 2. Smoke.

        W CF KF Fire
                mF
There is a coil in here and the color red looks like smoke and fire.

82"

INTERPRETATION

Test results as a whole indicate mild organic interference with thinking in an adult with constitutional maturational deficiency. The presence of organic features is indicated on intelligence test by low ratings on digit span, arithmetic, and digit symbols, in contrast to peak scores ranging from six to eleven points higher where more remote learning is involved. Drawing tests likewise reflect retardation in mental growth, along with distortion in the perception of spatial relationships, difficulty in organizing, and in maintaining angulation.

Maturational limitation is most apparent in the marked oversimplification seen on the H-T-P tests. Inconsistencies of performance recorded on intelligence test are repeated here; omission of essential details such as hands and feet on the figure of a person, pupils of the eye, a roof on the house, branches on the tree. These are compensated for by the presence of many windows, some of which are outside the framework of the building. The drawing of a person is infantile in the extreme and rates at the pre-school level. It is thus interesting to speculate on the dynamics of a brain structure which harbors knowledge of the Bard of Avon and yet reveals a body-image concept as immature as this.

The Rorschach protocol supports evidence from other tests in showing awareness of limitation, impotence, perplexity, anxiety, feelings of inferiority, a tendency to compensate by over-reasoning, as well as a definitely concrete approach. The tendency to personalize responses by introducing experiential material is a feature common to mongolism, and seems a defense against insecurity.

Explosiveness in the use of color and lack of more adaptiveness suggest poor control in the social area, with an inclination to become easily overwhelmed. This finding is in keeping with anxiety evident in his behavior, particularly his reaction to failure. Sufficient control exists, nevertheless, so that popular responses may be reported, and there is no immediate indication of an acute deteriorating process.

Prognosis is that a level of functioning lower than the original, and already apparent in his work, will become more pronounced as time elapses. This indication is also given in such responses as that to Card IX and the last response to Card X of the Rorschach protocol. Hence slow but progressive limitation in functioning ability over a period of years can be prognosticated. To date remarkable preservation of former ability is recorded.

Case IV   Questionable organicity in a seven-year-old girl with cretinism

THE CLINICAL PICTURE

Birth and development reportedly uneventful except for mild chicken pox at the age of three. Sitting up alone occurred at age nine months, isolated words appeared at one year, and walking alone took place at nineteen months. Words in sentence form were heard at two and one-half years.

Neurological examination and EEG at the time of psychological test were negative and normal, except that coordination seemed relatively poor. Speech was hesitant and indistinct.

INTELLIGENCE AND PERFORMANCE TEST RESULTS

On the Stanford-Binet test, a mental age of 5 years, 6 months was obtained, and an intelligence quotient of 80. These ratings are at the lower end of the low-average range, indicating some slowness but no serious retardation in development of verbal intelligence. A basal age was established at Year IV-6 with all tests at Year V creditable except folding-the-triangle and memory-for-sentences tests. At year VI all items were passed except bead design and numbers. A vocabulary score of 7 was considered average for her age.

Less success appeared on the Merrill-Palmer performance test. A performance score of 5 years, 0 months giving a quotient of 73 at the borderline level, was due essentially to poor motor coordination, since form perception was good but reaction time slow. Successes and failures ranged from forty-two months to seventy-one months, with the button tests and six-cube pyramid proving most difficult, while the Pink Tower and Manikin tests rated highest (66–71 months). Hand dominance did not appear to be well established, since constant shifting could be observed from one hand to the other.

RORSCHACH RECORD

Performance	Scoring and Inquiry
Card I	
5″ 1. A bird.	W F A P
	A little bird (whole blot covered by hand). (?) Just looks like it.
9″	
Card II	
4″ 1. A man.	W F H
	Two men—here is the head and the body. (?) Just look like it.
8″	
Card III	
5″ 1. A man.	W F H P
	Two men—here is his head, his body, and his feet. (?) That is his hand. (?) I don't know what that is. (lower D)
11″	
Card IV	
4″ 1. A fly.	W F A
	A big fly. He has a head and it looks like he has wings.
12″	
Card V	
5″ 1. A leg.	D F Ad
	It looks like a leg. (?) It looks like a chicken leg.
14″	
Card VI	
7″ 1. A spider.	W F A
	A big spider—his head and wings.
12″	
Card VII	
5″ 1. A spider.	W F A
	His body and his wings. (?) He's a big spider.

Performance	Scoring and Inquiry

12"

Card VIII

4" 1. Paint.

                      W CF Paint

All the pretty colors. (?) Like in a paint box.

    2. Two bears.

                    D F→FM A P

Here—his head and feet. (?) Looks like he's walking.

18"

Card IX

18" 1. A fly, I guess.

                        W F A

All of him—his head and wings (positional response).

25"

Card X

5" 1. A map.

                      W F Geo

The shape of it—like in a book.

    2. A leaf.

                      W F Pl

All the shape of it.

19"

INTERPRETATION

Relatively little evidence for organic interference with thinking is afforded in this test pattern. Findings are similar to those obtained from many retarded children of this age who are considered "unorganic" cases. It may be argued with some justification that the discrepancy between verbal and performance quotients points in an organic direction, and this is substantiated by poor motor coordination. A relatively low mental age on the Stanford-Binet as compared to an average vocabulary score is also suspicious. On the Rorschach test, developmental lag is apparent, but features common to mentally retarded children predominate rather than organic features. Perhaps contrasting responses, such as human figures which appear well seen and poor quality of the leaf response, would be in keeping with some interference. Certainly such evidence should be thought of as highly speculative, however, because of the meagerness of available material. Conclusions are tentative in the absence of subsequent tests.

MENTAL RETARDATION AND NEUROPSYCHOLOGY

Progress made in the difficult area of extricating organic factors highlights the need to discard the misleading conception of mental deficiency as a unitary entity. Among groups of brain-injured and non-brain-injured subjects, deviations of performance are of degree rather than of kind and reveal similarities rather than differences.

Capacities such as ability to shift, memory, and abstract thinking have been shown to be composed of numerous elements, and hence in need of further analysis. Such research will require more adequate testing instruments, as well as refinement of techniques. The value of longitudinal as well as cross-sectional studies, emphasizing etiology and the interplay of maturational and regressive factors, is already influencing the directions of research. For example, the mechanisms underlying developmental defect or central nervous system disorder may be more thoroughly explored. Certainly there is an increased interest in neuropsychological relationships among them.

BIBLIOGRAPHY

1. ARBITMAN, H. D. Rorschach determinants in mentally defective and normal subjects. *Train. Sch. Bull.*, 50: 143–151, 1953.
2. BENDA, C. E. *Mongolism and Cretinism.* (2nd Ed.) New York: Grune & Stratton: 1949.
3. BENDA, C. E. Prenatal maturational factors in mongolism. *J.A.M.A.*, 139: 979, 1949.
4. BENDER, L. A visual motor Gestalt test and its clinical use. *Amer. Orthopsychiat. Assoc. Monogr.*, 3, 1938.
5. BENSBERG, G. J. Performance of brain-injured and familial mental defectives on the Bender Gestalt test. *J. Consult. Psychol.*, 16: 61–64, 1952.
6. BIJOU, S., and WERNER, H. Language analysis in brain-injured and non brain-injured deficient children. *J. Genet. Psychol.*, 66: 239–254, 1945.
7. BROUSSEAU, K. *Mongolism.* Baltimore: Williams & Wilkins: 1928.
8. CANT, W. H. P., GERRARD, J. W., and RICHARDS, B. W. A girl of non-mongoloid appearance and normal intelligence. *J. Ment. Sci.*, 99: 560–563, 1953.
9. ENGLER, M. *Mongolism.* Baltimore: Williams & Wilkins: 1949.
10. HALPIN, V. Rotation errors made by brain-injured and familial children on two visual-motor tests. *Amer. J. Ment. Deficiency*, 59: 485–489, 1954.
11. HALPIN, V., and PATTERSON, R. M. The performance of brain-injured children on the Goldstein-Scheerer tests. *Amer. J. Ment. Deficiency*, 59: 91–99, 1954.
12. LEJEUNE, J. Somatic chromosomes in mongolism. Paper read before the A. Res. Nerv. & Ment. Dis., Dec. 11, 1959.
13. SARASON, S. B. Projective techniques in mental deficiency. *Character & Pers.*, 13: 237–245, 1945.
14. TENNIES, L. G. Some comments on the mongoloid. *Amer. J. Ment. Deficiency*, 48: 46–54, 1943.
15. WALLIN, J. E. W. Mongolism among school children. *Amer. J. Orthopsychiat.*, 14: 104–112, 1944.
16. ZIMMERMAN, F. T., BURGEMEISTER, B. B., and PUTNAM, T. J. The effect of glutamic acid upon the mental and physical growth of mongols. *Amer. J. Psychiat.*, 105: 661–668, 1949.

ADDITIONAL REFERENCES

1. BLACKETER-SIMMONDS, D. A. An investigation into the supposed differences existing between mongols and other mentally defective subjects with regard to certain psychological traits. *J. Ment. Sci.*, 99: 702–719, 1953.
2. HONZIK, M. P. Developmental studies of parent-child resemblance in in-intelligence. *Child Developm.*, 28: 215–228, 1957.
3. HUTT, M. L., and GIBBY, R. G. *The Mentally Retarded Child: Development, Education and Guidance*. Boston: Allyn & Bacon: 1958.
4. OGDON, D. P., and ALLEE, R. Rorschach relations with intelligence among familial mentally retarded. *Amer. J. Ment. Deficiency*, 63: 889–896, 1959.
5. SIEVERS, D. J. A study to compare the performance of brain-injured and non-brain-injured mentally retarded children on the differential language facility test. *Amer. J. Ment. Deficiency*, 63: 838–847, 1959.
6. YANNET, H., DEISLER, R. W., BAKWIN, H., STYLIANON, D. S., et al. Symposium on mental retardation. Los Angeles Children's Hospital. *J. Pediat.*, 50: 226–250, 1957.

VIII

➤➤

Cerebral Palsy

Cerebral palsy is known to be a result of aberrations in the motor control centers of the brain. Although it presents itself as a handicapping condition involving abnormalities of the muscles and skeletal system, sensory disturbances and loss of function in higher cortical centers are commonly associated with the motor disorders.

Lesions producing cerebral palsy vary widely in etiology and appearance, and it is often impossible to determine whether they result from a developmental defect, cerebral hemorrhage, or postnatal infection. As Josephy[9] points out, "often enough it is impossible to predict which specific lesion or even what type of lesion an autopsy may reveal." If malformations of the brain are basic, structural damage and loss of functioning ability may result, but a progressive deteriorating process is not indicated. Where a chronic degenerative disease process is evident, children are poor risks from an educational standpoint and prognosis is very poor. If, as in many cases, parts of the brain are intact and others have been destroyed by a traumatic process, no further interference is typical unless scar formations become more extensive.

Predisposing factors include many possibilities, such as congenital defects of the central nervous system, premature birth, traumatic labor of the mother, breech presentation, anoxia and cerebral hemorrhage, and vascular lesions. Postnatal traumas, infections, neoplasms and vascular conditions may also be predisposing. Hence the term cerebral palsy embraces both developmental and degenerative syndromes.

In discussing overt physiological features and underlying pathology, Putnam[15] makes the following observations:

1. Spasticity or hyperreflexia. Indicative of corticospinal tract disorders and characterized by motor deficiency, awkwardness, and some-

114

times by spasm of antigravity muscles. Myographic record and neurological examination are usually abnormal, with overactive reflexes, Babinski and Hoffman signs.

2. Athetosis and dystonia. Although similar as physiological entities, abnormal movements in the extremities are manifestations of athetosis, while abnormal tensions and postures in the axial muscles characterize dystonia. Brain stem origins are postulated with extrapyramidal rather than pyramidal tract involvement.

3. Alternating tremor and Parkinsonian rigidity are generally results of lesions in the globus pallidus and substantia nigra, embryologically related.

4. Ataxia caused by cerebellar deficiency is usually manifested in lack of coordination and control rather than in involuntary movement.

5. Transverse lesion of the spinal cord is characterized by extreme hyperreflexia, impulses spreading through the isolated segment of the cord.

On first consideration, one might expect that where a severe motor handicap exists, cortical centers would be apt to reflect impairment. However, no positive correlation exists between severity of motor handicap and degree of intellectual impairment. Severe motor handicap is often found with little or no involvement of cortical centers, while very slight degree of motor handicap may be accompanied by considerable interference with thinking on psychological test. Location, kind, and extent of brain damage, not presence of motor disability, determine test performance.

Clearly the term cerebral palsy is too comprehensive; detailed information must be obtained in individual cases before generalizations can be made. Much of the needed information is not available. For example, we lack knowledge as to whether symptomatology may be expected to be similar or different when either malformations or destructive processes constitute the underlying cerebral pathology.

Investigators disagree as to incidence of mental impairment among cerebral-palsied children. Phelps[13] reported that in children studied, approximately 70 per cent of the cases were free from organic interference with mental processes, and that a "normal" spread typical of the population at large existed among this 70 per cent. The remaining 30 per cent revealed brain damage involving intelligence and were mentally defective.

In reporting upon McIntire's findings, Phelps and Turner[14] stated that trend of his data indicated superior intelligence in 5 per cent of the children; high average in 10 per cent; average in 30 per cent; low average in 11 per cent; dull normal in 13 per cent; borderline in 5 per cent; feeblemindedness in 26 per cent.

In contrast to these results are figures for a group of thirty cerebral-palsied children, among whom Usher[17] recorded thirteen average, four borderline, and thirteen mentally defective. These findings are more in line with those reported by Burgemeister and Blum[3] in studying 100 cerebral-palsied clinic patients. These children ranged in age from two to eleven years, with a median age of four. The distribution of intelligence among these children was as follows:

Intelligence Level	Per Cent
Very superior	3
Superior	3
High average	5
Average	28
Low average	8
Borderline	3
Mental defective	50

Of these 100 cases 50 per cent were found to be mentally deficient, which is a percentage closer to that of Usher than those of Phelps or McIntire.

More recent research has confirmed the widespread incidence of retardation and shown the necessity for revising statistics downward. On the basis of the figures of Asher and Schonell,[2] Miller and Rosenfield,[11] Hohman,[7] and others, Perlstein and Hood[12] believe that more than 50 per cent of all types of cerebral palsy show I.Q.'s below sixty.

Summarizing a study of 1,003 cases, Hohman and Freedheim[8] reported that "mental retardation is tragically frequent in cerebral-palsied children." The age range for this group was from seven months to sixteen years. The number of cerebral-palsied children potentially educable for economic independence is placed by these investigators as probably well below 40 per cent.

MENTAL RETARDATION MEASUREMENT

Little information is gained by grouping cases by type of cerebral palsy because individual variation is the rule. The wide range of scores among various samples reported shows the need for more detailed study.

Until recently, incidence of mental retardation has been the focus of investigation, rather than the manner in which this particular reflection of brain damage reveals itself. Where speech is not impaired, valid results are usually obtainable with standard measuring instruments. Where both speech and motor handicaps exist, however, the dearth of suitable testing procedures is responsible for fragmentary findings: the neuropsychologist is faced with the task of measuring severe damage to motor centers and higher cortical areas with test materials that call for verbalization and motor skill. Since all standard procedures utilize these, none is applicable or accurate.

Understandably therefore, psychometrists have modified existing instruments to make them more usable. At best, scores obtained on such materials can give only rough approximations; at worst, results can be gravely in error. Strother,[16] commenting on this situation, says that an intelligence quotient cannot be obtained from abbreviated tests or batteries; scores are merely estimates of performance range or averages approximating a median mental age.

Because of the almost insoluble standardization problems, errors tend to mount. An example is the use of the Stanford-Binet Picture Vocabulary Test for multiple-choice. Here the examiner presents material to the cerebral-palsied child with unintelligible speech by saying, "What is this picture? . . . Is it a house? . . . Is it a shoe? . . . " and so on, until by a grunt or nod the child indicates he recognizes the object on the card. However, once a suggestion is made, the test item is admittedly less difficult for not requiring recognition and recall elements of the Stanford presentation. Credit thus given is, of course, distorting scores in favor of the cerebral-palsied patient. The writer believes that a tendency to overrate abilities of these handicapped children by such compensatory adjustment of materials accounts in large part for discrepancies in reported test results.

Another prevalent tendency is to invalidate results by failure to remain objective. Motivated by a feeling of sympathy often reinforced by seeing the physical energy expended by so many palsied children in following instructions, the examiner easily believes his hope, i.e., that the child knows more than he can express, and hence overestimates the child's ability.

Recognition of the need for tests adapted to the experience and limitations of cerebral-palsied children has led to the development of materials requiring a minimum of verbalization and motor skill. Where a combined speech and motor handicap is not present in severe degree, such approaches as those of the Ammonses[1] and Foulds and Raven[5] are useful, even though standardization problems beset the clinician in all cerebral-palsied populations.

The Columbia Mental Maturity Scale by Burgemeister, Blum, and Lorge[4] was designed particularly to measure intelligence of the child aged three to ten, with speech and motor handicaps too severe to be assessed adequately on standard intelligence test. Test materials consist of 100 items, each printed on a card 6×19 inches. One of the item cards is reproduced in Figure 5. The cards are of various colors; each item consists of a series of from three to five drawings: many of the drawings are also colored to attract and hold child interest throughout the testing session. The objects depicted are, in general, within the range of experience even of the handicapped child whose environment has been seriously curtailed.

FIG. 5. Sample item from Columbia Mental Maturity Scale.

In each item, the subject is to select from the series of drawings the one different from, or unrelated to, the others in the series. Intellectual discrimination required is the eduction of a principle for organizing the pictures so as to exclude just one. The bases for discrimination range from perception of rather gross differences in color or form to recognition of very subtle relations in pairs so as to exclude one drawing from a series of five. Items are arranged in order of difficulty.

Initial results with the Columbia Mental Maturity Scale indicate that the technique is a good one for measuring general intelligence, and superior for severely handicapped children otherwise inaccessible to testing. A second edition with revised norms and seventeen new items was released in 1959.

As with any instrument, its contribution varies with the individual and the condition under test. Hence a word of caution: the main limitation of the Columbia Mental Maturity Scale, as the author sees it, affects the child seriously deficient in ability to handle the particular kind of categorization demanded, i.e., the ability to detect similarities and differences. In several cases in the author's experience this weakness was so pronounced that children were able to respond only to the simplest items. Understanding of what was required seemed assured by correct answers at the lower end of the scale. Yet complete failure was encountered at higher levels, with quotients falling to the pre-school level. In all instances a Stanford-Binet test used as a control (Form L) gave scores from two to three years higher.

Categorizational difficulties of this kind do not appear dependent upon type of handicap or intellectual level, although all the children have intelligence quotients within the defective range. On evidence to date, this particular weakness in abstract thinking falls into no definite pattern and seems a highly individual reaction.

Infrequent as they may be, discrepancies need further investigation, especially since they are suggestive of organic perplexity such as Gold-stein[6] described in the "catastrophic" reaction of adult patients with frontal lobe injury. They must also be considered in evaluating useful-ness of the test.

Kogan and Crazer are at present experimenting with the Children's Picture Information Test.[10] This is a multiple-choice technique to meas-ure intellectual ability of very young cerebral-palsied children. Simple material is within their experiental scope; response consists of relating one of four offered pictures to a given picture. Preliminary results suggest this may be a valid index of intelligence, but more elaborate standardiza-tion studies are needed.

A survey of literature reveals that tests for children with extreme language and motor handicaps are still in an embryonic stage. When intellectual impairment is recorded, it is assumed to be the result of brain damage, but level of intellectual ability, as a baseline for estimating extent of interference, is unknown in most instances. Also, techniques appropriate to such cases must, of necessity, be limited in scope, render-ing measurement far more difficult than in other types of disturbance. Since mental retardation without, or with, brain damage tends to obscure signs of organic interference, the prevalence of mental deficiency among cerebral-palsied children adds to the dilemma. Nowhere is there more urgent need for a battery of techniques to combine with observa-tions of behavior. As a corollary, additional instruments are an absolute requirement of future research with cerebral-palsied children, as cases below illustrate.

CASE HISTORIES

Case I   Evidence of slight mental growth in an eight-year old girl with severe cerebral palsy, microcephaly, cerebral hemorrhage, and mental retardation

THE CLINICAL PICTURE

An only child, with history of a breech presentation after thirty-six hours of labor. Cerebral hemorrhage at birth confirmed by spinal tap. Child was pale at birth and not expected to live more than a few days. Development was extremely slow; child sat up alone at the age of three; walked at four years with the help of braces. No words had been heard up to the time of psychological test, but girl imitated the sound "O."

Neurological examination at the time of psychological test revealed a microcephalic head with predominant right-sided spasticity; both upper and lower extremities were involved. Right arm remained flexed and athetoid movements of the right hand were observed. Neurological signs present included right Hoffman; left Chaddock; left and right Babinski.

PSYCHOLOGICAL TEST BATTERY I (AT EIGHT YEARS)

During the test session the child was hindered in moving about by braces, and was seated on the floor. Drooling was continuous, with the tongue hanging from the mouth much of the time. Behavior was characterized by periodic activity and inactivity, seemingly without purpose. Sometimes rhythmic movements of the trunk were noticeable, but most of the time the child just sat quietly without appearing to be alert to outside stimulation. The parents recognized this as being typical of behavior at home, very little motivation being reflected in her actions.

Little interest was shown in test materials except to throw them to the floor in most instances. The left hand only was used throughout.

Gesell Infant Intelligence Test

MOTOR DEVELOPMENT. Basal age at 7 months with all tests passed up to 15 months except those requiring fine movements of the hand and pulling self to standing position, although the latter can be done with help. An average rating of 13 months was obtained on this section of the test.

LANGUAGE. Basal age 8 months. Highest success at 12 months which was adjusting to simple commissions. Imitation of the sound "O" credited as only indication of rudiments of speech. Average performance here 10 months.

ADAPTIVE BEHAVIOR. Basal age 8 months. Credited with pulling string and obtaining ring; attending to scribbling demonstration, and rattling a rattle. Average rating 9 months.

PERSONAL SOCIAL BEHAVIOR. Basal age 8 months. Cooperation in rhythmic games (swaying to singing) and waving goodbye creditable, as well as repeating a performance laughed at at 12 months. Best score cooperation in dressing at 15 months. Average rating here 10–11 months.

The average over-all rating for items on this scale was 11 months. In terms of ratio of mental age to chronological age, an exceptionally low rating was obtained (about 11 per cent), indicating an extremely severe handicap.

Kuhlmann-Binet

Score 10.8 months, agrees well with Gesell results.

Vineland Social Maturity Scale

(By mother's report) S. A. 14 months.

PSYCHOLOGICAL TEST BATTERY II (AT TEN YEARS)

Gesell Infant Intelligence Test

MOTOR DEVELOPMENT. Gain of 1 month only. Rating now 14 months. Received credit for better prehension.

LANGUAGE. Gain of 4 months in twenty-six months. Rating now 14 months. Credited with saying "da-da" and with using expressive jargon.

ADAPTIVE BEHAVIOR. Gain of 5 months bringing the rating up to 14 months. New learning includes bringing inset block and formboard into exploiting relationship and securing two cubes given by the examiner, and then three cubes.

PERSONAL SOCIAL BEHAVIOR. Gain of 3–4 months in twenty-six months. Now rates an average of 14 months here.

Kuhlmann-Binet

14.5 months. Gain of 3.6 months in twenty-six months.

Vineland Social Maturity Scale

16 months. Gain of 2 months in twenty-six months.
Development quotient if given would be 11 per cent as it was on first test.

INTERPRETATION

This case is of interest because it illustrates an exceptionally severe degree of mental retardation associated with physical signs of severe cerebral palsy. Also significant is the fact that in spite of an extremely low level of functioning, the same rate of learning was maintained during the interval of twenty-six months between psychological tests as had been recorded originally. This indicates continued growth rather than mental deterioration and would be consistent with a static neurological condition.

One might expect the same slow rate of learning to continue, with ability to consolidate gains. In terms of prognosis, acceleration is probably not to be hoped for, when damage is so extensive and severe after ten years. Behavior at the infant level seems almost inevitable as the ultimate outcome, so far as may be judged from psychological tests and the clinical picture.

Case II   Dramatic mental growth in a two-year-old girl with spastic hemiplegia

THE CLINICAL PICTURE

Birth and development reported normal up to age four months, when the infant sustained a head injury in a bad fall from a highchair, with unconsciousness lasting several minutes. Diagnosis of spastic hemiplegia involving upper and lower extremities on the right side. Following this mother reported child was "very temperamental" and cried a lot.

Neurological examination at time of psychological test confirmed diagnosis of spastic hemiplegia. Walking was observed to be rigid with legs stiffened, and accomplished only by holding on to the mother. EEG was not obtained.

Behavior during the psychological test session was one of interest and cooperation, although at times a stubborn streak intervened.

PSYCHOLOGICAL TEST BATTERY(AT TWO YEARS)

Gesell Infant Intelligence Test

MOTOR DEVELOPMENT. 15 months. Coordination poor.

LANGUAGE. 8–9 months

ADAPTIVE BEHAVIOR. 15–18 months

PERSONAL SOCIAL BEHAVIOR. 15–18 months
Uneven development is indicated in this case. Except for language, progress of 1 to 1½ years is recorded. On the average, retardation is apparent, high borderline ability being revealed.

Kuhlmann-Binet

Rating 14.4 months, or about 58 per cent of the expected progress.

Merrill-Palmer

21 months, suggesting much less retardation than other tests in spite of poor coordination. Form perception seemed very good.

Stanford-Binet

Only one test passed (the form-board), showing a mental age of 19 months. If an I.Q. were given, which is dangerous at this age, it would be close to 80, or the low-average level.

Vineland Social Maturity Scale

By mother's report, 16 months.

All psychological tests given show some degree of retardation, although the amount varies with the instrument used.

INTELLIGENCE TEST II (AT FIVE YEARS)

Stanford-Binet rating 6 years, 9 months, I.Q. 131, at the very superior level of intelligence. A basal age was established at Year IV-6 with all tests passed at Year V with the exception of copying a square. Although not below her age level, in view of the rest of her work ranging to Year XI before an upper limit is reached, this exception is suspicious of organic interference compatible with the history and initial lag.

Merrill-Palmer score above 6 years, 6 months, showed exceptionally good motor skill.

RORSCHACH RECORD

Performance	Scoring and Inquiry
Card I	
17″ I don't know.	
1. A sky.	W C'F Clouds Because it looks all black. (?) Like black clouds—like a thunderstorm.
38″	
Card II	
11″ 1. A fire.	W CF C'F Fire mF It looks all red and black. It looks like something burning.
22″	
Card III	
15″ 1. Some girls. They can't see. They don't have any eyes.	W M H P They have a nose and mouth, but no eyes. They are holding a ball, but they can't play because they can't see.

Performance	Scoring and Inquiry
34"	
Card IV	D F A
13" 1. A rooster.	He has a long neck and he looks like a rooster.
27"	
Card V	
18" 1. A dog.	D FM A
	It looks like two dogs. I can see just the tail and the legs mostly. It looks like they're chasing something.
19"	
Card VI	W Fc AObj
14" 1. A chicken.	He has a long neck and a big body. He looks like he's killed and he has feathers.
26"	
Card VII	
11" 1. Some pussy cats.	D FM A
	Here are their heads. They have their hands out like they're playing.
17"	
Card VIII	
11" 1. Sheep—these.	D FM A P
	They look like they're climbing on something. (?) I can't tell what.
18"	
Card IX	D F A
12" 1. Cows.	Here are the eyes and the nose and his mouth. (?) I can only see his head. He has ears like a cow, too.
21"	
Card X	D F At
9" 1. Bones.	Here at the tops they look like bones in your body. (?) The shape of them. I've seen them in pictures.
19"	

All limits tested showed ability to recognize concepts suggested.

INTERPRETATION

The second psychological test performance pattern shows remarkable acceleration over the first. Recovery from her traumatic head injury which resulted in spastic hemiplegia is believed to account for this. *Significantly, such recoverability potential was not obvious on initial test. These findings emphasize the importance of caution in prognosticating outcome, especially at such an early age.* Outcome in any case is a function of variable developmental progress and particular recovery potential.

Except for her difficulty in copying a square on the Stanford-Binet, no evidence exists for the possibility of organic interference there. This particular inability is suspicious because it reflects much less competence in handling spatial relationships than anticipated. In the Rorschach, familiar signs of concern for blackness, attraction to redness in the cards, followed by absence of color responses in the last three cards, and an emotional adjustment out of keeping with the advanced intellectual development recorded, all seem to point to the likelihood of some organic residue. The relative meagerness of the record might also be in keeping with this view. Nevertheless, her functioning at the very superior level of intelligence and acceptable social adjustment (by report) affords little evidence for interference serious enough to attribute directly to brain damage.

Case III   Absence of mental acceleration in a three-year-old boy with cerebral palsy (spastic type), mental retardation, and convulsions

THE CLINICAL PICTURE

Breech presentation was reported, although birth seemed normal. Convulsions began twenty-four hours after birth. A slight hemorrhage was also noted on top of head. Spasticity followed on the left side including upper and lower limbs. Convulsions stopped following this, with no seizures until age nine months when an isolated attack occurred. Another seizure was noted at thirteen months. Convulsions usually started on the left side and later became generalized. Reported to have sat up alone at eleven months. Neither talked nor walked at time of initial test.

Neurological examination at that time revealed less movement on the left side than on the right. Involuntary movements of the left upper and lower extremities were also noted. A left Babinski and Chaddock were present. A diagnosis of cerebral palsy (spastic type) with left-sided preponderance was made with mental retardation and convulsions. EEG tracing was abnormal with convulsive features compatible with grand mal seizures.

PSYCHOLOGICAL TEST RESULTS I (AT THREE YEARS)

Psychological testing was difficult because of lack of cooperation. The patient refused many toys, throwing them to the floor. The handicaps of not being able to use his left hand, poor coordination of the right hand, absence of speech, stubbornness, and an over-protective father all combined to invalidate results.

Gesell and Cattell Test Results

Minimal scores of 12 months were obtained on both of these instruments. The only exceptional feature of the test patterns was language comprehension, which appeared to be much higher than expression, suggesting development in that area nearer 2 years. With this feature as an index to his highest possible functioning level, ability nearer two-thirds the expected development was indicated under optimal conditions.

From the father's report, credit on the Vineland Social Maturity Scale was given at 8 months, with speech and motor handicaps limiting learning to a severe degree.

In spite of initial testing inaccuracies, mental retardation was clearly indicated in all areas of development. The degree of retardation was open to some question because of inadequacies in measuring instruments and the absence of cooperation.

PSYCHOLOGICAL TEST RESULTS II (AT TEN YEARS)

Improvement in motor ability was noted on neurological examination. The boy was beginning to walk alone, assisted by braces on both legs. Left upper and lower extremities still revealed some spasticity and the left side continued to show less movement and greater weakness than the right side. Speech was recorded as indistinct and unintelligible, although the patient made a great effort to be understood. He also became impatient at lack of understanding. Gesturing and pointing predominated. EEG recording was considered normal, with convulsions well controlled by medication.

Stanford-Binet results were still not valid because of speech difficulty and motor handicap involving use of the right hand only; poor co-ordination in that hand ruled out drawing tests. By actual test a mental age of 4 years, 2 months, I.Q. 42, was obtained on the Stanford-Binet material. (A basal age was given at Year III-6, with the highest success at Year VI, namely, picture completion.) The patient's intelligence seemed higher than this by observation, and his highest achievement at Year VI appeared a better index to his general verbal intelligence than the total rating.

In view of this the Columbia Mental Maturity Scale was given, and on that a rating of 6 years, 7 months, I.Q. 67, was secured. Since the handicap involved both speech and motor aspects of behavior, the Columbia test appeared preferable and gave results consistent with the boy's optimal functioning on standardized test.

Merrill-Palmer ratings agreed closely with those on the Stanford material, being 4 years, 1 month, I.Q. 41. The patient was penalized by slow reaction time and inability to button buttons. Form perception appeared relatively good, however, as indicated by credit for all of the Decroly forms within 160 seconds. This rates at 60–65 months.

RORSCHACH RECORD

Performance	Scoring and Inquiry
Card I	
5″ 1. A plane.	W F Obj
	Covers whole card with hand and says "Here."
10″	
Card II	
7″ 1. A shoe.	D F Obj
	Points to top red and then to his own shoe, saying, "Shoe."
11″	
Card III	
5″ 1. Tie.	D F Obj
	Points to center and puts hand on neck. Then points to leg of "man" and rubs his own arm.
11″	
Card IV	
7″ 1. Ducks.	D F Ad
	Points to side projections and says "Ducks."
2. Pants.	Points to lower center and then to his own pants.
10″	
Card V	
8″ 1. Rabbit.	d F Ad
	Points essentially to the ears in the center.
15″	
Card VI	
9″ 1. Fish.	D F A
	Points to the side projections.
19″	
Card VII	
14″ 1. A duck.	W F A
	Covers whole card with hand.
24″	
Card VIII	
4″ 1. Animal.	D F→FM A P
	Points to usual bear and moves in chair as if walking. When asked if

Performance	Scoring and Inquiry
	the animal is doing that, patient smiles and says "Yes."

13"

Card IX

11" Points to top orange but speech   D   CF?   Fire?
      not intelligible. Sounded like
      "Tire" (maybe fire). Since pa-
      tient always agreed with a sug-
      gestion there was no way of
      being certain.

27"

Card X

10" 1. Birds flies. (waved hands in   D   ?   FM   A
         manner of a bird flying)

17"

INTERPRETATION

Over a test-retest interval of nearly seven years, mental retardation continued, with about two-third the expected rate of progress, implying a fairly static rate of development. These data were consistent with the neurological picture: evidence of considerable brain damage, but no deteriorating process. On the other hand, since psychological testing only confirmed evidence and contributed nothing new to the neurologist, it again exposed the inadequacies of present measuring instruments in general. Practically nothing is known of this child's emotional development or adjustment, nor about dynamics of motivation. At best, a rough approximation of intelligence was the major finding.

DISCUSSION OF CASES

Motor handicap is evidently the only element common to the several developmental and degenerative syndromes included under cerebral palsy. The classification is obviously too comprehensive to help the neuropsychologist to define type or limit of aberration.

Techniques did reveal the existence of interference, the assumed result of brain damage reflected as mental retardation. Neuropsychological procedures, however, elicited very few direct signs. Findings support the view that a positive correlation does not exist between severity of symptomatology and degree of intellectual impairment; in fact, wide individual patterning is clear. The latter is shown in the rate of mental growth observed: all three cases were mentally retarded on initial test; two maintained a fairly constant but slow rate of development between test and retest; the third, on the other hand, upon retest had attained a very high level of intelligence not anticipated initially. The phenomenon was attributed to recoverability of the brain from traumatic head injury.

Data also point up the inadequacy of present testing instruments where speech and motor handicaps must be dealt with in the same individual.

CEREBRAL PALSY AND NEUROPSYCHOLOGY

Studies to date are limited almost entirely to measurement of intellectual functioning. Practically nothing is known about the personality of cerebral-palsied children. The major contribution of neuropsychology has been an effort to devise testing instruments to estimate the intelligence of those with severe speech and motor handicaps. In this way, the mean intelligence quotient for cerebral-palsied groups was found to fall below that of the population at large. Such a finding might be anticipated where organic interference with functioning is present. Many children with cerebral palsy were, in fact, shown to be mentally defective. A negative correlation is, however, generally to be expected between severity of motor handicap and level of intelligence.

Wide individual variation in extent and expression of brain damage is the rule. Impairment has not been localized within precise areas of the brain or beyond clues afforded by the nature of the handicap itself.

Retests repeated over long intervals are now needed to assess psychological alterations paralleling neurological changes. Further attempts are in order to investigate etiology of cerebral palsy, i.e., the effect of developmental vs. degenerative factors on performance. As with the concept of mental deficiency, this exploration will lead to abandonment of the present unsatisfactory definition.

BIBLIOGRAPHY

1. AMMONS, R. S., and AMMONS, H. S. *Full-Range Picture Vocabulary Test.* Louisville, Ky.: Louisville Univer.: 1948.
2. ASHER, P., and SCHONELL, F. E. A survey of 400 cases of cerebral palsy in childhood. *Arch. Dis. Child,* 25: 360–379, 1950.
3. BURGEMEISTER, B. B., and BLUM, L. H. Intellectual evaluation of a group of cerebral palsied children. *Nerv. Child,* 8 (2): 177–180, 1949.
4. BURGEMEISTER, B. B., BLUM, L. H., and LORGE, I. *Columbia Mental Maturity Scale.* (2nd ed. 1959) Yonkers, N.Y.: World Books: 1954.
5. FOULDS, G. A., and RAVEN, J. C. An experimental survey with progressive matrices (1947). *Brit. J. Educ. Psychol.,* 20: 104–110, 1950.
6. GOLDSTEIN, K. H. Mental changes due to frontal lobotomy. *J. Psychol.,* 17: 187–208, 1944.
7. HOHMAN, L. B. Intellectual levels of cerebral palsied children. *Amer. J. Phys. Med.,* 32: 282–290, 1953.

8. HOHMAN, L. B., and FREEDHEIM, J. Further studies in intelligence levels in cerebral palsied children. *Amer. J. Phys. Med.*, 37: 90–97, 1958.

9. JOSEPHY, H. The brain in cerebral palsy. A neuropathological review. *Nerv. Child*, 8(2): 152–169, 1949.

10. KOGAN, K. L., and CRAZER, R. Standardization of the children's picture information test. *J. Clin. Psychol.*, 15: 405–411, 1959.

11. MILLER, E., and ROSENFELD, M. D. The psychologic evaluation of children with cerebral palsy and its implications in treatment. *J. Pediat.*, 41: 613–621, 1952.

12. PERLSTEIN, M. A., and HOOD, P. N. Infantile spastic hemiplegia. III. Intelligence. *Pediatries*, 15: 676–682, 1955.

13. PHELPS, W. M. Characteristic psychological variations in cerebral palsy. *Nerv. Child*, 7: 10–13, 1948.

14. PHELPS, W. M., and TURNER, T. A. The farthest corner. Elyria, Ohio: Nat. Soc. Crippled Ch. & Adults, Inc.: 1945.

15. PUTNAM, T. J. The neurology and neurosurgery of cerebral palsies and related disorders. *Nerv. Child.*, 8 (2): 170–176, 1949.

16. STROTHER, C. R. Evaluating intelligence of children handicapped by cerebral palsy. *Crippled Ch.*, 23: 82–83, 1945.

17. USHER, E. An integrated approach to cerebral palsy. *Delaware State J. Med.*, 18: 196–199, 1946.

ADDITIONAL REFERENCES

1. BROWER, L. M. Factors inhibiting progress of cerebral palsied children. *Amer. J. Occ. Ther.*, 10: 293–295, 1956.

2. DOLPHIN, J. E., and CRUICKSHANK, W. M. The figure-background relationship in children with cerebral palsy. *J. Clin. Psychol.*, 7: 228–231, 1951.

3. GINGRAS, G., SUSSET, V., LEMIEUX, R. R., CHEVRIER, J. M., HUOT, G., VOYER, R., SKUHROVSKY, G., and QUIRION, C. A clinical and statistical study in cerebral palsy rehabilitation. *Canada M. Ass. J.*, 80: 342–346, 1959.

4. PERLSTEIN, M. A. Expanding horizons in cerebral palsy. *Amer. J. Phys. Med.*, 35: 135–143, 1956.

5. POSER, C. M. Cerebral palsy: the need for reevaluation of obsolete concepts. *J. Kansas M. Soc.*, 60: 131–134, 1959.

6. RICHARDS, T. W. Movement in the fantasy of brain-injured (cerebral palsied) children. *J. Clin. Psychol.*, 14: 67–68, 1958.

IX

>>

Traumatic Head Injuries and
Intracranial Neoplasms

The three preceding chapters have been concerned with brain pathology apparent at an early age. Studies show that lesions occurring during the first few years of life usually have a far more deleterious and generalized effect upon psychological development than those occurring in adolescence or adulthood. Mental retardation and deficiency are common when lesions occur early, favoring the theory that equipotentiality of cortical development is present in infancy to a degree not demonstrable later (Lashley,[13] Coghill,[4] Hooker[8]). Variability, selectivity, and individuality are more characteristic of adults than of children, with significantly more independence and specialization of function. At the same time, intelligence per se is of less and less importance in the total pattern of adjustment. Hence the study of individuals suffering from brain injuries and tumors that first appear at or after adolescence usually centers on problems of interference with certain aspects of general intelligence rather than overall amentia. These individual aspects operate in a complex pattern, dependent upon former learning and capacity for readjustment.

Case histories presented below are limited to known or suspected pathology occurring after the childhood period of cortical development. While a developmental continuum rather than a dichotomy is the case, a chronological division seems meaningful in the light of clinical findings.

TRAUMATIC HEAD INJURIES

In closed head injuries, postconcussive trauma, and like conditions, it is well known that neurological and psychological components interact.

On the neurological side, symptoms may either persist over long periods of time or disappear rapidly. Immediate and/or delayed evidences of pathology are characteristic. Complications include hemorrhages, atrophy, scar tissue, softenings, fluid imbalance—alone or in combination, together with many others (Strauss and Savitsky[26]). These symptoms suggest potential pathology in traumatic injuries, although scar tissue remaining after surgical ablation is usually believed to be static. Follow-up of patients with head injuries for a considerable length of time is therefore essential, especially when neurological signs are positive. Epilepsy, psychoses, and permanent mental defects are not uncommon adjuncts.

Subjective complaints include headaches, dizziness, insomnia, vasomotor anomalies, aphasia, inability to concentrate, memory impairment, and mental dullness. Many invade the psychological domain and show great similarity to a neurosis. Reaction to trauma varies widely from individual to individual, and raises a question of whether symptoms have a physiological or psychological basis. Merritt[17] reports that posttraumatic phenomena are "more apt to occur in patients who had markedly neurotic symptoms before injury." Ruesch, Harris, and Bowman[23] are among those who believe that pretraumatic personality has more effect upon posttraumatic behavior than sequelae of the injury. Schilder[24] also stresses pretraumatic personality makeup as the key to later response, and is of the opinion that hysteria is the neurosis most typically observed following head trauma. A further assumption that individuals predisposed to hysteria are prone to head injury is harder to defend, but worthy of consideration.

Severity of the injury appears to be another factor determining head trauma reaction. Very severe blows to the head sometimes have the same effect as ECT (electro-convulsive therapy) in eliminating anxiety and hypochondriacal symptoms, while mild damage tends to aggravate psychogenic components. Landis and Bolles[12] have speculated that loss of familiarity, so obvious in patients following ECT, may be explained in terms of amnesia and aphasia. Their theory credits feelings of familiarity with being the associative linkage between memory and experience. Serious injury, like ECT and similar shock-producing procedures, severs or weakens such connections with resultant confusion in thinking and orientation. Once feelings of familiarity are disrupted or eliminated, elements recognized are no longer related to past experience in realistic and meaningful ways. It is as if associations had so weakened that ideas are no longer connected as they were in the past, or as they should be in normal mental life.

Such a theory would explain continuance or reinforcement of previously existing anxiety patterns in cases of mild head trauma as reflecting greater preservation of familiarity feelings. This seems a sound observation and might be applicable as well to problems of relapse following temporary alleviation of symptoms by tranquilizing medication or surgical intervention.

Head-injury cases have occasioned the use of neuropsychological findings in medico-legal problems. Until a few years ago, court testimony by psychologists was rarely acceptable to judges and lawyers. At present, however, neuropsychological testimony is being sought by progressive legal personnel. Because financial remuneration is the prime motivation in accident cases, symptoms are often exaggerated or prolonged when litigation begins. Determination of whether elements of malingering, psychoneurosis, psychosis, and/or organicity are present can be made more accurately by introducing neuropsychological techniques.

INTRACRANIAL NEOPLASMS

The onset of behavioral changes in individuals with neoplasms is often gradual and progressive in nature; loss in functioning ability is characteristic. Pathologic changes observable in various types of intracranial tumors are related to the nature and location of the tumor. Changes depend partly upon the destructive nature of the growth and partly upon secondary effects of increased intracranial pressure. Practically nothing is known about the etiology or mode of growth of primary intracranial tumors (Merritt[17]).

Although diagnosis is less of a problem if headaches, vomiting, and papilledema are present, these identifying signs of increased intracranial pressure often appear late rather than early. Their precursors are masked frequently by neurotic or psychotic behavioral features, making detection of lesions difficult. Waggoner and Bagchi[30] are among those reporting individual cases in which mental symptoms appeared first; they advocate early EEG's to minimize mistakes in diagnosis. Sometimes autopsy reveals intracranial neoplasms left completely unsuspected because of misleading psychological symptomatology.

According to findings of Soniat,[25] of a total of 128 consecutive patients, more than half (51.5 per cent) showed psychiatric symptoms attributable to the effects of cerebral damage produced by tumors.

Studies such as Soniat's are of interest because they furnish information not only on the incidence of psychiatric symptoms with pathological etiology, but also on types and locations of tumors. Figures on incidence and location of pathology appear in Table 3.

Soniat's cases confirm a recognized heterogeneity of location, although by far the greatest number of tumors accompanied by psychiatric symptoms appear in the regions of the frontal and temporal lobes.

Table 3. Incidence and Location of Brain Tumors[25]

Location of Tumor	Number of Patients	Number of Psychiatric Symptoms
Frontal lobe	45	32
Parietal lobe	22	8
Temporal lobe	25	19
Occipital lobe	1	1
Cerebellum	14	0
Pons	3	1
Medulla	1	1
Third ventricle	2	1
Fourth ventricle	2	0
Cerebellopontine angle	7	0
Suprasellar region	2	1
Parasellar	1	1
Optic chiasm	1	0
Fifth cranial nerve	1	0
Left lateral ventricle	1	1
Total	128	66

Soniat further reported "a similarity in incidence and nature of psychiatric symptoms exhibited by patients with tumors of the frontal lobe and those of the temporal lobe," except that olfactory or visual hallucinations were manifest in the latter group.

The types of brain tumor producing these psychiatric symptoms were listed by Soniat as shown in Table 4.

One might expect diffuse and widespread pathology to have more adverse effect upon psychological test ratings than that which is discrete and localized in a small area. Soniat's figures are of value, therefore, in revealing that tumors having the highest incidence of psychiatric symptoms were infiltrating tumors.

Psychological studies of brain injury and intracranial pathology are scattered and fragmentary. As a rule they comprise a small number of cases or isolated case histories, so that conclusions are tentative.

Goldstein and Scheerer's[5] report on the aftereffects of wartime brain injury furnishes excellent descriptive material, but many attributes cited often accompany lesions in other parts of the cortex also.

Milner[18] regarded visual difficulty as the main deficit of temporal-lobe pathology, even in unilateral lesions. These affected visual retention and learning in humans and monkeys. The loss noted in ability to comprehend or interpret complex picture material is interpreted therefore as "not an agnosis in the strict sense, nor is it a sample of forgetting of learned discrimination."

Table 4. Types of Brain Tumors and Incidence of Psychiatric Symptoms[25]

Type of Tumor	Number of Patients	Number of Psychiatric Symptoms
Meningioma	23	9
Glioblastoma multiforme	44	32
Astroblastoma	5	3
Astrocytoma	23	11
Oligodendroglioma	8	7
Spongioblastoma polare	1	1
Hemangioblastoma	3	1
Medulloblastoma	3	
Sarcoma	3	
Unclass. glioma	2	
Ependyoma	1	
Neurofibroma	8	
Craniopharyngioma	1	
Papillary adenocarcinoma of choroid plexus	1	1
Glioma of optic chiasm	1	
Unclass. tumor	1	1
Total	128	66

McFie and Piercy[15] approached the problem of localization by studying the relation of laterality of lesion to performance on the Weigl Sorting Test. Seventy-four patients were included in the study, which showed that incidence of failure was related to presence of lesions in the dominant hemisphere and unrelated to the presence of dysphasia. On the Weigl test, patients with left-sided lesions proved significantly inferior to patients with lesions in the so-called non-dominant right side, regardless of whether the lesion was located in the frontal, parietal, or occipital lobes. These findings are in disagreement with those of Anderson[1] using the Wechsler-Bellevue, but reports are brief and conclusions without reservations unjustifiable.

McFie and Piercy[16] believe there is a particular relationship between frontal-lobe lesions and impaired performance on a test involving arrangement of pictures to tell a story. Although other intellectual abilities may be impaired by lesions in various locations, a lowering in retention and learning seemed related to size of lesion rather than to location.

Trends rather than significant differences were found by Hanvik and Anderson[6] in studying effects of focal brain lesions on recall and on production of rotations on the Bender Gestalt. Among forty-four adult males with lesions in the dominant and nondominant hemispheres, slightly poorer recall scores were found for patients with dominant hemisphere lesions than for those with nondominant lesions. The latter, on the other hand, showed more of a tendency to rotate figures on the Bender Gestalt.

Results of Wortis, Herman, and London[31] suggest that in cases of subdural hematoma mental disturbances occur, with concrete functioning relatively well preserved, but with abstract thinking impaired. Reduction in spontaneity, difficulty in perception of spatial relationships, and mood alterations are also reported.

According to Kral and Dorken,[11] lesions of the basal ganglia do not appear to cause intellectual impairment but are responsible for changes of mood and/or impulsiveness, in addition to motor phenomena.

In a study by Battersby, Teuber, and Bender,[3] eighty veterans were divided into three groups. Twenty patients suffered from parieto-occipital lesions, twenty from penetrating frontal injuries, and forty from peripheral injuries, making them serviceable controls. Under these conditions, patients with frontal-lobe injuries made no worse showing on performance than those with parieto-occipital damage. This is in contrast to the reports of several other investigators who used different tests.

Affective disturbances in fifty patients with and without brain damage were investigated by Reitan.[27] The Minnesota Multiphasic Personality Inventory was administered and differences between patients with frontal- and parietal-lobe damage were recorded. The former showed denial of anxiety, attitudes of acceptance, affability, self-confidence, schizoid trends, and rather low levels of aspiration. Those with parietal-lobe lesions presented a preponderance of neurotic-like symptoms, such as anxiety, depression, guilt, introversion, feelings of inadequacy, and somatic concern. The brain-damaged group also rated higher on the paranoia, psychasthenia, schizophrenic, and manic scales than the non-injured group.

Several investigators have reported on individual cases, using the Rorschach test for appraisal of organic damage in patients with head injury or tumor (Tallman and Klopfer,[28] Tallman,[27] Machover,[14] Ostrander[20]).

The well-known early work of Harrower-Erickson[7] on a group of pre- and postoperative subjects with brain tumors indicated that location of lesion was unimportant. A statement was also made that constriction and uniformity were the outstanding characteristics of tumor cases. Later, following an investigation of patients with focal epilepsy where only one in ten showed a similarity to the preceding Rorschach pattern, Harrower-Erickson modified previous views and stated that obviously these attributes were "not characteristic of all types of cerebral lesions."

Eighteen brain-lesion cases were compared by Piotrowski[21] with ten patients having non-cerebral disturbances of the central nervous system and five conversion hysteria cases. He found an average of 6.2 Rorschach signs of organicity for the cortical-subcortical group, and one of only 1.5 for the group having no cerebral involvement but some organic disease of the central nervous system. Each case in the cortical group also had more signs than any individual in the non-cortical group, no member of the cortical group having less than four signs, and no member of the non-cerebral group having more than three signs.

Using different cases, Koff[10] and Orchinik, Koch, Wycis, Freed, and Spiegel[19] reported upon the emotional response to brain damage as revealed by the Rorschach. In Koff's study of brain-concussion war casualties tested shortly after injury, screening of patients was accomplished by establishing the presence of at least five of the Piotrowski signs of organic brain damage. Koff's findings are of special interest because 91.97 per cent of patients thus selected were shown to have elevated spinal fluid proteins, a neurological indicator of central-nervous-system disturbance. Conversely, strong anxiety and hypochondriacal signs were associated with low spinal-fluid protein, leading to the deduction that these are of psychogenic rather than organic origin.

In the Orchinik study of nine patients with thalamic lesions, preoperative personality traits were found to influence results of thalamotomy only because of their permanence. No evidence was obtained for postoperative changes in the Rorschach, even in the face of alterations in behavior. (This is a common problem of psychoneurological research; it is often impossible to account for behavioral changes by psychological test. In the writer's opinion there is often a lag between behavioral alteration and Rorschach change. Retest after a longer interval of time might have resulted in closer agreement between the two criteria of change.)

In a review of the literature, Klebanoff, Singer, and Wilensky[19] point out that earlier optimism about the utility of psychological tests as an aid in localizing brain pathology has been dispelled because of limitations of anatomical localization and inadequacy of testing instruments. They conclude that psychological techniques generally have not differentiated patients with presumptive injury to specific cortical areas. Teuber[29] believes that localization claims should be limited to three gross areas, namely, the parieto-occipital, frontal, and intermediate regions. Baker[2] advocates caution in generalizing but recommends the Rorschach along with other tests, not only for localization purposes, but also as a means of studying the emotional makeup of the brain-injured individual. In this way valuable information is gained about techniques developed by the individual patient for handling organic interference. This assists in diagnosis and prognosis more than an inquiry limited solely to problems of intellectual functioning.

Premorbid personality, aspiration level, emotional adjustment, demands of the individual's particular environment, such as financial pressures, job responsibilities, and other factors, enter increasingly into the clinical psychologist's deliberations in the study of brain pathology. Recent information shows the advantage of total personality evaluation rather than concern for intellectual functioning alone. A much larger number of matched cases with controls, more detailed information on case history, and improved testing tools are needed for future research in this important but poorly understood area.

CASE HISTORIES

Case I   Severe head injury in a twenty-nine-year-old man

THE CLINICAL PICTURE

History consequent on automobile accident, in which patient was thrown to the pavement from a truck and remained unconscious for sixteen days. Orientation was disturbed; he did not recognize his wife at first. Gradual return of memory occurred over four-month period before psychological evaluation, but patient complained he was still "all mixed up" at time of testing.

The patient, a Negro, had supervised the family farm after the death of his father. Besides responsibility for crops, he had done carpentry work, building barns for himself and friends, and rebuilt motors in cars. For six months he served in the U.S. Army as a truck driver, and left with an honorable discharge, accelerated because of father's illness.

At the time of accident, the patient was driving a truck for a firm transporting materials between New York and Pennsylvania. His employer reported him as always reliable, keeping all schedules and finding his way along all routes without difficulty, showing interest and initiative in his work, making good suggestions and catering to customers. He was zealous in protecting his boss and job and had secured several new customers for the firm. No one had questioned his intellectual ability, which was assumed to be average.

Neurological examination and EEG tracing showed no evidence of focal injury and were considered normal at the time of psychological test, four months after the accident. These negative findings were, however, inconsistent with both the clinical picture and subjective complaints of the patient.

PSYCHOLOGICAL TEST RESULTS I

During the psychological test session, the patient had trouble understanding written and oral instructions. He reported that memory loss seriously interfered with holding a job, that he often forgot directions, got lost, and could not be trusted with responsibility. (These facts were verified by his former employer, who had attempted to rehire him.) His wife complained that he had forgotten how to travel, was no longer able to sing, whereas he had belonged to a church choir previously, that he had forgotten dance steps, and how to cook. Irritability was displayed in disciplining his children, and jealousy in his wife's direction, in contrast to his former pleasing, stable personality.

As the patient worked, it was clear that motor coordination and mechanical ability were poor. Nevertheless, he was cooperative and tried hard to comply with requests. Failure disturbed him badly. There was no doubt he was aware that his functioning was poor, as he verbalized dissatisfaction in remarks such as "I had nine years of school. I ought to know that. I know I had it in school," or "I want to go back to work. Do you think they will take me soon?"

WECHSLER-BELLEVUE SCALE RESULTS

Verbal-scale quotient	71
Performance-scale quotient	46
Full-scale quotient	57

The patient's verbal-scale quotient showed functioning at the borderline level. The other two quotients fell well within the defective range. The highest rating recorded was on the comprehension test, at the low average level, while all other scores were much lower.

Information	3	Picture arrangement	1
Comprehension	10	Picture completion	2
Digit span	4	Block design	3
Arithmetic	1	Object assembly	0
Similarities	5	Digit symbol	2

Patterning on the performance scale was even, but only the simplest items were understood. All ratings were considered minimal due to severe interference with thinking. An estimate of at least low average, probably average, ability, was made as his intellectual potential. Although mechanisms accountable for loss in functioning were not entirely clear, organic aspects of loss were much more impressive than psychogenic components. This pointed to severe brain damage, in the opinion of the examiner.

RORSCHACH RECORD I

Performance	Scoring and Inquiry
Card I	
30″ I don't know.	
62″ 1. Some kind of an animal.	W F A P
	I don't know what kind of an animal this is. It has a couple of wings. (?) A butterfly, I guess.

Performance	Scoring and Inquiry

79″

Card II

15″ 1. Just the dark part—don't have no legs.

D   F   Ad

All of it looks like a body, but it has no legs. I guess it's an animal. I don't know what kind.

2. This looks like a man here.

W   F   Hd

All of it looks like a man, but all it has is a body. I don't know whether it's a man or an animal. I guess it's the body of a man.

64″

Card III

18″ 1. You mean the black? This looks like a heart here.

D   FC   At

It's red here like a heart and it looks like a heart.

2. A man.

W   F   H↔A   P

He has two legs instead of arms. He looks more like an animal. Here is his body and legs. (?) I guess he's a man. It's hard to tell.

57″

Card IV

35″ 1. An elephant.

W   F   A

All of this. Here is his head and his tail and his legs. (?) He's big like one.

56″

Card V

25″ 1. This I don't know either. A rabbit.

D   F   Aobj

He has a head with ears and a big body. (?) He looks like he's dead.

53″

Card VI

48″ No animal. I don't know what.

— — — —

I don't know this one.

69″

Card VII

20″ 1. The United States.

W   F   Geo

It looks like a map in a book. I saw it in school.

42″

Card VIII

68   All one.

75″ 1. Some kind of animal.

D   FM   A   P

It looks like a rabbit. It looks like it's climbing on land from the shape of

Performance	Scoring and Inquiry
	it. It has one, two-three-four legs; no, three legs, I guess. (?) I don't know what happened to his ears. I can't see them.

78"

Card IX

55" I don't know this one.

— — — — —

I don't know what this is.

67"

Card X

22" 1. A spider.

D   F   Aobj   P
It looks like a dead spider. Like the shape of one with all the legs.

31"

The patient was not able to see human movement in the cards when limits were tested and became very much upset because of his incapacity.

INTERPRETATION I

Post-traumatic signs are apparent in this patient's work. The lowering of both quotients on the Wechsler favors this interpretation, as well as the marked discrepancy between verbal and performance quotients with the verbal score higher. Ratings on all tests requiring new learning or immediate memory indicate dysfunction compared to comprehension score which is low average.

On Rorschach test, a very meager record was obtained, with perplexity, impotence, poor form quality, vague whole responses, absence of human movement, texture, and acceptable color responses. Attraction to red and black was also noted initially, as well as difficulty in seeing the usual men in Card III. The interpretation of two legs instead of an arm and a leg was in keeping with regression on an organic basis. Obviously, feelings of inadequacy and confusion existed, and might or might not be the result of injury, in the degree observed.

FOLLOW-UP AND RETEST (TEN MONTHS LATER)

For ten months after first psychological test, clinical progress was very slow. Improvement was insufficient for him to hold steady work. He was reported as a "willing and cooperative worker," who "tried all tasks presented to him," but one whose production was so poor that no one could afford to hire him. Repetitive tasks involving more than one hand operation confused him. Slight memory improvement was noted, but inability to perform well enough to earn a living continued to upset the patient. Because compensation from injury was involved, psychological tests were repeated following this ten-month interval. Neurological examination and EEG tracing continued to be negative.

Improvement on psychological test was to be anticipated on a basis of time alone, in the absence of neurological findings. The second psychological test was held fourteen months after the head injury. A comparison of Wechsler-Bellevue subtest scores shows the following gain:

	First Test	Second Test 10 Mos. Later	Point Gain
Information	3	6	3
Comprehension	10	10	0
Digit span	4	4	0
Arithmetic	1	3	2
Similarities	5	5	0
Picture arrangement	1	5	4
Picture completion	2	7	5
Block design	3	7	4
Object assembly	0	5	5
Digit symbol	2	2	0
Verbal-scale quotient	71	78	7
Performance-scale quotient	46	75	29
Full-scale quotient	57	75	18

The verbal-scale quotient on retest was 78 as compared to 71 originally, indicating verbal ability near the low-average range on test. Greatest improvement on this section occurred on information involving remote recall and on arithmetic. Digit span continued to be one of the low ratings.

On performance tests, improvement was definite and the quotient raised from 46 to 75. These twenty-nine points from the defective to the borderline level were a result of better work on all tests except digit symbols. There the same low rating remained. Of special interest is the fact that the first five block designs were correctly completed within time limits. Upon first test the patient could complete only one.

RORSCHACH RECORD II

Performance	Scoring and Inquiry

Card I

25″ 1. A bug with the head off.

         W F Ad P
I don't know what kind of a thing this bug is, but it has wings and a body.

38″

Card II

30″ 1. A hog with the head cut.

         W F Aobj
The whole thing looks flattened out like it's stretched (?) Just the shape of it. I know, like a skin.

Performance   Scoring and Inquiry

57"

Card III

35" 1. A bug crawling around. It found something dead standing up. One is holding the other.

D)
   } W   FM   A
D)

This part looks like a large bug and two small bugs here. I don't know what the red is. (?) The big bug has a body and legs. I can't see the head.

49"

Card IV

29" 1. A hog that just died and somebody cut him open.

W   Fm   Aobj

This looks like the inside that's opened up. (?) The shape of it. The body and legs in front and back. I can't see the head.

58"

Card V

17" 1. A hog somebody killed. Part of him is lying out not cut up yet.

W   F→Fm   Aobj

Here are his legs and it looks like he's been all stretched out. (?) The other hog [Card IV] looked more like he's cut open down the middle. I don't think they cut this one up yet. (?) He's dead because he's all spread out.

47"

Card VI

27" 1. A cooter crawling—walking on his feet. Something scared him.

W   FM   A

He looks like he's running away. Here's his head and his legs and his body.

42"

Card VII

15" 1. A hog. They cut him up, laid him out. Picked him up.

W   cF   mF   Aobj

He looks dead or cut up. Like a lot of pieces of meat. Dark meat.

36"

Card VIII

16" 1. A rabbit walking, not on land, out in the water. He's climbing on land.

D   FM   A   P
D   CF   Water

The water is all around. The color looks like it. (?) Blue and rabbits have four feet.

Performance	Scoring and Inquiry

28"

Card IX

47"　1. Land and earth near water. Water has got it surrounded. Valleys are cut out between the water.

W　C/F　Geo
The whole thing just looks like it. I've seen pictures like that. (?) Colored pictures.

66"

Card X

18"　1. Two hogs. Somebody killed them. They're hanging on a pole.

D　Fm　FC　Aobj
Up at the top it looks like the shape of hogs hanging there and this color looks like wood. (?) Brown like wood. The hogs have a body and four feet and this thing has tied them onto the wood.

32"

When limits were tested, patient accepted men in Card III but saw them with two legs instead of a leg and an arm. No other human movement could be elicited.

INTERPRETATION II

On second intelligence test, the full-scale quotient was fifteen points above the original quotient of 57. This indicated that the patient was now able to function generally at borderline level, whereas initially performance fell within the defective area. A potential of low-average ability seemed within striking distance, therefore, according to test results. Whether the man would ever regain the capacities he was reputed to have had prior to the accident remained questionable, however. Some permanent impairment seemed likely on the basis of test and retest and the clinical picture, although this conclusion was admittedly speculative.

The second Rorschach has more responses than the first, with no cards refused. Content with more dynamic action is also included. Elaboration is fuller, indecision less, and reaction time shorter. Both records are pathological, nevertheless, with responses less than 15, a great many poor whole responses, repetition, perseveration, evasion, attempts to rationalize anxiety, as in map responses and references to anatomy. Although less impotence and perplexity appear in the second record, inner turmoil (small m) is greater, interestingly—a sign which might be compatible with a milder degree of trauma than was at first reflected. This would be in keeping with the clinical picture, i.e., some expected neurological improvement with passage of time, in the absence of positive neurological findings.

Case II Questionable head injury in a thirty-five-year-old man

THE CLINICAL PICTURE

History of head injury one year prior to psychological testing. The patient was found unconscious beside a dumbwaiter shaft and hospitalized. As superintendent of the building he claimed he had been looking for the dumbwaiter when it fell four floors, hitting him on the head. No one witnessed this accident and no cuts or bruises were noted upon hospital admission immediately following.

Neurological examination was negative and the EEG abnormal with dysrhythmia and slowing, but without focal signs. Ten days after the accident the patient had a grand mal seizure and a diagnosis of epilepsy was made. One year later the diagnosis was unchanged.

At the time of psychological test, one year after alleged injury, the patient was still unable to work, and "feeling worse all the time." History included a college education with engineering training. Details of his job history were incomplete, the patient claiming his head "bothered" him and he couldn't remember "exactly." He complained of severe headache throughout the test session and frequently closed his eyes. Exceptional tension was revealed in shaking of the hands to such an extent that he often knocked materials out of position and had to slide cards along with the palms of his hands rather than pick them up. Repeated complaints of memory loss were verbalized. The patient was unable, or unwilling, to describe circumstances under which injury had occurred. He said he had forgotten such things as his height, birthdate, address, and college. Excuses were that he had been "sitting home" so long he "naturally" wouldn't know the answers. "Spells" in which he lost consciousness were mentioned, some severe enough to require hospitalization. The patient denied having had any before the accident.

PSYCHOLOGICAL TEST RESULTS

Psychological testing was difficult and time-consuming because each answer was considered very carefully before the patient responded. At one point he admitted being worried because he felt the examiner would try to prove him "crazy." He volunteered information revealing embarrassment at home from remarks of the neighbors. The patient claimed they considered him a "nut." He believed the reason was because he had been "upset" prior to the accident. As he said, "You know you do funny things, and I ran after my wife with a knife." He insisted, nevertheless, that this "one mistake" ought not to be held against him, and said that his wife had taught him not to do anything which might further alienate his former "friends."

WECHSLER-BELLEVUE SCALE RESULTS

Information	3	Picture arrangement	6
Comprehension	7	Picture completion	7
Digit span	2	Block design	8
Arithmetic	9	Object assembly	5
Similarities	5	Digit symbol	4

Verbal-scale quotient	78	Borderline
Performance-scale quotient	84	Low average
Full-scale quotient	80	Low average

Most questions had to be repeated because the subject claimed he had not been listening. Occasionally he did seem preoccupied with his own ideas, but most of the time gave the impression of stalling.

All scores were considered minimal because of severe emotional blocking, yet the pattern of his work indicated that he ought to rate above average in general intelligence under optimal conditions.

RORSCHACH RECORD

Performance	Scoring and Inquiry

Card I*
42" ∨ I must make sure I'm right.

64" 1. ∨ A bridge.

W   S   F   Fc   Obj
This over here looks like the shape of a bridge and it has water underneath it. (?) It's the shape of it and the black and white that makes it look like a bridge and water. (?) The darkness of shading.

78"
Card II
85" 1. ∨>∧ An atom bomb.

W   CF   mF   Atom
          CF'
The red and black look like fire and smoke with flames coming up.

91"
Card III
120" 1. ∨∂∧ Inside of your head.

W   F   At
This looks like the brain itself. (?) The shape of it. I've seen pictures of it. I was in the hospital, you know.

134"
Card IV
161" 1. >∨∧ One of the things I see in my night-mares—a monster.

W   F→FM   A
He seems to have a head and claws and a tail and big feet. (?) He looks

* See p. 71. Additional symbol ∂ indicates rotation of card.

Performance	Scoring and Inquiry

Scoring and Inquiry
like an awful monster I would like to
get away from. (?) So big.

173"
Card V
45" 1. ∨∧ A bird with two heads.

W   F→FM   A

Here are two heads—no—its mouth
is wide and the wings are open. Here
are the feet. Some kind of a bird that
catches something. (?) Yes, the
mouth is wide open.

72"
Card VI
247" 1. ∨∧ A butterfly on a mountain.

D→W   F→FM   A

The top—part of it—no, I guess it's
coming out of a cocoon. This would
be a cocoon, I suppose because the
butterfly is coming out of it.

259"
Card VII
27" 1. A bunch of clouds.

W   KF   Clouds
     mF

The shape of the whole thing looks
like a lot of clouds. (?) Thunder
clouds probably because they look
sort of heavy and broken apart by
the wind. They are pieces.

34"
Card VIII
26" 1. The inside of a skeleton—
pieces of insides, no, that
could not be because bones
here are not white—maybe
it is.

W   CF   At

The whole thing looks like a skeleton
with blood and bones. I've seen pictures like this. (?) Colored pictures in
books.

41"
Card IX
129" 1. Two   monsters   fighting.
They're trying to get out of
a fire.

D)   W   FM   A
D)   CF   mF   Fire

The horns and claws on top reminded
me of monsters. (?) I don't know
what kind. They look like animals of
some kind. I can see their heads and
bodies and here are the flames going
up where they are trying to get out.

Performance	Scoring and Inquiry

146"
Card X
38"   1. A bunch of insects.

         D   FM   A   P
These look like spiders crawling around with a lot of legs.
         D   FM   A
These two are standing against a pole.
       D→W   C$_{des}$ Color
They all look like they're in a drop of water. (?) The colors I think.

53"

INTERPRETATION

The pattern on the Wechsler-Bellevue is unusual because of its variability, easy tests being failed and hard ones creditable. Averaged scores on immediate memory and learning are higher than those for remote learning and recall. This finding is atypical of severe organic interference with thinking. Individual test items, too, accentuate the erratic nature of performance, i.e., the patient could not remember the name of the President of the United States, or the number of weeks in a year, while at the same time he was able to complete seven arithmetic problems orally within time limits. The latter tests were, in fact, done very quickly, with an average reaction time of twelve seconds. The most difficult block design was completed within time limits and extra credit for speed was earned on the first two easy reproductions. Block designs and arithmetic scored the highest ratings. Both tests are particularly sensitive to the presence of brain damage which affects intellectual functioning. In addition, the performance quotient for the battery as a whole was 84 (low average), while the verbal rating was six points lower, 78, which is borderline. With a reported history of college education and at least high-average basic optimal intelligence a marked lowering in functioning level was indicated.

The Rorschach protocol reveals an unusually long reaction-time for the first six cards, which might be interpreted on an organic basis. The sudden speeding up and unevenness in response to Cards VII, VIII, and X, on the other hand, seem more typical of emotional interference. Absence of human movement in the original protocol, as well as minimal texture response, concern with anatomy, perplexity, explosive use of color, attention to blackness, poor and vague whole responses, suggest some organic interference. All these, however, are features found in epilepsy without head trauma. Evaluation of the extent to which the

Table 5. Pertinent Factors Affecting Disability Claims

	Case I	*Case II*
Nature of Head Injury Established	Accident witnessed. Thrown from truck after collision. Coma of 16 days.	(No physical signs of injury: bruises, swelling, cuts, etc.) Unconsciousness of several minutes noted. Grand mal seizures 10 days later.
Speculation		Dependent upon subjective report of patient who cannot remember details. Claims hit on head with dumbwaiter. Possible psychomotor epilepsy (attempted attack on wife with knife with amnesia for incident) prior to alleged accident.
History	Dependable job history. Considered well adjusted.	Very poor job history with instability and maladjustment. Labeled "psychopathic personality" by welfare agency.
Armed Forces	Honorable discharge after six months.	Discrepancy in testimony. At time of court hearing denied any service record, but social worker's notes gave statement earlier by patient that he had served.
Neurological Examination	Negative at time of psychological test.	Negative at time of psychological test.
EEG	EEG normal. No focal signs.	EEG dysrhythmic and slow, consistent with epilepsy. No focal signs.
Educational Background	Nine grades of school.	College education with training in engineering.
Psychological Test Behavior	Cooperative with much effort.	Very evasive, reluctant to supply information. Extremely threatened by test situation.
Psychological Test Findings	Even test pattern with organic features on intelligence test material. Organic and neurotic signs on Rorschach, with former more prominent.	Unevenness of test pattern with unorganic quality on intelligence test. Organic and neurotic signs on Rorschach with strong neurotic overlay.

reported head injury contributed to functioning disability therefore was difficult, especially in view of the life history.

A comparison of information available for Cases I and II is made below to stress the desirability of interpreting data as part of a large Gestalt. In that way, contributions from psychological testing prove most meaningful and accurate.

Both patients were compensation cases for injuries reported during employment. In Case I more facts could be established from evidence presented than in Case II, where far more ground for speculation existed. Table 5 presents a summary of pertinent factors on the basis of which disability claims were decided.

In the first case, a substantial settlement was made on the basis of psychological-test evidence. This is an example of the assistance psychology can sometimes offer the neurologist. Without this psychological-test evidence it is extremely doubtful whether the patient would have fared so well. The neurologist in charge of the case admitted frankly, "There certainly ought to be brain damage with such a history, but I couldn't have proved it in court from my findings alone."

Decision on the second case is still pending, awaiting further investigation of discrepancy in the patient's testimony regarding service in the Armed Forces. Although the presence of convulsive seizures has been confirmed, date of onset is uncertain.

Psychological-test findings, containing a statement that head injury cannot account for the marked lowering in functional level recorded on psychological tests, have been incorporated into the neurologist's report. He has testified at a preliminary court hearing that evidence attributable directly to the head injury is not convincing. As he says, "I don't believe one blow on the head such as was reported could make that much difference to this man." The neurologist's opinion is that pre- and post-accident behavior are very similar, and not suggestive of traumatic brain damage in the degree claimed.

If records from some branch of the Armed Forces show previous poor performance, they will bolster the general impression gained of little post-traumatic personality change. If the patient did not serve at all, he must then explain why he said he did during hospital admission a few years ago. Possibility of a very good record in service appears remote; he probably would admit this willingly, unless convulsive seizures are recorded. In that event, his whole case will collapse.

Case III   Focal head injury in a thirty-nine-year-old woman

THE CLINICAL PICTURE

Housewife with history of head injury two weeks prior to psychological examination and testing. Patient was entering automobile as her husband backed the car assuming she was already seated in the rear. Patient's head struck by rear door frame, causing immediate severe pain in occipital region radiating down her neck, but not causing unconsciousness. Scalp was sensitive to touch in the left parieto-occipital region. Severe headaches, dizziness upon bending, anorexia, and vomiting appeared and persisted up to the time of study.

Skull X-ray was negative for fracture. Neurological examination was negative, with questionable weak right grip. EEG was abnormal, with focus in the left parieto-occipital area, the known site of injury.

Educational background was limited, with only four grades completed in Europe before coming to this country twenty-four years before. She gave the impression of being embarrassed by this deprivation and said, "However, I do do dressmaking."

During the first part of test session, the patient was detached and inaccessible. She asked frequently to have questions repeated, saying, "I don't get you." Complaints of excruciating pain were often made during psychological testing and she seemed tense, anxious, depressed, and ill at ease. She fatigued easily.

WECHSLER-BELLEVUE SCALE RESULTS

Information	4	Picture arrangement	4
Comprehension	6	Picture completion	4
Digit span	9	Block design	8
Arithmetic	7	Object assembly	10
Similarities	2	Digit symbol	9

Verbal-scale quotient	80	Low average
Performance-scale quotient	91	Average
Full-scale quotient	85	Low average

RORSCHACH RECORD I

Performance	Scoring and Inquiry
Card I	
13″ 1. A butterfly.	W F A P
	The shape of it looks like a butterfly. The body is a little small for the wings, but it looks like a butterfly—just the shape of it.
24″	
Card II	
12″ 1. This looks like blood.	D) D) CF Blood
	The red color made me think of blood. (?) All of the red.
2. A butterfly smashed—it has blood on it.	W Fm Aobj D CF Blood
	It looks like it had all been squashed and it has blood on it: on the body.

Performance

Scoring and Inquiry

(?) That's all I can see, just the body, really, and the wings that look kind of squashed.

41"
Card III
6" 1. Skeletons—a butterfly skeleton.

W S F AAt
The whole thing in the middle looks like a skeleton of a butterfly, but there's no body inside. Here are the wings and the feet, but I can't see the body. (?) Bones. I see bones.

D Fm A
Now I see two little squirrels. They have long tails and they look like they's hanging from something.

17"
Card IV
15" I can't make out what's this.

28" 1. It looks like a cow upside down.

D F Ad
All you can see is the head and the tail. (?)I don't know why it looks like a cow. It just does. The shape of it, I think.

41"
Card V
17" 1. The skin of an animal.

W Fc Aobj
The whole thing looks like a fur piece, like you put on your neck. (?) Some dark fur. I don't know what kind of an animal it is.

28"
Card VI
10" 1. That's another skin of the animal. I can't see the animal.

W Fc Aobj
All I can see is another piece of fur, but this might be a head of something. I don't know. I can just see the fur and not the animal. (?) This is some lighter fur. The other was darker.

27"
Card VII
12" 1. Piece of fur.

D)
D) W Fc Aobj
This is more fur. It looks like the other one only it has more pieces.

Performance	Scoring and Inquiry

28"

Card VIII

28" 1. Two tigers climbing on the tree.

D FM A P
Here is the head and the tail and the feet.
(?) The shape of them is like tigers and they are climbing up on something. I said a tree maybe. I don't know. They are climbing up something. That I know.

38"

Card IX

23" 1. Monkeys.

D FM A
They are climbing up something. I don't know what. (?) They have a head and a tail and a body. They look like monkeys to me.

37"

Card X

20" 1. An animal.

D F→FM A
You find them in the road? Like a squirrel. It's sitting there like a squirrel. (?) I can see the head and the tail and the body.

2. Another one trying to jump on the tree.

D FM FC A
There's two of them trying to jump on the tree. These are bigger squirrels. (?) They could be brown squirrels. I don't know. I think they could.

52"

In testing the limits, the examiner found the patient able to see human movement quite readily.

INTERPRETATION

The first Wechsler-Bellevue pattern is of special interest here because most of the usual organic features are absent. The performance quotient, for example, is higher than the verbal and the patient earned two of her highest scores on digit span and digit symbol, which are supposed to be sensitive to the presence of organicity. Her block-design rating was also relatively high.

When the pattern is examined more closely, the lowest scores on the verbal section are seen to be on information and similarities. In interpretation, the low information score was attributed to limited educational background and not considered linked to posttraumatic symptomatology. The low similarities rating seemed to indicate weakness in ability to categorize readily. But while this may have been exaggerated as the result of the injury, it appeared fairly basic to the woman's intellectual makeup. Perseveration from one question to another pointed in the direction of a "stickiness" sometimes found in the Rorschach.

A number of organic features in the first Rorschach would fit the post-traumatic syndrome, namely total response less than fifteen, absence of human movement, attraction to red, color avoidance after initial outburst, references to anatomy and blood, perseveration on "butterfly" and "fur" concepts, expressions of perplexity, meagerness of content, reference to damage (butterfly being smashed), and some poor form. In testing the limits, the examiner found readiness to see human movement and accuracy of description suggestive of strong neurotic overlay and exaggerated anxiety such as is found more often with mild head trauma than with severe brain damage. An interpretation of mild organicity with favorable prognosis was made on the basis of initial tests.

FOLLOW-UP AND RETEST (EIGHT MONTHS LATER)

After eight months during which the patient was placed on medication and followed by the neurologist, psychological testing was requested.

Neurological examination and EEG were both normal, with focus no longer apparent in EEG tracing. During second test session, the patient was more at ease and reported feeling better.

WECHSLER-BELLEVUE SCALE RESULTS

Comparison of the first and second test patterns is given below:

	First Test	Retest 8 Mos. Later
Information	4	4
Comprehension	6	7
Digit span	9	7
Arithmetic	7	9
Similarities	2	4
Picture arrangement	4	7
Picture completion	4	6
Block design	8	9
Object assembly	10	8
Digit symbol	9	10
Verbal-Scale quotient	80	83
Performance-scale quotient	91	97
Full-scale quotient	85	90

RORSCHACH RECORD II

Performance	Scoring and Inquiry
Card I	
5″ 1. A butterfly.	W F A P

The whole picture looks like a butterfly. I can see wings and the head and the tail. It is shaped like one.

Performance	Scoring and Inquiry

18"
Card II
35"   1. ∨ A chest.

D) F/C   At
D) W   CF   Blood

It looks like the lungs. It is shaped like the lungs and the color helps to make it look like that. (?) The red looks like blood down here. I don't know what this red is.

41"
Card III
10"   1. ∨ A bow tie.

D   F   Obj   P

The shape of it is like a bow tie. (?) Just the shape of it. The men have ties like that.

D   FM   A

Two little squirrels with long tails hanging on something. I can't see what.

19"
Card IV
5"   1. ∨ An animal skin.

W   Fc   Aobj   P

I can see the tail, the animal's nose, and his fur on his body. (?) I don't know what kind of an animal. A cow maybe.

14"
Card V
4"   1. A piece of fur.

W   Fc   Aobj

This looks like a fur piece, a fur neck piece. (?) It looks like fur, that's all. I don't know what kind.

2. A bat flying.

W   FM   A   P

And I saw a bat, too, flying. Here are his head, his wings, and these things (antennae).

15"
Card VI
12"   1. ∨∧ A skin.

W   Fc   Aobj   P

This is another piece of fur from some animal. I can't see much of the animal. His head is here and his fur. That's all.

Performance	Scoring and Inquiry

18"
Card VII
19" 1. ∨∧ Animal tails and pieces of fur together.

D)
D)W Fc Aobj
D)
Theses are pieces of fur like you see sometimes. They have tails and pieces of fur they put together to make a coat or a fur piece. It might be squirrel fur. It is a light-colored fur.

26"
Card VIII
7" 1. Two little animals that would like to climb up.

D FM A P
They look like bears—baby bears—and they are trying to climb up something. Here is the head and the body and the four feet. (?) They must be baby bears. They look too small for regular bears.

16"
Card IX
23" 1. ∨∧ ∧ A tree and two animals want to climb on it.

D FM A
That looks like a rabbit, the head and tail. It is shaped like a rabbit and it's climbing up here.

2. Faces.

D Fc Hd
They are men's faces—here is a moustache and the eyes and nose.

49"
Card X
12" 1. Two animals want to jump on top of the tree.

D FM A
Little baby squirrels here. Here is their head and they look like they're jumping to get on top of the tree.

2. Crabs.

D FM A P
They have a lot of legs and look like they're crawling all around.

3. Caterpillars.

D FC FM A P
They are shaped like it and they are green like caterpillars and they look as if they might be eating something.

67"

Human movement was seen readily when the limits were tested.

INTERPRETATION

The second Wechsler-Bellevue test confirmed the first impression of good recoverability potential. Gains of three points, six points, and five points were obtained for verbal-, performance-, and full-scale quotients, respectively. This brought the full-scale quotient to the average range of intelligence, the level suggested initially as her potential. Nevertheless, some interference was still believed to make scores minimal, especially digit span and object assembly, lower than on original test. Otherwise, improvement on second test was general on both sections of the scale, with greater gains on performance than on verbal items.

The second Rorschach record, although meager, reveals improvement in quality. Four popular responses were added (bow tie in Card III, bat in Card V, crabs and caterpillars in Card X). There was no evidence of perplexity, less emphasis upon anatomy, freer and more controlled use of color, less perseveration, and more dynamic content. Absence of human movement again had to be modified in interpretation in view of ready response during testing of the limits. This favored repression as underlying mechanism, rather than organic impotence.

In the three preceding cases of head injury, surgical intervention was not warranted. In the two following cases, psychological evaluation was verified by neurosurgery.

Case IV   Left fronto-temporal meningioma in a fifty-four-year-old man

THE CLINICAL PICTURE

History negative until two months prior to psychological testing. About two months before hospital admission, patient complained of severe headaches on the left side and nausea upon opening his eyes in the morning, with vomiting almost immediately. For the next eight weeks, symptoms continued to worsen. He was tested psychologically under threat of immediate surgery, when his hospital chart was not available to the examiner.

High-school education was reported; the patient had earned his living as a painter, was married with three children. As far as could be learned, adjustment had been good.

Cooperation was good during the test session, although patient complained frequently of his headache. Anxiety and insecurity showed, too, in apologetic remarks, and head pains were blamed for inadequacies of performance.

WECHSLER-BELLEVUE SCALE RESULTS

Information	9	Picture arrangement	6
Comprehension	8	Picture completion	6
Digit Span	4	Block design	0
Arithmetic	9	Object assembly	7
Similarities	5	Digit symbol	4

Verbal-scale quotient	92	Average
Performance-scale quotient	88	Low average
Full-scale quotient	87	Low average

The pattern of this man's work shows him functioning well in some areas, but with difficulty in others. On the similarities test, for example, he kept giving differences rather than likenesses, suggesting impairment in this phase of abstract thinking. Four digits were repeated in given order and four in reverse order. Although scores were slightly lower on this test, no serious interference was recorded; for the entire verbal section the quotient was within the average range.

Complete failure on block designs was the outstanding feature of the performance section. There the patient became quite confused and could reproduce only the simplest pattern after time limits. Digit-symbol material was also lower than expected, but this sometimes occurs on a basis of age and here ought not be attributed solely to the presence of focal pathology. The discrepancy favoring verbal over performance scores also is too small to be more than suspicious. Hence an evaluation of the over-all picture would place most significance on similarities and block-design ratings as suggesting organicity (No disturbances in vision or coordination were apparent on test.).

RORSCHACH RECORD

Performance	Scoring and Inquiry
Card I	
12" I don't know. It's two halves of something.	
29" 1. Maybe some animal.	W S F Ad It might be an animal's head, the ears and the eyes and the mouth. Maybe a wolf's head or a fox's head. I really don't know.
41"	
Card II	
46" 1. Maybe this is a picture of your body.	W F At This looks like your chest. I've seen pictures of it. This shouldn't be here (S).

Performance

2. Two dogs, maybe.

Scoring and Inquiry

D   FM   A   P

These look like puppies. They seem to have their noses together, kissing.

59"

Card III

22"   1. This looks like two dogs standing on something.

W   FM   Fm   A

Here is the head and the body and the legs. One of the legs is falling off. (?) I don't know what they are standing on.

2. I don't know what this is, maybe blood.

D   CF   mF   Blood

The red color makes it look like blood. Over here it's running down.

47"

Card IV

31"   1. This looks like another picture of your body. Your spine, I think.

W   F   At

The middle of this looks like your backbone going up to the head, but there's no head here. (?) I've seen these pictures in magazines.

48"

Card V

10"   1. This looks like a bat that's sort of shot.

W   Fm   A   P

It looks like a broken down bat. The wings are torn here. I guess it's half dead. Here is the head and here are the wings.

24"

Card VI

23"   1. This might be an X-ray picture of your body. You can see the backbone here and the back here. This might be the head up here, but it's too small. My head is bothering me. Otherwise I'd do better.

W   Fk   At

The backbone is right here. (?) It looks more like an X-ray than the other ones did because you can see the spine like it looks in an X-ray, see it better than before.

34"

Card VII

47"   I don't know this.

58"   1. Just a lot of broken pieces of something. I don't know what. Maybe some bones.

D)

D)W   mF   Meat

D)

Here are all pieces of something. (?) I didn't mean bones. It's more like

Performance

Scoring and Inquiry

pieces of meat. The shape of them, all different pieces.

62"

Card VIII

36" 1. Two animals over here.

      D F→FM A P

These look something like bears. They seem to be walking or something. I can see the head and body and legs.

    2. Some bones in here.

        D F At

This looks like your chest, I think. Maybe it's your backbone. I don't know. I'm not good at this.

69"

Card IX

31" 1. Somebody painted something but I don't know what.

      W CF Paint

Pretty colors, like in a paint box.

    2. Here is your spine again.

        D F At

The line down the center. This one looks very plain—like a backbone.

48"

Card X

21" 1. This looks like your windpipe.

        D F At

The shape of it looks like your windpipe.

    2. > These could be spiders.

      D F→FM A P

They have a lot of wiggly legs. They could be spiders.

    3. This way it could be a tulip, or some sort of a flower.

      W FC Pl.

The shape and color make it look like a flower—a tulip, I think.

69"

When the limits were tested, the patient could not find or accept either human movement or the controlled color responses that are popular. He did point out a fur rug correctly, after it was suggested.

INTERPRETATION

Curtailment of productiveness was clearer from the Rorschach record than from his intelligence-test pattern. Affective control appeared weaker than ideation on both tests, however, and pointed to a lowering in functioning level. Organic features apparent in the Rorschach were absence of human-movement response and inability to see it when testing the limits; impotence, perplexity, overemphasis upon anatomy, repetition, mention of disastrous properties like "broken," "broken down," and explosive use of color.

Because deficiencies in abstract thinking were noted on intelligence test, along with lability of emotional control there and on the Rorschach, some frontal-lobe involvement was hypothesized. Interpretation did not exclude the possibility that other cortical areas might also be affected.

Psychological retest was not requested after surgery, but the patient was followed by the neurosurgeon as an out-patient. Six months later, he was functioning well and all symptoms had disappeared except that memory for numbers seemed poorer than before.

Since memory is particularly sensitive to neurosurgical intervention, one might be tempted to assign the patient's complaint to operative procedure. This would be highly speculative, however, because pre-surgery digit span was slightly lower than patient's other verbal work. Absence of adequate baseline leaves the following questions unanswered:

1. Was pre-operative memory deficiency the result of focal pathology?
2. Was it the result of aging?
3. Was it exaggerated by the presence of focal pathology after showing signs of defect on a basis of age?

If this memory function improves with time, temporary interference because of surgical intervention will be indicated. If it does not improve, or worsens, the reason will remain enigmatic in the absence of an adequate pre-history.

Case V   Right cystic glioblastoma in a fifty-four-year-old man

THE CLINICAL PICTURE

History of a sudden fall to the ground unconscious, three months before hospitalization, and while patient was working as usual in a service station. Upon regaining consciousness he was very confused and for three hours had difficulty in speaking. Although speech later improved somewhat, he never regained full command of words. Intermittent periods of confusion with complete speech loss had continued over the three-month interval. Severe right-sided headaches were practically constant following the first lapse into unconsciousness and less severe headaches prior to that time were reported. Neurological findings were not known at the time of psychological testing.

Background showed limited education, and work as a service-station attendant for many years. Patient had a grown son and daughter who spoke well of their father, describing him as a "kind man," dependable and honest. His wife confirmed their report, adding that he had always been a good provider and made a "comfortable" living.

During the psychological test session he tried hard to cooperate. He complained frequently of severe headache and was easily fatigued. A great deal of confusion was present. Anxiety marked his attempts to express himself, which were poor. Awareness of failure was definite. Throughout the session he apologized for his speech handicap, making

clear how much it embarrassed him. From behavior and such conversation as he managed, a presumption of at least low-average intellectual
ability seemed justifiable.

WECHSLER-BELLEVUE SCALE RESULTS

Wechsler-Bellevue subtest scores fell into the following pattern:

Information	1	Picture arrangement	0
Comprehension	1	Picture completion	1
Digit span	1	Block design	0
Arithmetic	0	Object assembly	2
Similarities	0	Digit symbol	0

Verbal-scale quotient	59	
Performance-scale quotient	60	
Full-scale quotient	58	Defective by test

All subtests showed serious interference with thinking, particularly in
the block designs, where turning of the blocks at all angles was noted.
The simplest pattern was not completed, although the patient persisted
for as long as three or four minutes on each of the first few designs.
Three digit symbols were completed within time limits, indicating that
the patient understood what was required but could not work fast
enough to receive credit.

If scores are interpreted literally, they show little evidence of a lowering in functioning level, with no discrepancy between verbal and performance quotients and minimal variability of subtest ratings. However,
observations of behavior and approach to the materials, especially block
designs and the digit-symbol test, suggest the entire pattern was lowered
so much that the usual distinctions were not apparent.

DRAW-A-MAN TEST

When asked to draw a man, the patient refused, claiming he could
not remember what one looked like. He could not be persuaded to
comply.

RORSCHACH RECORD

No definite responses to the cards were verbalized. Instead, concern
for symmetry was expressed by pointing and remarking, "Same here and
here." He seemed unable to find words. "I can't say it," "Sorry, I can't
help it," and "I can't figure this one," were his comments on all cards.

In testing the limits he was unable to find even popular forms. Extreme
perplexity and confusion were apparent.

INTERPRETATION

On the basis of behavior during test session and response to materials,
the interpretation was one of organic pathology with serious inroads on

ideation and affect. Indications of aphasia placed the difficulty in the area of the parietal lobes, while his general behavior and response to block-design material were more suggestive of frontal-lobe damage. Remaining information was too limited for further speculation.

Two days after psychological testing, ventriculargram revealed a large right-sided lesion. A diagnosis of intracranial tumor (cystic glioblastoma) was made with a huge focus covering the right frontal, temporal, and parietal lobes. Postoperative psychological study was not possible.

Case VI   Left sphenoid-ridge meningioma in a fifty-nine-year-old woman

THE CLINICAL PICTURE

History showed patient had complained of numerous pains, particularly back pains, six months before hospitalization. Gait disturbances were apparent, with shuffling and unsteadiness. Confusion in thinking developed, with considerable memory loss. Symptoms had worsened progressively.

The patient was a housewife, with education limited to elementary school. Marital adjustment had been adequate, so far as could be determined.

Neurological procedures revealed a left sphenoid-ridge meningioma at time of psychological evaluation. During test session she was cooperative and tried hard. She frequently verbalized discomfort and asked for permission to walk. She would then rise, shuffle to the wall, lean against it, and say, "Now I feel better." Returning to her chair, she would resume the test at hand.

Her reaction to failure was interesting: self-critical and keenly aware of limitation at times, she would just as frequently laugh at mistakes and express amusement at her inability to cope with problems. Memory impairment of which she had complained was obvious in her inability to recall her permanent address, though she could remember that of a nursing home where she had stayed three weeks before. From her test-session behavior and conversation, potential intelligence seemed average.

WECHSLER-BELLEVUE SCALE RESULTS

Information	4	Picture arrangement	4
Comprehension	5	Picture completion	2
Digit span	3	Block design	6
Arithmetic	0	Object assembly	9
Similarities	5	Digit symbol	3

Verbal-scale quotient   75   Borderline
Performance-scale quotient   86   Low average
Full-scale quotient   80   Low average

DRAW-A-MAN TEST

The figure of a man shown in Figure 6 was obtained.

FIG. 6. Figure of a man drawn by a 59-year-old woman with left sphenoid ridge meningioma 10 days prior to surgery.

RORSCHACH RECORD I (TEN DAYS PRIOR TO SURGERY)

Performance	Scoring and Inquiry

Card I

2″ 1. An oyster.

W F A

This was two rats, wasn't it? Not rats. Wait until I get these bats straightened out. Not rats.

2. Could be a fish.

I don't see the oysters now, but I do see it like—well, this is a fish's body. It's big and small. A wing and this is a tail. (?) I don't know, maybe a rat or an oyster.

95″

Card II

15″ 1. Two dog's heads or two bears.

D FM A P

They've just come together and ready to fight. Their eyes and two heads and they're going to fight. Their noses are close together. (Turns card) No. They are bears.

D CF Meat

Would you say this is meat because it's red?

Performance	Scoring and Inquiry

31″

Card III

19″ 1. Two little colored boys or I don't know what you call it.

W F→M FC′ H P
Its' cute, isn't it? Cute little eyes they have. Little feet in black and white shoes. (?) Ready to fight because big fellows are taking their parts.

2. A chicken, huh?

D F A obj.
They are holding two chickens.

46″

Card IV

12″ 1. Two dogs with their heads together leaning up against two posts.

D FM Fc A
Here is their ear. They are posing, looking up at each other. (?) Some kind of woolly dogs, I guess.

28″

Card V

5″ 1. This is a rat or could be a bat. Do you know what a bat is?

W F FC′ A P
Here are their legs and that looks like feathers. It doesn't look like a rat so much as a bat spread out with horns. A bat is that color. (?) Black. (?) Feathers—I mean the way the wing sticks out on the card.

19″

Card VI   Oh—uh.

37″ 1. A butterfly. Say, whoever made these things was quite clever. One of these flying butterflies. Guess that's what it is.

W F A
Not an ordinary bat. I don't know what kind. It has a nice little head. I've seen them like that. It looks like the whole thing is a butterfly or a bat flying.

50″

Card VII

8″ 1. This is some kind of a—all I can think of is one of those things that comes to the seashore. Some kind of an "anbul." The way they look at each other.

D FM A
Two somethings all getting ready to fight because they're looking at each other. Two little "jacks" going to fight each other in the woods. Their little faces are like this (points) and they're standing on something.

Performance	Scoring and Inquiry

38"

Card VIII

8" 1. Might be two rats, Um, two rats or little bears. Guess that's all I can think of. Wish I knew whether that's right.

        D FM A P
It looks as if they'd crawled up there, for what I don't know. (?) Rats, I guess. (?) They have only three legs. Is that their tail? I guess so.

21"

Card IX

6" 1. Looks like a reindeer's head.

        d F Ad
Yes, I see the reindeer's head. It's very pretty. (?) The shape of his nose, I like.

    2. Oh, dear, I'm no good on this one at all. Red and green and yellow. No, I can't get it.

        D Cn→CF Obj
It's a sea shell because it's beautiful because of the colors and the design.

70"

Card X

    Oh, goodness.

    1. Looks like a sea shell that somebody has drawn to be pretty. It's beautiful, the colors.

        D CF Obj
I don't know where the sea shell is, but it's so pretty.

    2. Frogs, I think, only they're not beautiful.

        D FC FM A
Two animals, yes, frogs because they're green. Seem to be moving.

I never was very good in these things. It's a pretty thing. Did I get any of them right?
270"

INTERPRETATION I

On the verbal section of the Wechsler-Bellevue, the rating at borderline level revealed more than usual interference with thinking. Some appeared due to emotional blocking associated with limited education, as on the information test. Panic reaction was encountered on oral arithmetic; the patient responded correctly only to the first simple problem. She kept explaining that she was no longer able to make change, and could not go to the store, to her great distress. A right-handed preference was shown; no visual or motor difficulties were noted.

Poor work on picture completion and digit symbols would be consistent with loss in functioning ability; but, significantly, block designs were relatively well done. Performance quotient likewise was significantly higher than the verbal, which is atypical of organic interference. It was suspected, however, that both quotients were lowered because of organicity, which erased expected relationships between them.

Difficulty in drawing a person in profile often reflects a lowering in functioning level, but is not pathognomonic of focal pathology. Age was also a consideration. But a tendency to reverse details, as was done in the mouth, is more frequently the mark of focal pathology, in the writer's experience, than of more diffuse disturbance.

The patient's difficulty in walking and balancing and her shuffling gait make the right leg on the figure interesting, i.e., it looks as if it were heavy and hard to lift. Asymmetry of the left and right sides of the drawing are suspicious of organicity also. Below the neck the right side shows more distortion than the left, involving psycho-physiological exaggeration consistent with later neurological findings.

Few responses, perplexity, impotence, repetition, automatic phrasing, concern for correctness and variable form level, are clear in the Rorschach protocol as evidence for organic factors interfering with thinking. On the other hand, human movement, animal movement, color, and texture in the main record indicate considerable facility, as is true of the several popular responses. Flexibility and spontaneity were more in keeping with performance test than with verbal ratings.

Ten days after psychological test, a left sphenoid-ridge meningioma was removed. After six months, the woman was retested.

FOLLOW-UP AND RETEST (SIX MONTHS LATER)

The patient's behavior had improved considerably. Complaints were few, except that she still spoke of a back pain, although less severe, and reported feeling much better in general. Ratings obtained on retest after six months, as well as point gains on subtest scores, are given below.

WECHSLER-BELLEVUE SCALE RESULTS

	Pre-operative score	Post-operative score	Point gain
Information	4	4	0
Comprehension	5	11	6
Digit span	3	9	6
Arithmetic	0	2	2
Similarities	5	3	−2
Picture arrangement	4	5	1
Picture completion	2	8	6
Block design	6	5	−1
Object assembly	9	15	6
Digit symbol	3	7	4

These point gains resulted in a sharp rise in postoperative quotients:

	Pre-operative	*Post operative*	*Point gain*
Verbal-scale quotient	75	83	8
Performance-scale quotient	86	109	23
Full-scale quotient	80	96	16

DRAW-A-MAN TEST

See Figure 7.

FIG. 7. Figure of a man drawn by patient (see Fig. 6) with left sphenoid ridge meningioma 6 months after surgery.

RORSCHACH RECORD II (SIX MONTHS POST-SURGERY)

Performance	Scoring and Inquiry

Card I

21" 1. Looks like it could be an eagle.

W F→FM A P
Here are the wings and the head and it's flying.

2. A lion or a bear.

D F A
It has the same head as a bear.

3. Could be a flower.

D F Pl
This might be the pot, not the flower.

4. Now this could be an oyster —not an oyster—a lobster.

dr F Ad
The head of a lobster and this little thing is his body.

120"

Card II

4" 1. A dog's head and he's been in a fight.

D FM Fc A P
Here are his ears and his head. He has a bone in his mouth. (?) A woolly dog.

Performance	Scoring and Inquiry

2. There's blood all around it. All over it. That's all I can see.

  D   CF   Blood
The red stuff all looks like blood. It's the right color.

50"

Card III

8" 1. This looks like it might be a monkey.

  W   F→FM   A
This looks like a monkey. This is his head and his leg and they're fighting over something. (?) This is his other leg.

2. And the red I don't know. What's that for? That's all, anyway.

  D   CF   Blood
I guess the red stuff is blood again.

69"

Card IV

35" 1. And this, isn't this funny? They all look like dogs or monkeys.

I don't see the monkeys.
  W   F   Obj

2. This might be a piece of furniture.

A flower pot? It has handles on it.

71"

Card V

15" 1. ∨∧ It looks like a flying squirrel. I thought of these animals always.

  W   FM   A   P
See his head and two legs and wings? He's flying.

32"

Card VI

9" 1. This looks like a lion's fur.

  W   Fc   Aobj   P
Here—a leg and here, here, and here. This head could be off and you can see the light and darker parts look like fur.

23"

Card VII

7" Well, I don't know about this.

15" 1. This looks like fur of some kind. I don't know why I feel that way. I can't make much out of it.

  W   Fc   Aobj
I just see around the neck held together here. It looks fluffy.

74"

Card VIII

35" 1. ∨ By golly, this is something. A purse. A purse with colors on it.

  W   S   FC   Obj
The color of it is like a purse. You can carry it about by the handle.

Performance

2. ∧ That's some kind of animal. These things strike me just as they did before. Isn't that funny?

Scoring and Inquiry
D   F   A   P
I don't know what kind of an animal would be up there. A bear, maybe.

78"

Card IX

20" 1. By golly, I don't know . . . This is the thing that impressed me the last time—could be a sky—an etching. You know the way the colors come out in the sky sometimes.

W   CF   Painting
All of these could be sky colors. A painting of sky colors. That's what it is.

2. That could be a dog.

D   F→FM   A
That could be a dog or a wild boar. A boar, I think. The way he's standing there.

84"

Card X

Last one?

27" 1. Well, I don't know . . . It looks like a rabbit's head.

d   F   Ad
The shape of the head. That's all I can see of the rabbit.

2. Looks like two little monkeys.

D   FM   A
Two little monkeys standing up fighting with each other.
D   FM   A   P
Some kind of fish. Lobsters standing there.

46"

Human movement was readily seen in testing the limits.

INTERPRETATION II

Postoperative improvement was dramatic on every performance subtest except block designs. Furthermore, the same relationship between quotients was maintained, i.e., ability which had been hypothesized was verified on retest, but had to be revised upward because of a possibility of further improvement over a longer time interval. Some slight residues of organicity compatible with the condition were believed to remain.

The second human figure was better proportioned than the first. Even though some difficulty remained in carrying out the profile idea, this was much less obvious. No reversal of mouth details nor asymmetry remained. Such findings could be considered in keeping with the removal of focal pathology.

Less confusion, more productiveness, greater variety of content, improved form level, and more popular responses appear in the second Rorschach protocol. Some impotence and perplexity show, nevertheless, and human movement does not appear as it did originally. Although there is less tendency to use color, the second record shows that an explosive, uncontrolled reaction still predominates when color does enter. The basic personality is seen as intact, an immature and rather naive emotional makeup. On the whole, postoperative findings indicate more positive gains than losses, but still show some organic features. A favorable prognosis is implied in the over-all gains on intelligence, drawing, and Rorschach tests, and this is compatible with neurological progress.

DISCUSSION OF CASES

Organic features interfering with functioning were detected by psychological techniques in all six cases presented. These appeared as individualized patterns and indicated varying degrees of dysfunction. Although findings agreed well with neurological evidence and opinion, certainty as to accuracy varied from one instance to the other.

In one patient psychological-test results showed severe head injury seriously affecting capacity to perform. This was later verified by retest and clinical improvement. In another, report of dysfunction was complicated by the presence of epilepsy and a most unstable pre-accident personality. In still another, causal relationship between reported memory loss and surgery could not be established because similar complaints were made prior to removal of a left fronto-temporal meningioma. Age was also a complicating factor. All cases reveal the complexities of psychoneurological problems and the necessity for considering as a whole all available information to obtain a meaningful baseline for interpreting test results. The cases also illustrate the advantages of cooperative effort among members of a neuropsychiatric team.

NEUROPSYCHOLOGY AND TRAUMATIC HEAD INJURIES AND INTRACRANIAL NEOPLASMS

Neuropsychological studies have demonstrated considerable accuracy in detecting the presence of focal pathology. Yet the difficulty has been localized only within fairly large areas of the brain, except in a few individual cases. Inadequate testing instruments and limitations of anatomical localization account for this discrepancy. Even when testing has uncovered dysfunction unique to one particular area, such as the frontal lobe, surgical intervention has often revealed damage involving surrounding areas as well. Hence determination of degree and type of interference rather than site of origin has to date been the most useful application of neuropsychological techniques.

Attempts are now being made to devise more refined techniques and to establish better pre-illness or pre-operative baselines. Broad configurations must also be investigated, such as the relationships between pre- and post-traumatic personality traits likely to affect symptomatology. Separation of psychological from physiological elements in symptoms is often difficult.

BIBLIOGRAPHY

1. ANDERSON, A. L. The effect of laterality localization of brain damage on Wechsler-Bellevue indices of deterioration. *J. Clin. Psychol.*, 6: 191–194, 1950.
2. BAKER, G. In Klopfer, B., *Developments in the Rorschach Technique:* 318–428. Yonkers, N.Y.: World Book: 1956.
3. BATTERSBY, W. S., TEUBER, H. L., and BENDER, M. B. Problem-solving behavior in men with frontal or occipital brain injuries. *J. Psychol.*, 35: 329–351, 1953.
4. COGHILL, G. E. The early development of behavior in the amblystoma and in man. *Arch. Neurol. & Psychiat.*, 21: 989–1009, 1929.
5. GOLDSTEIN, K. H., and SCHEERER, M. *After Effects of Brain Injuries in War.* (2nd ed.) New York: Grune & Stratton: 1948.
6. HANVIK, L. J., and ANDERSON, A. L. The effect of focal brain lesions on recall and on the production of rotations in the Bender Gestalt test. *J. Consult. Psychol.*, 14: 197–198, 1950.
7. HARROWER-ERICKSON, M. R. Personality changes accompanying cerebral lesions. I. Rorschach studies of patients with cerebral tumors. *Arch. Neurol. & Psychiat.*, 43: 859–890, 1940.
8. HOOKER, D. The reflex activities of the human fetus. In Barker, R. G., et al., *Child Behavior and Development.* New York: McGraw-Hill; 1943.
9. KLEBANOFF, S. G., SINGER, J. L., and WILENSKY, H. Psychological consequences of brain lesions and ablations. *Psychol. Bull.*, 51: 1–41, 1954.
10. KOFF, S. A. The Rorschach test in the differential diagnosis of cerebral concussion and psychoneurosis. *Bull. U.S. Army, Med. Dept.*, 5–6: 170–173, 1946.
11. KRAL, V. A., and DORKEN, H. The influence of subcortical (diencephalic) brain lesions on emotionality as reflected in the Rorschach color responses. *Amer. J. Psychiat.*, 107: 839–843, 1951.
12. LANDIS, C., and BOLLES, M. M. In *Psychosurgical Problems.* Mettler, F. A. (Ed.). New York: Blakiston: 1952.
13. LASHLEY, K. S. Functional determinants of cerebral localization. *Arch. Neurol. & Psychiat.*, 38: 371–387, 1937.
14. MACHOVER, K. A case of frontal lobe injury following attempted suicide. (Drawings, Rorschach.) *Ror. Res. Exch. & J. Proj. Tech.*, 11(1): 9–20, 1947.

15. McFIE, J., and PIERCY, M. F. The relation of laterality of lesion to performance on Weigl's sorting test. *J. Ment. Sci.*, 98: 299–305, 1952.

16. McFIE, J., and PIERCY, M. F. Intellectual impairment with localized cerebral lesions. *Brain*, 75: 292–311, 1952.

17. MERRITT, H. H. *Textbook of Neurology*. Philadelphia: Lea & Febiger: 1955.

18. MILNER, B. Intellectual function of the temporal lobes. *Psychol. Bull.*, 51: 42–62, 1954.

19. ORCHINIK, C., KOCH, R., WYCIS, H. T., FREED, H., and SPIEGEL, E. A. The effect of thalamic lesions upon the emotional reactivity (Rorschach and behavior studies). In *Life stress and bodily disease. Res. Pub. A. Nerv. & Ment. Dis.*, 29: 172–207, 1951.

20. OSTRANDER, J. M. A report of Rorschach and Wechsler-Bellevue records of a man after the removal of tumor from the frontal lobes. *Ror. Res. Exch. & J. Proj. Tech.*, 12(1): 65–71, 1948.

21. PIOTROWSKI, Z. Rorschach studies of cases with lesions of the frontal lobes. *Brit. J. M. Psychol.*, 17: 105–118, 1938.

22. REITAN, R. M. Affective disturbances in brain-damaged patients. *Arch. Neurol. & Psychiat.*, 73: 530–532, 1955.

23. RUESCH, J., HARRIS, R. E., and BOWMAN, K. M. Pre- and posttraumatic personality in head injuries. In *Trauma of the central nervous system. Res. Pub. A. Res. Nerv. & Ment. Dis.*, 24: 507–544, 1945.

24. SCHILDER, P. Neuroses following head and brain injuries. In *Injuries of the Brain and Spinal cord and their coverings*: 298–328. Brock, S. (Ed.). Williams & Wilkins: Baltimore: 1949.

25. SONIAT, I. L. I. Psychiatric symptoms associated with intracranial neoplasms. *Amer. J. Psychiat.*, 108: 19–22, 1951.

26. STRAUSS, I., and SAVITSKY, N. Head injury: neurologic and psychiatric aspects. *Arch. Neurol. & Psychiat.*, 31: 893–955, 1934.

27. TALLMAN, G. Further results of retesting Mr. A. *Ror. Res. Exch.*, 3: 35–36, 1938.

28. TALLMAN, G., and KLOPFER, B. Personality studies of cases with lesions of frontal lobes. III. Rorschach study of bilateral lobectomy case. *Ror. Res. Exch.*, 1: 77–89, 1936–1937.

29. TEUBER, H. L. *The Biology of Mental Health and Disease*. New York: Hoeber: 1952.

30. WAGGONER, R. W., and BAGCHI, B. K. Initial masking of organic brain changes by psychic symptoms. Clinical and EEG studies. *Amer. J. Psychiat.*, 110: 904–910, 1954.

31. WORTIS, S. B., HERMAN, M., and LONDON, J. Mental changes in patients with subdural hematomas. In *Trauma of the central nervous system. Res. Pub. A. Res. Nerv. & Ment. Dis.*, 24: 274–282, 1945.

ADDITIONAL REFERENCES

1. BATTERSBY, W. S., KRIEGER, H. P., POLLOCK, M., and BENDER, M. B. Figure-ground discrimination and the "abstract attitude" in patients with cerebral neoplasms. *Arch. Neurol. & Psychiat.*, 70: 703–712, 1953.

2. GRASSI, J. R. The graphic Rorschach as a supplement to the Rorschach in the diagnosis of organic intracranial lesions. *Psychiatric Quart.*, Suppl. 21, 2, 312–327, 1947.
3. GRINKER, R. R., and WEINBERG, J. Neuroses following head and brain injuries. In *Injuries of the Brain and Spinal Cord and their Coverings:* 329–341. Brock, S. (Ed.). Baltimore: Williams & Wilkins: 1949.
4. GURDJIAN, E. S., and WEBSTER, J. E. Experimental and clinical studies on the mechanism of head injury. In *Trauma of the central nervous system. Res. Pub. A. Res. Nerv. & Ment. Dis.*, 24: 48–97, 1945.
5. MASSERMAN, J. H., and PECHTEL, C. How brain lesions affect normal and neurotic behavior. *Amer. J. Psychiat.*, 112: 865–872, 1956.
6. WALTON, D. On the validity of the Rorschach test in the diagnosis of intracranial damage and pathology. *J. Ment. Sci.*, 101: 370–382, 1955.

X

>>>

Psychosurgical Problems

Surgery is undertaken not only for excision of focal pathology in such neurological disorders as epilepsy, intracranial neoplasms, and intractable pain, but also for the relief of severe emotional disturbances. One of these, excessive anxiety, is prominent among symptoms for which surgery may be indicated. Since the frontal lobes are known to be involved in anxiety and general affective expression, psychosurgery has been directed to them.

As early as 1941, Freeman[3] attributed foresight and insight to the frontal lobes; he believed surgical intervention could modify ideas of self-concern. Later he postulated that primitive visceral consciousness was represented in the posterior region of the frontal lobes, with more complex awareness located in prefrontal segments.

Animal studies have shown that specific learning defects occur in many cases after damage to the frontal lobes, particularly deficits in retention of habits recently acquired. In keeping with this finding, Landis and Bolles[11] conceive of the frontal lobes as harboring feelings of familiarity, i.e., associations related to former experience. According to this theory, feeling of familiarity is the associative link binding components of present experience and memory together. When interferences such as ECT, head injury, or surgery occur, loss of familiarity often results. Recognition of elements is intact, but familiarity feelings are defective. Hence patients cannot integrate present and past experiences or give appropriate meaning to stimuli.

In 1952 Mettler[12] reported that the symptom most noticeable in lobectomized primates and topectomized humans was that they neglected peripheral stimuli furnishing possible clues, and were fixated upon an immediate field of stimulation. Changes after psychosurgery are interpreted as an over-responsiveness to immediate sensory impression and a reduction of affect for elements connected with past experience. Loss of self-conscious anxiety, loss of anguish in intractable pain, and lack of foresight become logical under this hypothesis.

Significantly prior to Mettler's comments on personality change, Jones[10] confirmed observations of Freeman and Watts[4] indicating that tendency to project oneself into the future was apparently decreased following operative procedures. Forty prefrontal lobotomy patients were studied. Observations suggest an analogy between lobotomy effects and those sometimes produced through use of tranquilizing drugs: i.e., in drug therapy freedom from anxiety often involves a decrease in motivation and drive, formerly utilized to advantage.

Results of psychosurgery are difficult to evaluate. One of the most important reasons is the variety of operative techniques used on different parts of the frontal lobes, including the lobotomies—frontal, prefrontal, partial, transorbital, lateral transorbital, bimedial, and lower medial, as well as topectomy, leucotomy, venous ligation, and lobectomy. Lack of uniformity in operative procedures thus makes postoperative behavioral generalizations difficult.

Greenblatt and Solomon[7] summarized contributions of frontal surgery to an understanding of brain-functioning mechanisms of human adaptation. They call attention to Yakovlev's report[20] of widespread parasurgical necrosis, particularly when suction methods were used. Extreme degeneration of fronto-pontine fibers was also demonstrated. Further, efferent projection tracts connecting frontal lobes to areas of varying complexity must be considered in assessing lobotomies and anatomico-behavioral correlations.

Threat of postoperative convulsions has been greatly reduced by improved operative techniques. However, Greenblatt and Solomon[7] report that electroencephalographic changes occur for five years or more and that an unusual number of macrophages appear in patients who survive five years or longer. Findings indicate neuropathology continuing "well beyond the expected degenerative period."

Complexity of reorganization is required following psychosurgery: mere subtraction of postoperative from pre-operative behavioral characteristics is an inadequate basis for a theory of frontal-lobe functioning. For such an evaluation, gross autonomic differences following surgery, as well as specific areas of involvement, must be considered.

The disorders of patients constitute another stumbling block to generalization. Psychotic and severely disturbed neurotics are the most suitable for surgical treatment. A high correlation cannot be postulated between behavioral changes expected in these conditions and those of individuals functioning normally.

Technical disparities are frequent among clinical studies. Where qualitative observations were used as criteria of personality change, quantitative measurements were often overlooked. Some investigators have emphasized objective test results without clinical confirmation. Noncomparability of retest intervals, lack of adequate pre- and post-operative measures, and absence of proper control cases are among factors limiting the usefulness of findings. Anyone who has tried to administer psychological tests to severely disturbed psychotics also knows the difficulty of obtaining cooperation because of confusion and strong emotional resistance. Mental deterioration is sometimes sufficient to defy accurate measurement by test.

As a whole, psychosurgery has shifted from total to partial removal of tissue, from extensive to limited operative areas, and from bilateral to unilateral intervention.

PSYCHOLOGICAL TEST RESULTS WEIGHED

Affective changes, intellectual losses, and specific ability impairments have come under the scrutiny of psychologists. Deficiencies in intellectual functioning are of particular interest, although the number of cases available for study has been small. Time is also an important consideration, and investigators do not agree upon how long unfavorable symptoms persist after surgery. Freeman and Watts,[4] Paul and co-workers,[15] Partridge,[13] Greenblatt and coworkers,[6] and Porteus and Kepner,[17] for example, seem more inclined than others to believe that brain damage is lasting in many cases. Brickner[2] also reported a fairly permanent lowering in functioning level after bilateral frontal lobectomy.

In contrast, much more favorable results were obtained by the Columbia-Greystone Associates[12] in one of the most elaborate procedures undertaken. There biological, psychiatric, and psychological aspects of psychosurgery were studied among psychotic patients. Very little physiological change was reported following surgery. Results favored topectomy rather than lateral transcranial lobotomy. Where, however, topectomy failed and transcranial lobotomy was done subsequently, no improvement occurred.

A number of psychosurgical patients were able to return to society. A clear positive correlation was obtained between social recovery and decrease in both anxiety and complaint scores. Mechanisms responsible for this correlation were quite elusive.

Varied psychological tests conducted by Zubin[21] included the Wechsler-Bellevue Scale, Porteus Maze Test, two sorting tests, and tests measuring ability to shift (Weigl and Homograph). Interest centered upon general intellectual changes and upon special-ability alterations such as those of memory, retention, maintenance of set, and perceptual functioning. Pre- and postoperative testing sessions were recorded; some controls were used, but were not equated for all variables.

Zubin found that ability to shift showed some loss in verbal and performance ratings, but that postoperative losses were regained by most patients within three months. Except in cases of extensive venous ligation there was "no lowering of intelligence beyond the initial pre-operative level." Four patients with more extensive posterior involvement of the frontal lobes showed a relatively greater deficit in functioning ability during the immediate postoperative period than others on the Porteus Maze, the Wechsler verbal section, and the Homograph. On the latter tests, only partial recovery after three months was recorded, while a decline on the Wechsler-Bellevue Scale was apparent for as long as six months. Inability to benefit from practice after operation was noted on the Wechsler-Bellevue performance scale.

Zubin's studies indicated no permanent impairment of intellectual functioning following lobotomy in psychotic patients. Mettler did report, on the other hand, during the period immediately after surgery, a tendency to be governed by the immediate field of stimulation, which is characteristic of brain-injured patients who are "stimulus bound." Inasmuch as psychotic patients selected were presumed to be free of brain damage, such a conclusion points to operation as the precipitating cause.

About the same time, Petrie[16] reported a demonstrable loss of social comprehension in neurotic patients and loss in ability to handle intellectual tasks requiring abstract thinking. Recently Tow's[18] careful studies confirmed intellectual losses among postoperative neurotic patients, including diminution in attention, discrimination, perception, insight, foresight, abstract thinking, and creativeness.

Research using Rorschach and other creative techniques, yielded varying results. Wittenhorn and Mettler[19] found a "lack-of-conceptual-control" score in the Rorschachs of topectomized patients. As shown in responses where form perception was absent or minimal in relation to color or shading, performance was poorer than that of control subjects.

Using the graphic Rorschach, Grassi[5] reported a tendency to exclude peripheral stimulation. Although no reduction in intelligence on Wechsler-Bellevue items was found, "blot dominance" was prevalent after operation. Six months later, blot-dominated behavior was markedly reduced.

In eight psychotic patients after transorbital lobotomy, Allison and Allison[1] found four Rorschach factors different from those of the controls: 1) decrease in m per cent, 2) decrease in FK per cent, 3) increase in W per cent, and 4) increase in reaction time. In these cases transorbital lobotomy was alleged to have resulted in a lessening of inner tension, of introspection, self-awareness, and insight, as well as in loss of ardent enthusiasm and active interest.

Hunt[8] used the Kent-Rosanoff Word Association Test in forty lobotomy cases and recorded postoperative improvement in most. Hutton and Bassett[9] used projective techniques with patients before and after prefrontal leucotomy, including a story-telling test stemming from the TAT, but in this sentences appeared. Other tests involved drawings. The authors concluded that creative ability was diminished by prefrontal leucotomy.

Follow-up studies after intervals of at least five years have now begun to appear (Paul, Fitzgerald, and Greenblatt,[14] Greenblatt, Robertson, and Solomon[6]). Paul and coworkers emphasize the superiority of bimedial lobotomy, 65 per cent of chronic intractable psychotics having shown significant improvement after five years. In contrast, only 44 per cent of patients undergoing full bilateral lobotomy improved, and only 31 per cent of patients in their series exposed to unilateral intervention.

In general, it seems fair to conclude that nonpsychotic as well as psychotic individuals show definite functional losses following psychosurgery. Recoverability in a considerable degree is probable over time. In psychotic cases, however, choice of baseline is important in evaluating outcome. If ultimate postoperative behavior is compared to pre-operative status striking gains are the rule. Marked reduction in tension and anxiety with resultant improvement in social adjustment is characteristic. When status before illness is a criterion for judging postoperative progress, considerable functional loss is usually found to prevail.

More exact conclusions await further research. Where improvement in behavior is obtained, mechanisms responsible need to be understood. Where loss is recorded, nature and duration must be more thoroughly investigated. Factors such as changes in motivation, retention ability, and learning capacity are some of the variables not yet equated. Here, again, improvement in psychological techniques themselves is needed, and better control cases as well.

A baffling question still unanswered is why in some instances much improvement in behavior is noted after psychosurgery, only to be followed by a relapse into former patterns after many months. Another unexplained phenomenon is the occasional appearance of more disturbance after surgery than was present before. These problems are closely allied to the question of what is responsible for the occasional degradation of personality and morale that occurs. The author has seen at least two postoperative patients whose pre-operative personality was far more desirable. One of these was a tense, compulsive, anxious psychoneurotic on first psychometric test (male, age twenty-five), who was friendly and put forth great effort. Behavior was quite acceptable socially.

Following lobotomy he regressed to a vulgar, belligerent individual who was definitely obnoxious. This demoralization was not temporary, but resulted after two years in commitment to a psychiatric hospital, with poor prognosis.

The second was a twenty-three-year-old male schizophrenic who had had little treatment before lobotomy. (ECT has not been given and tranquilizing drugs as we know them today were not available.) Contact was sufficiently well maintained during pretreatment psychological test to obtain a high-average intelligence quotient. An adequate Rorschach confirmed the evaluation. Following prefrontal lobotomy this patient became so inaccessible that it was impossible to test him. Institutionalization was required; he spent all of his time pacing up and down corridors, refused to talk to anyone except his mother, with whom he fought whenever she came. He was unwilling to dress or to eat, and in general presented a picture of marked regression. This condition still persisted after three years when the patient was last seen.

Isolated instances like these emphasize the necessity for better diagnostic criteria before attempting psychosurgery. Mettler[12] has suggested factors to help in estimating degree of probable effectiveness of surgery. They are of interest to the clinical psychologist because they illustrate how an individual's whole life figures in such decisions. Mettler mentions diagnosis, age of onset, response to ECT, subjective impressions of behavior, absence of "painful" affect, degree of "deterioration," and time-span of institutionalization as possible clues to success in a degree warranting instigation of surgical procedures. Greenblatt and Solomon[7] believe "marked tension" is a factor of paramount importance. They report that even with very disorganized patients, if this tension exists, operation can be worthwhile. For those with minimal or "below normal" tension, results, on the other hand, tend to be quite disappointing. These authors feel that investigators cited in the literature could have weighted their statistics in favor of psychosurgery if they had included only high-tension cases. In any event, no one clearcut pattern of preferred personality emerges; as in so many other areas of neuropsychology, broad and complicated Gestalten still remain unexplored.

CASE HISTORIES

Case I   Unilateral lobotomy in a fifty-eight-year-old manic-depressive woman

THE CLINICAL PICTURE

History showed frequent hospital commitments over a period of twenty years for "manic-depressive psychosis." Only temporary, intermittent relief had been secured from ECT and other procedures. During these intervals the patient remained at home with her husband and two grown children. The family was of high socio-economic status, and the woman had a college degree.

During the pre-operative psychological test session, she was in a hypomanic state, talking continuously, finding it very hard to sit still, and going out of contact often. Much confusion and agitation were apparent. Clinically, she seemed above average in intelligence. A thorough intelligence test was not attempted. She was given the block-design test from the Wechsler-Bellevue Scale and the entire Shipley-Hartford Scale.

All seven of the block designs were completed within time limits with a score of 11, an average rating. This was considered minimal, nevertheless, because she was talking constantly as she worked.

SHIPLEY-HARTFORD SCALE RESULTS

Vocabulary rating	37
Abstract thinking	22
Conceptual quotient	60

Her vocabulary score of 37 is exceptionally high. Forty words defined correctly would receive maximal credit. If this one measure were accepted as indicative of intelligence, it would reflect very superior capacity. This is especially true because so much confusion in thinking was noted in her conversation.

On the abstract-thinking section, interference was much more noticeable. There a rating of only 22 resulted in a conceptual quotient of about 60 percent, which is considered pathologically low.

RORSCHACH RECORD I

Performance	Scoring and Inquiry

Card I

27"   1. Three witches.

$\left.\begin{array}{l} D) \\ D) \end{array}\right\}$ W   M   FC′   (H)

There's two on the side and one in the middle. (?) They're witches because they have capes on and they're black. These two and, yes, this one, have their arms out and up like this (demonstrates).

43"

Card II

32"   1. Two bears—black bears.

D   FC′   FM   A   P

They seem to be dancing. They have their noses up there, and their ears

Performance   Scoring and Inquiry
                                               here. (?) They just look like bears,
                                               that's all.

45"
Card III
23" 1. Two skeletons might be   W   M   (H)   P
          dancing around a pot.   Here they are and here's the pot. (?)
                                               They look like skeletons because they
                                               have bones which are not joined to-
                                               gether. (?) Skeletons of men—yes—
                                               no—yes—men. Here is their leg, their
                                               body. (?) Oh yes, their heads and
                                               their arms.

47"
Card IV
47" 1. The fur of an animal.   W   Fc   Aobj
                                               The shading of this makes it look like
                                               a silver fox.

69"
Card V
22" 1. A beaver skin.   W   Fc   FC'   Aobj
                                               A black fur piece. This is certain.

31"
Card VI
24" 1. Another beaver skin.   W   Fc   Fm   Aobj   P
                                                        FC'
                                               It's torn. I see fur, black fur. It looks
                                               like a fur piece.

32"
Card VII
21" 1. A map.   W   Fm   Geo
                                               This looks like a map in a book. It
                                               has broken pieces. That's funny. (?)
                                               The broken pieces. (?) They don't
                                               look like any special place. A map.

34"
Card VIII
27" 1. These I don't know. Just   W   CF   Colors
          colors.   This looks like a blotch of colors.

37"
Card IX
19" 1. A child's painting or sur-   W   CF   Art
          realist art.   It looks like Dali's painting. (?) A lot
                                               of colors and they don't make sense.

| Performance | Scoring and Inquiry |

29"

Card X

17" 1. Looks like a lot of fishes.

                                                    D FM A P

These look like crabs walking all around.

29"

When the limits were tested, the patient identified FC responses readily.

INTERPRETATION—I: PRE-OPERATIVE(TEST 1)

Although the Rorschach record was meager and the patient refused to elaborate further or give any more responses, it did not reveal any strikingly manic signs, certainly not to a degree compatible with her clinical behavior. Affective elements, however, dominate the protocol.

Except for the readiness with which human movement was seen in the first card, the record has an organic tinge and suggests a lowering of functioning level. Reasons would be difficult to assign, nevertheless, because the latter might be due to deteriorative processes of the psychosis itself or partly the result of aging; it might plausibly be the aftereffect of repeated series of ECT over twenty years. In addition, anxiety and depression are clear.

FOLLOW-UP AND RETEST 1 (EIGHT DAYS POSTOPERATIVE)

Following the first psychological test unilateral lobotomy was performed, and testing was repeated eight days after surgery.

During the session the patient was again talkative, but much more subdued and less agitated.

Increased interference on blockdesign material was noted in a drop from 11 points (pre-operative score) to 7 points postoperatively. Because testing followed the operation so closely, this was compatible with expected trauma and not considered to indicate genuine or permanent loss. Features accounting for the lowered rating included confusion and slower reaction time.

Shipley-Hartford scores showed the following changes:

	Pre-operative	Post-operative
Vocabulary	37	35
Abstract thinking	22	12
Conceptual quotient	60	34

Vocabulary suffered little loss, while abstract thinking was markedly lowered. The latter resulted in a drastic decline in conceptual quotient, since that is based upon ratios between the two components of mentation.

RORSCHACH RECORD II (EIGHT DAYS POSTOPERATIVE)

Performance   Scoring and Inquiry

Card I

20" 1. Satan and his pal around a
        pot. Three witches in a fire.

D)
D) W M FC′ (H)

Mephistopheles or Satan around his
cauldron. (?) It's so black. (?) The
witches are on the side and in the
middle. You can't see Satan but he's
there. It's so black.

32"

Card II

 2" This is—the devil take it.

12" (?) It's so blarey.

W M FC′ H
        FC
        Fc

Two old gals thought they'd paint the
town red. (?) Picked up boy friends.
(?) They have capes and red hats on.
They look like they have been drink-
ing.

14"

Card III

 4" 1. They give this one in the
        [magazine] article. I forget
        the red spots but the two
        dudes are having a drink.

⚹ W M Fc H P
        FC′

Two dudes doing the same as the
gals. (?) They're dudes because they
look so funny. (?) The costumes are
fancy and black.

23"

Card IV

 2" 1. Oh, that's like the first one. A
        black bear skin.

W Fc FC′ Aobj
        Fm

Just a bear skin. (?) It looks like a
fur piece. (?) Hung up to dry,
maybe.

29"

Card V

 4" 1. A black bear skin—no . . .
        a fox skin.

W Fc FC′ Aobj

I said a fox skin. That's what it looks
like. (?) I can tell if a fur looks like
a fur piece.

Performance	Scoring and Inquiry

21"

Card VI

4" 1. A beaver or muskrat.

W Fc Aobj P

A moleskin, no, I mean muskrat. It looks lighter than the black one.

18"

Card VII

8" 1. ∨ That's the female of the men [Card III] only no red.

W M Fc H

The ladies of the night. They have quite a hairdo and they seem to be turning around. (?) Their skirts are here, I guess.

19"

Card VIII

4" 1. Oh, like a coral reef—with flying fish.

W CF A

A blowfish. (?) The pretty coloring and the shape of it.

16"

Card IX

5" 1. More flying fish.

D FM A

Sea horses wiggling their feelers at each other. (?) Just the shape of them. (?) I can see most of them— their head and belly, but not their tails.

16"

Card X

5" 1. All the blowfish in creation. A lobster symphony.

W CF Sym
D FM A

A chromatic rhapsody. (?) Lots of color and the shapes look like fishes all over the place crawling around.

17"

In testing the limits, the patient was able to find or accept all concepts suggested.

INTERPRETATION—II: POSTOPERATIVE (TEST 2)

Even though the postoperative record is as short as the initial one, it is clearly more dynamic. Much more happy-go-lucky content typifies it, less inhibition, and lack of concern for social consequences, such as is reported in the literature. It is significant psychologically that in contrast to increased interference and confusion on tests requiring abstract thinking, affective areas show some relief of tension even at this early date.

The protocol does, in fact, look less "organic" than the first record. At the time, these findings appeared to warrant expectation of good prognosis.

FOLLOW-UP AND RETEST II (EIGHT WEEKS LATER)

On second postoperative test, the patient's block design score returned to 10 after having fallen from 11 to 7. The last rating was very close to the pre-operative score of 11 and indicated that with more time, a rating higher than the original would probably be obtained, with no permanent ill effects of psychosurgery reflected on material of this type.

The Shipley-Hartford abstract-thinking score did not show quite the same degree of recoverability. The initial score of 22 was not reached, but rather one of 16, after an initial drop to 12. This left a pathological functioning discrepancy between old and new learning (44 per cent loss).

RORSCHACH RECORD III

| Performance | Scoring and Inquiry |

Card I

9" 1. If you're checking I saw three witches last time.

    W   Fc   FC'   Aobj
                Fm

24" 2. A drying bat skin hung up.

No—not now—now it looks like a skin spread out and tacked on a wall to dry by the front feet and hooks. (?) A bat because it's black.

52"

Card II

10" 1. Two bears dressed up for Hallowe'en.

    D→W   FC   FC'   (A)   P
                Fc

They have Hallowe'en caps on their heads but it should be finished. (Points to space between red hat and black bear.) A red and black costume on. They look as if they are thirsty. (?) The gay color and the suggestion of red through here (black part).

24"

Card III

3" 1. Two roués around a punch bowl.

    W   M   Fm   H   P

They are fairly young and a little fat. His eye is far up in his head. There's a supercilious look on his face and a glass of claret. Somebody got mad at them and threw it. (?) They're leaning down. Maybe they came back to

Performance	Scoring and Inquiry

get more. (?) Part of the punch bowl here.

14"
Card IV
4" 1. A bear skin.

W   Fc   FC'   Aobj
This looks like the fur of a black bear. Yes, a black fur piece.

2. A nightmare hobgoblin.

W   F   Aobj
Eyes that look like a skate and head, fins, and floppers. (?) It looks flat.

25"
Card V
4" 1. A black silver fox you can give me for Christmas.

W   Fc   FC'   Aobj
Half the animal here and half here. You can see the forepaw and the hind legs. They are skinned. Here is the head and it's stretched out like a fur piece.

19"
Card VI
3" 1. A nice beaver skin you can have made into a coat for me.

W   Fc   Aobj   P
There's a streak of light down the center. This looks like the underneath side, not the fur side.

17"
Card VII
5" 1. The Dollie Sisters.

D→W   M   Fc   H
They have heads with a scarf or head-dress on, a shoulder wrap. No legs, though. How can they dance with no legs? Maybe this is a footstool. If they kneel on it long, they'll get tired.

24"
Card VIII
9" These, I'm not sure.
   1. Fantastic—surrealistic—a Dali.

W   CF   Art
The coloring and imagination makes this look like a Dali. (?) Doesn't look like anything special.

17"
Card IX
4" 1. Dali went to the extreme.

W   CF   Art
He put in all the paints he could at the moment. (?) I don't know why.

Performance	Scoring and Inquiry

15″

Card X

6″ 1. Crabs.

> D   FM   A
> Two crabs, Mr. and Mrs. Standing there. (?) I don't know which is which.

2. Little fishes looking around.

> D   FM   A   P
> These are not eels. They may be fiddler crabs since they have so many legs.

3. Two devil fishes climbing up a thing to get out of the tank.

> D   FM   Fm   A
> They don't have nice eyes. Maybe they're devil fish. (?) Only devil fish would have these kind of eyes. (?) Mean-looking eyes.

26″

All limits tested showed ability on the part of the patient to respond appropriately.

INTERPRETATION—III: POSTOPERATIVE (TEST 3)

The third Rorschach record is by far the best, even though a psychotic process is still clear. Since work involving intellectual functioning also indicated improvement, the patient was considered a good prognostic risk. This later proved to be the case, with noticeable diminution in the extremes of affect clinically, and greater stability over a period of time. Anxiety was markedly reduced.

Case II   Pre-frontal lobotomy in a twenty-three-year-old postencephalitic woman

THE CLINICAL PICTURE

History uneventful until age eleven, when an acute encephalitis produced unfavorable personality changes. She was reported to "carry on," and to become extremely difficult to manage. Negativism and hostility were marked. Screaming, loud talking, and insulting remarks to family and friends led to placement in a school away from home. Changes in schools were frequent because of unpredictability, running away, sexual play, and general inability to adapt.

When all other measures had failed, pre-frontal lobotomy was performed at the age of twenty-one. For a year thereafter behavior was reported to have improved markedly, and the girl was kept at home without disruption of family life. Social adjustment was fairly adequate.

During the year prior to psychological testing, behavior again reverted to its former pattern of temper tantrums and emotional outbursts, making home life unbearable. The girl was also preoccupied with the notion that her father intended to kill her mother, suggesting hostility on her own part toward the mother. Aggressive behavior in the mother's presence was noted upon approach to the patient in the wating room.

In contrast, the patient was overly polite during testing, saying, "Yes, doctor," and "Thank you, doctor," to almost every question. She was, in fact, so overly solicitous that the examiner was afraid her attitude might suddenly change to open hostility. However, the patient remained co-operative and agreeable throughout. She frequently asked whether she was doing well and showed concern when confronted with failure. In spite of this, her general deportment was much more adolescent than ex-pected.

INTELLIGENCE AND PERFORMANCE TEST RESULTS

On the Stanford-Binet test a quotient of 76 was obtained, using a six-teen-year-old norm. In terms of mental age, this was 11 years, 4 months. The scatter of successes and failures was very wide, ranging from a basal age at Year VIII to an upper limit at the Average Adult level. The most striking features were poor work on drawing tests and consistent failure of memory material. Vocabulary and abstract words, on the other hand, were creditable at Year XIV. (The latter is of special interest because word comprehension was far in excess of her ability to think abstractly.) The pattern of her work in general indicated emotional instability and a lowering in functioning level suggestive of an organic syndrome often seen among postencephalitic patients.

Without pre-operative psychometrics it was impossible to determine whether any residue of psychosurgery remained. This appeared extremely unlikely, since greatly improved behavior was reported during the first postoperative year, and the patient appeared as alert as before.

Scores on the Arthur Point Scale (Form 1) also showed a wide scatter, from below 5 years on the Seguin Form-board to 13 years on the Mare and Foal Test. The maze tests and block designs were relatively low, rating only 7 and 8 years, respectively. (The same impression was gained on performance test as on verbal material, namely, that scores obtained were minimal due to interference with thinking.) Using a sixteen-year-old norm, a performance quotient of 58 was earned, with a score of 8 years, 8 months. Definitely lower than her verbal rating at the borderline level, this falls in the defective range. The discrepancy between the two quotients, favoring the verbal, was considered another feature consistent with organicity. Since twelve years had passed since the reported en-cephalitis and poor behavioral manifestations, rather severe brain damage was evidenced, of a sort more apt to show deterioration than recoverability over time.

RORSCHACH RECORD

Performance	Scoring and Inquiry

Card I

5″ 1. Looks like a great big moth or bat with wings spread out ready to fly.

W FM A P

A bat, I guess because it looks so big and has big wings and a small head. It could be a moth, too. I don't know.

10″

Card II

10″ 1. Looks like two witches sitting up together

W M FC′ (H)
        Fc

The head and body look like witches. (?) They just do. They have black costumes on.

14″

Card III

7″ 1. Looks like two Negroes standing holding two chickens.

W M FC′ H P

These look like Negroes because they have heads that are shaped like that and they're black. (?) The chickens are dead.

17″

Card IV

9″ 1. Looks like a great big moth.

W F Aobj

This one looks dead. It has a head and wings and a big tail.

16″

Card V

7″ 1. Looks like a great big butt.

W F Meat

Looks like a ham butt. (?) The shape of it. Like a piece of meat.

17″

Card VI

31″ I don't know.

— — — —

I don't know.

34″

Card VII

9″ 1. Looks like two Scottie dogs.

D FM Fc A

They have ears and a face and a body. (?) Standing up looking at each other.

Performance	Scoring and Inquiry

26"

Card VIII

5" 1. Two bears.

D   FM   A   P

They're walking. They look like bears walking. (?) The head and the four feet look like bears.

12"

Card IX

26" Got me.

— — — —

I don't know.

39"

Card X

34" I don't know.

— — — —

D   F   A

A moth at the top. (?) The shape of it and here is

W   F   Ad

part of another moth, the wings and feet. (?) Just the shape.

As the limits were tested the patient picked out a fur rug in Card V when the concept was suggested and spoke of the blackness making it look like that. Card VIII was used in its entirety as a colored butterfly (FC—). The colored butterfly concept on Card III was refused, but patient said all the red looked "like fire." She also rejected notion of a bow tie on Card III, saying it didn't look like one.

INTERPRETATION

Although the Rorschach record indicates higher intellectual ability than was recorded on test, it has organic features suggestive of diffuse brain damage. These include few responses, rejection of cards, automatic phrasing, repetition, poor form level, references to blackness, vagueness, inability to elaborate, and poor whole responses. The first part of the record is much better than the note on which the protocol ends. The record lends support to other test findings suggesting the likelihood of mental deterioration and reduced adequacy in functioning at time of test. Certainly the patient's inability to use color constructively would be in keeping with her reported asocial behavior and lapses in control. The poor judgment frequently shown would be consistent with frontal lobe damage, but is also a characteristic of some postencephalitic patients. Therefore it may not be credited to the operative procedure except as a speculation. The writer's opinion is that in the use of color and shading this record, as a whole, is poorer than that generally obtained from patients with postencephalitic symptoms, and thus the possibility of focal damage may not be ruled out.

DISCUSSION OF CASES

Results in the first of these two cases are in keeping with those most frequently reported in the literature: definite loss in abstract thinking immediately following psychosurgery. This loss tended to subside after an interval of eight weeks. In contrast to intellectual loss, however, alleviation of anxiety in a manic-depressive patient, and freeing of inhibitions, were striking on Rorschach test immediately following lobotomy. Gains increased after an eight-week interval.

In the second case, severe brain damage from an old encephalitis twelve years prior to testing had definitely invaded affective and intellectual realms. Marked behavioral improvement for a year followed a lobotomy, but gains were not held beyond that point. Initial improvement seemed attributable to surgical intervention. Although relapses of this nature are not uncommon, they do tend to make the patient a poor prognostic risk.

PSYCHOSURGICAL PROBLEMS AND NEUROPSYCHOLOGY

Studies show neuropsychological techniques to be successful in detecting changes in performance consistent with the postoperative clinical picture. Some disagreement exists among investigators, however, regarding nature and duration of post-traumatic residuals directly attributable to operative procedures. Temporary rather than permanent impairment in intellectual functioning has been the rule.

Behavioral changes after psychosurgery show features similar in many ways to those produced by tranquilizers and shock, except that a careless attitude seems more prevalent among lobotomized patients than among those given other therapeutic measures. The neuropsychological bases for changes observed remain obscure, and equally so are bases for selection of patients sure of a good prognosis. Follow-up testing may provide information about localization of function and permanent or temporary impairment to the central nervous system. The development of less drastic measures of treatment during the past few years has reduced the number of psychosurgical cases to be studied.

BIBLIOGRAPHY

1. ALLISON, H. W., and ALLISON, S. G. Personality changes following transorbital lobotomy. *J. Abnorm. & Social Psychol.*, 49: 219–223, 1954.
2. BRICKNER, R. *The Intellectual Functions of the Frontal Lobes.* New York: Macmillan: 1936.
3. FREEMAN, W. Brain-damaging therapeutics. *Dis. Nerv. System*, 2: 91–94, 1941.
4. FREEMAN, W., and WATTS, J. W. *Psychosurgery.* (2nd ed.) Springfield, Ill.: Charles C Thomas: 1950.

5. GRASSI, J. R. Impairment of abstract behavior following bilateral prefrontal lobotomy. *Psychiatric Quart.*, 24: 74–88, 1950.
6. GREENBLATT, M., ROBERTSON, T., and SOLOMON, H. C. Five-year follow up of one hundred cases of bilateral prefrontal lobotomy. *J.A.M.A.*, 151: 200–202, 1953.
7. GREENBLATT, M., and SOLOMON, H. C. Studies in lobotomy. In *The brain and human behavior. Res. Pub. A. Res. Nerv. & Ment. Dis.*, 36: 19–34, 1958.
8. HUNT, T. The application of the Rorschach test and a word-association test to patients undergoing prefrontal lobotomy. *Psychol. Bull.*, 37: 546 (abs.), 1940.
9. HUTTON, E. L., and BASSETT, M. Effect of leucotomy on creative personality. *J. Ment. Sci.*, 94: 332–350, 1948.
10. JONES, R. E. Personality changes in psychotics following pre-frontal lobotomy. *J. Abnorm. & Social Psychol.*, 44: 315–328, 1949.
11. LANDIS, C., and BOLLES, M. M. In *Psychosurgical Problems.* Mettler, F. A. (Ed.). New York: Blakison: 1952.
12. METTLER, F. A. In *Psychosurgical Problems.* Mettler, F. A. (Ed.). New York: Blakiston: 1952.
13. PARTRIDGE, M. *Prefrontal Leucotomy.* Springfield, Ill.: Chas. C Thomas: 1950.
14. PAUL, N. L., FITZGERALD, E., and GREENBLATT, M. Bimedial lobotomy: five-year evaluation. *J. Nerv. & Ment. Dis.*, 124: 49–52, 1956.
15. PAUL, N. L., FITZGERALD, E., and GREENBLATT, M. Five-year follow-up of patients subjected to three different lobotomy procedures. *J.A.M.A.*, 161: 815–819, 1956.
16. PETRIE, A. Personality changes after prefrontal leucotomy. *Brit. J. M. Psychol.*, 22: 200–207, 1949.
17. PORTEUS, S. D., and KEPNER, R. DeM. Mental changes after bilateral lobotomy. *Genet. Psychol. Monogr.*, 29: 3–154, 1944.
18. TOW, P. M. *Personality Changes Following Frontal Leucotomy.* London: Oxford Univer. Press: 1955.
19. WITTENHORN, J. R., and METTLER, F. A. A lack of perceptual control score for the Rorschach test. *J. Clin. Psychol.*, 7: 331–334, 1951.
20. YAKLOVLEV, P., HAMLIN, H., and SWEET, W. Anatomical study of lobotomy—survey of six specimens from 11 to 235 days postoperative survival. In *Lobotomy*, Ch. 13. Greenblatt, M., Arnot, M., and Solomon, H. C. (Eds.). New York: Grune & Stratton: 1950.
21. ZUBIN, J. In *Psychosurgical Problems.* Mettler, F. A. (Ed.). New York: Blakiston: 1952.

ADDITIONAL REFERENCES

1. LEWIS, N. D., LANDIS, C., and KING, H. E. (Eds.). *Studies in Topectomy.* New York: Grune & Stratton; 1956.
2. NEWMAN, J. Prefrontal lobotomy as a means to improve the hospital adjustment of chronic psychotic patients. *J. Abnorm. & Social Psychol.*, 51: 581–584, 1955.

XI

▸▸

Multiple Sclerosis

Multiple, or disseminated, sclerosis is a central-nervous-system disease recognized most often between the ages of twenty and forty years. Although essentially a young-adult disorder, isolated cases have been recorded at almost every age. For example, Low and Carter[16] have reported three children under ten in whom diagnosis seemed reasonably certain after thorough evaluation, while Friedman and Davison[11] set sixty-three years as the most advanced age of onset among their patients.

Multiple sclerosis is characterized pathologically by the existence of demyelinated nerve tissues scattered in erratic fashion throughout the nervous system. Bing and Haymaker[3] have demonstrated by autopsy verification that no two pathologic pictures are identical, attesting to the individualistic nature of symptomatology. According to Putnam[19] neuropathologists are in "practically complete agreement" that the gliosis is secondary to tissue damage, and that each lesion goes through an acute stage (Marburg). Acute lesions affect white matter of the cerebral hemispheres particularly, although not limited to these regions. As Merritt[17] points out, plaques "are most numerous in the white matter of the cerebrum, brain stem, cerebellum and spinal cord, but the gray matter of the nervous system and the roots of the spinal and cranial nerves may be affected." Lesions in the brain tend to form around the lateral and third ventricles. They "vary in size from that of a pinhead to huge areas encompassing the major portion of one lobe of the hemisphere."

In early stages, predominating symptoms usually fall more or less into clinical types, i.e., in the spine, brain stem and cerebellum, or the cerebrum. As the disease progresses, evidence of damage in all parts of the nervous system usually appears.

Like that of idiopathic epilepsy and many cases of mental retardation, the etiology of multiple sclerosis is still undetermined. Earlier theories such as those of Putnam[19] have been challenged. Vascular changes were stressed by Putnam, and a "peculiar lability of the clotting mechanism" credited with producing symptoms. Pneumonia, trauma from falls or accidents, pregnancy, menstruation, and over-exertion have been cited as factors precipitating initial attacks, or relapses; but convincing evidence of the direct bearing of these influences is lacking. Merritt[17] reports that now the most plausible theory is that the disease is based on a reaction to some unknown allergin. Ziegler,[23] on the other hand, believes that speculations on allergenic mechanisms apply to some multiple-sclerotic patients only. Attention is called to similarities of clinical manifestations in multiple sclerosis and rheumatic fever. Among these are the transient nature of attacks which may or may not leave permanent damage, a hypersensitivity of reaction, and greater prevalence of both in colder climates. Ziegler speculates therefore that the term multiple sclerosis may eventually be found to refer to a group of diseases having diverse etiologies.

SYMPTOMATOLOGY AND PROGNOSIS

Because pathology is so widespread, symptoms are numerous: weakness of extremities, awkwardness, tremor and stiffness of the hands, unsteadiness of gait, difficulty in walking and loss of balance, numbness of limbs and paresthesias, pain, loss of sphincter control, visual difficulties with narrowing of visual fields, headaches, dizziness, ringing and buzzing sounds, speech disorders, affective lability and intellectual impairment involving memory loss and inability to concentrate. As the disease progresses more severe manifestations such as convulsions and psychoses may appear.

Remission of initial symptoms is the rule, with substantial spontaneous recovery in many cases. Over a period of time, nevertheless, relapses are characteristic. Prognosis is better for milder symptoms at the onset and for isolated complaints. Because the long-term prognosis in a majority of cases is poor, many fatalities are reported after fifteen or twenty years. Isolated instances, on the other hand, show a life span of as long as fifty years following onset of symptoms. Later onset usually favors life expectancy, i.e., there is less chance of curtailment of normally expected years of life. Limburg[15] has estimated an average life expectancy of twenty-seven years for multiple sclerotics in general.

The course of multiple sclerosis as determined by autopsy-proved cases has been reported upon by Carter, Sciarra, and Merritt[8] for forty-six patients. The average time from onset to hospital admission for these cases was six years; average duration of life was thirteen years, with an average of nine years after onset of illness to bedridden state. Patients showed a rapid decline after incapacitation; approximately three-fourths of them died within five years. Infection was the greatest single cause of death, and developed in 70 per cent of the patients.

Fifty-eight per cent of cases in the Carter, Sciarra, Merritt study reported as having mental disorders died within two years after the appearance of mental changes; 71 per cent died within four years, and 84 per cent within six years. These are significant clinical findings. The appearance of mental deterioration also proved ominous prognostically, since 83 per cent of patients died within two years after the onset of deterioration, and 100 per cent within four years. Appearance of mood disturbances in nine years left an average life expectancy of four years. With affective disturbances, the average life was longer than when intellectual impairment was recorded. Carter and associates also mention the appearance of a "superficial sensory level" which seemed to influence prognosis unfavorably. Following this symptom, an average life expectancy of only two years was recorded.

Such evidence illustrates how accurate psychological evaluation might provide the neurologist with valuable prognostic indices.

Interest in mental deterioration has been keen in psychological circles concerned with multiple sclerosis. As early as 1943, Sugar and Nadell[21] found disagreement among clinicians in reviewing literature dealing with associated intellectual changes. Evidence of mental deterioration was reported by several investigators, but not by others. Varying techniques, lack of pre-illness baselines, and poor control cases accounted for most of these discrepancies. In time, it became more apparent that interference with intellectual functioning, i.e., memory loss, difficulty in assimilating new material, and the like, depends upon such variables as differences in distribution of multiple lesions (which is highly individual), nature and severity of symptoms, time of onset, and duration of the disease. There has been no adequate large-scale psychological study which takes into account all these factors. On the whole, and under rather poor experimental conditions, the number of investigators reporting positive findings is greater than that reporting negative findings on the loss in intellectual efficiency (Baldwin,[1] Brown and Davis,[6] Burgemeister and Tallman,[7] Cottrell and Wilson,[9] Diers and Brown,[10] Ombredane[18]).

Neurologists and psychologists agree that emotional lability is usually integral to multiple-sclerotic behavioral manifestations. There is less assurance about whether these psychogenic components are products of the demyelinating process itself or important factors in etiology of the disease. Clinical studies show great similarity of affective disturbances in many cases, a coincidence pointing to premorbid personality with hysterical inclination. Should research corroborate these speculations, multiple sclerosis could be considered a psychosomatic disorder rather than a neurological disease in the strict sense.

This hypothesis is supported by several investigators. Surveying the literature, Schumacher[20] reported that neurotic manifestations have often concealed first evidences of central lesions, thereby causing many false diagnoses of hysteria.

Using twenty-six cases and control patients with various psychosomatic conditions, Grinker, Ham and Robbins[12] investigated psychodynamic factors in multiple sclerosis. The following features are listed as characteristic of multiple-sclerotic patients studied:

1. An evaluation of the mother as close to perfection and a relationship in which the child never reached her emotionally, but showed no resentment.

2. The father pictured as a "nice fellow," but often strict.

3. Good relationships with siblings.

4. Relationships with others never close and without emotional warmth, remaining affable but somewhat detached.

5. Men were interested in sports, substituting muscular activity in adolescence for sexual satisfaction. Late sexual activity and late marriage with no close libidinal relationships were prominent.

6. Substitutes for direct expressions of angry feelings at frustration were prominent, and the multiple sclerotic portrayed as a conformist of the highest order and proud of it. Overt rebellion absent in childhood and later life, and an easygoing, happy-go-lucky attitude dominant.

Grinker and associates are of the opinion that development of neurological symptoms is precipitated by intense resentment or muscular strain. Attention is called to anger as a basic mechanism and its repression in the premorbid personality. It is argued that all physiological symptoms of multiple sclerosis indicate a gradual regression to a state of functionally-helpless infancy.

Since in humans, myelination of much of the central nerve-fiber system occurs during the first years of life, the hypothesis is advanced that a "disturbance of structure occurs," causing gradual demyelination, and rendering the patient neurologically the infant he always was psychologically. Following vascular spasms produced by inner rage there may be acute clinical disturbances which increase from time to time because of severe frustrations denied any other expression.

Langworthy[14] likewise believes multiple sclerosis may have an hysterical basis in early stages. Evidence, according to Langworthy, appeared clearer in the Rorschach than on the Wechsler-Bellevue test material.

Grinker and associates report euphoria apparent in the early stages.

This feature has been remarked on by several clinicians with considerable disagreement. Brickner[5] reviewed more than two hundred cases and found only 10 per cent frankly euphoric and another 10 per cent frankly depressed. Burgemeister and Tallman[7] also found more depression than euphoria in forty patients. Differences in sampling seem to account for reported discrepancies.

Similarities and differences in Rorschach results are reflected in a comparison of findings in the Blatt-Hecht[4] and Burgemeister-Tallman studies.

Comparative Rorschach Results in Two Studies of Multiple-Sclerosis Cases

	Blatt & Hecht[4]	Burgemeister & Tallman[7]
Number of patients	21	40
Average age	33.1 yrs.	30 yrs.
Age range	22–45 yrs.	13–52 yrs.
Duration of illness	2 wks.–10 yrs.	Less than 1 yr. to 10 yrs. Aver. 3 yrs.
Total number of responses:	*Aver.*	*Aver.*
Fewer than	20	15
Human movement (M) repressed—number	1 or 2	1
Animal movement (FM) greater than M	Yes	Yes
Color (pure C) and Color-form (CF) responses greater than form-color (FC)	Yes	No
Rejection of cards VI, VII, IX (suggestion of sexual conflict)	Yes	No (very few rejections)

Blatt and Hecht stated that regression, suppression, evasion, and other personality traits predate the illness and reflect an oversensitivity to emotional stress. The Burgemeister and Tallman findings agree with this hypothesis, but show the need for more adequate pre-illness baselines. Much better controlled studies are also essential before such lability may be assigned to hysterical tendencies. The author is of the opinion that some constitutional weakness may eventually be discovered to account for the production of both hysterical inclination and neurological symptomatology of a regressive nature, evident on Rorschach test.

Beck's[2] summary of seven multiple-sclerotic Rorschach records reveals signs of organic brain damage. Common neurotic features include "flat affectivity, emotional passivity, low or absent phantasy, vulnerability to anxiety shock and an overhanging feeling of threat of danger." Unusual symbols were reported: trees and grass associated with the theme of restricted growth, i.e., "deteriorated," "dried up," and "no life." De-

structive elements such as these are also very striking in the Burgemeister and Tallman records.

Using the Wechsler-Bellevue, Rorschach, and Szondi tests, Harrower[13]
commented upon the absence of tension among multiple-sclerotic patients, particularly concerning bodily symptoms. Sixty-one patients were
characterized by Harrower as showing excessive dependency, submission
and compliance, as well as over-cordiality in social relationships. Her
findings regarding the absence of tension, however, illustrate the general
state of disagreement at present since Grinker, Ham, and Robbins[12] interpret the characteristically calm outward attitude of the multiple
sclerotic as a defense against "deeply concealed inner tension," and
Wortis[22] describes patients who were markedly anxious, irritable, and in
states of agitated depression when studied.

A great deal more work is needed on criteria for assessing the psychological components of this chronic, progressive illness.

CASE HISTORIES

Case I   Early multiple sclerosis in a forty-year-old housewife

THE CLINICAL PICTURE

History of disturbance originating about one year before hospital
admission, when the patient's daughter drowned. Thereafter she complained of depression and extreme fatigue after the slightest exertion.
Two months later numbness of the legs appeared, with difficulty in
walking and maintaining balance. Symptoms progressed during a ten-
month interval until time of psychological testing.

Patient's husband described her as "companionable." They had been
married since her graduation from junior college.

EEG findings were mildly and diffusely abnormal; discharge diagnosis
after hospital workup was multiple sclerosis.

Except that the patient kept yawning and calling attention to the
habit, her behavior was not exceptional during the test session. Cooperation was good.

WECHSLER-BELLEVUE SCALE RESULTS

On the Wechsler-Bellevue Scale she earned scores given below:

Information	10	Picture arrangement	8
Comprehension	14	Picture completion	9
Digit span	4	Block design	8
Arithmetic	6	Object assembly	11
Similarities	9	Digit symbol	7

Verbal-scale quotient	98	Average
Performance-scale quotient	100	Average
Full-scale quotient	100	Average

Nothing on the verbal section points to organic factors, except perhaps that she repeated only three digits in reverse order. The scatter of successes and failures is very wide, however, reflecting emotional instability. A slightly low score on digit symbols involving new learning is offset by the total performance quotient's being higher than the verbal. Hence, on the whole, the test detects very few organic features directly interfering with these types of intellectual activity. Emotional lability is much more apparent.

DRAWING TESTS

Drawings are shown in Figures 8 and 9. The figure of a man is fairly well done, except for minor irregularities of spatial organization. The peculiar angle of head attachment indicates problems of maintaining balance, and asymmetry of the arms and legs may be noted as significant in view of patient's own complaints of numbness in the limbs and unsteadiness in walking. Only very mild organicity was judged to be suggested.

FIG. 8. Figure of a man drawn by a 40-year-old woman with early multiple sclerosis.

Unreliability of performance appeared indicated in the House-Tree-Two-Persons Test; she drew two trees as well as two people. The people and one tree are off balance, but otherwise indicate only rather poor judgment and anxiety and depression.

FIG. 9. House-Tree-Two-Persons drawing by patient (see Fig. 9) with early multiple sclerosis.

RORSCHACH RECORD

Performance	Scoring and Inquiry

Card I

10″ 1. ∨∧∨ Looks like some kind of a bat.

    2. ∧   Another animal.

W F A P

It looks like a moth or a bat. Could be either. The wings head, body.

D F A

An elephant. Has a big trunk.

19″

Card II

3″ 1. Well, looks like the circus. Possibly an elephant with a fancy hat. The hat is falling off.

D→W FM FC A P

               Fc

               Fm

They seem to be acting like in the circus. Have red hats on and seemed to be dressed up.

21″

Card III

12″ 1. Looks like two men dancers. What the red is I don't know.

    2. A butterfly.

    3. Pretty girls in the background, no doubt.

    All the same things, aren't they? Ink spots with things left out.

W M H P

Two men seem to be dancing. They have their hats in their hands.

D FC A P

The shape and the color.

D M FK H

They seem to be standing in the background.

56″

Card IV

17″ 1. ∨ It may be some kind of nature coming out of a cocoon. I'm nature con-

D→W FM A

This looks like the first one. Like a moth or a butterfly.

Performance

scious, because my son has a collection.

56"

Card V

5" 1. That's just plain like a bat.

W F A P

Scoring and Inquiry

This one really looks like a bat.

26"

Card VI

35" 1. ∨ I suppose if you stretch it, it looks like a mildewed piece of bread.

W Fc Fm Food

This is a wild guess. I forgot what I said. Moldy cake? I'll bet you it looks like your appendix. I never saw one.

41"

Card VII

Oh, my.

40" 1. ∨∧ You've got two faces up there but it doesn't cover the whole thing. Make it into somebody washing their hair on Sunday afternoon.

W M Fc H

Little girls' faces. Our little neighbor washing her hair.

67"

D F Statue

1. A statue in the park down here.

W KF Clouds

2. Heaven knows what the rest is, unless clouds.

Card VIII

That's pretty, isn't it?

5" 1. They look like a moth or butterfly. They all do, but that's because I'm so conscious of them. Such pretty colors.

W FC A

The pretty one. Must be some moth or a creature of the ocean.

34"

Card IX

10" 1. Oh, that must be a musical comedy. I'm nearsighted and can't see their faces.

W CF N

I remember that, I think, from Key West. A beautiful thing out of the ocean.

41"

Card X

10" 1. Good grief. This looks like Key West with sea horses.

D FC FM A P

Sea animals crawling around. They are beautiful. Beautiful colors.

Performance	Scoring and Inquiry
2. And crabs.	D FM A P

Lots of legs on these.

They say there are beautiful colors
down there.
42"

INTERPRETATION

Limited number of responses, considerable perplexity and verbalized inadequacy, personal references, automatic phrasing, repetition, suggestion of perseveration in remarks such as "they all look like a moth or butterfly," and references to something deteriorating (mildewed bread)—are features consistent with organicity. In addition, the record shows a superficial quality and "cheapness" often found among psychoneurotic patients with lability of affect and hysterical inclination. Whether this is the result of the multiple-sclerotic process or the premorbid personality is not demonstrable here. Nevertheless, the fact that symptoms appeared shortly after the trauma of her daughter's death suggests emotional shock as a possible precipitating factor. Both intelligence and Rorschach results favored interpretation of a large emotional overlay that may be a causative factor in the disease process, the dynamics of which are not yet clearly understood.

Case II   Early multiple sclerosis in a
twenty-six-year-old professional woman

THE CLINICAL PICTURE

History of symptomatology during three years before time of psychological test. Complaints included numbness of the limbs, unsteadiness of gait, questionable diplopia, and difficulty in swallowing.

Patient was college-educated and a social worker for two years before symptoms appeared. For three subsequent years, prior to hospital admission for neurological evaluation, she had been a substitute teacher in kindergarten.

At the time of psychological test EEG was diffusely abnormal. During the psychological test session, the patient fatigued early and seemed rather anxious and depressed. Otherwise there was nothing notable about her behavior. She was interested and cooperative.

WECHSLER ADULT INTELLIGENCE SCALE (WAIS)

Information	10	Digit symbol	6
Comprehension	14	Picture completion	7
Arithmetic	7	Block design	7
Similarities	12	Picture arrangement	7
Digit span	16	Object assembly	5
Vocabulary	12		

Verbal-scale quotient	110	High average
Performance-scale quotient	74	Borderline
Full-scale quotient	96	Average

Organicity is clear in the pattern of work; digit symbol, arithmetic, and all tests on the performance scale reveal a lowering in functioning level consistent with organicity. Variability of ratings on the verbal section also reflects emotional lability and difficulty in maintaining consistent control. Since her best work on the verbal scale fell within the superior range, this fact plus her conversation and college history made a loss of efficiency practically certain. In the writer's experience, however, such a disparity between verbal and performance quotients solely on a basis of organic inroads on thinking is unusual at age twenty-six without mental confusion in a pathological degree. Here, emotional interference was felt to be the prime factor explaining her poor showing on so many subtests, which may or may not be related to pathology in neurological terms.

DRAWING OF A PERSON

The figure of a person (Fig. 10) was well done and supported the impression gained generally on intelligence test that anxiety was a

FIG. 10. Figure of a person drawn by a 26-year-old woman with diagnosis of multiple sclerosis, psychoneurosis, hysteria, and depression.

factor prominent in symptomatology. No signs of distortion in the perceptional relationships are reflected, proportioning is fair, and clothing indicated. The only feature which could possibly be construed as indicating organicity would be the very slight asymmetry of the head, arms, and body. In the omission of the pupil in each eye and in general outline, the drawing resembles much more closely those of psychoneurotics than those of patients with central-nervous-system disorders.

RORSCHACH RECORD

Performance	Scoring and Inquiry

Card I

15″ 1. Two ballet dancers. I don't know what the foot thing is in the middle.

        D   M   Fc   H
They are girls and they have a foot on the floor. They are balancing their full skirts.

32″

Card II

8″ 1. Two little children playing with their hands up, sitting on something.

        D   M   Fm   H
Here are their heads, body, and hands. The hands are up in symmetrical position.

22″

Card III

11″ 1. Looks like waiters dipping water up from the fountain, dressed up.

     W   M   FC′   H   P
           Fc
They have black outfits. They have a pitcher in their hand.

  2. A lamp hanging from the ceiling.

        D   Fm   Obj
The shape of it, dangling.

  3. A butterfly.

        D   F   A   P
The shape of it essentially, the body and wings.

54″

Card IV

12″ 1. A little boy all dressed up for Hallowe'en.

     W   M   Fc   H
          Fm
His arms are outstretched and he has his father's shoes on. He's trying to look ferocious. His hands are out here in a monkey costume.

36″

Card V

14″ 1. Just a butterfly.

     W   F   Aobj   P
The feelers and the wings here suggested it. (?) It looks pretty flat—pasted.

Performance	Scoring and Inquiry

30"

Card VI

34" Let me see.

56" I don't know.   — — — — —

                                                 Rejected.

Card VII

9" 1. Two little children on the   D   M   H
     floor at school making faces   Fm
     at each other.   They are two little girls. Here is their
                                      hand below.

29"

Card VIII

11" 1. Two animals climbing up a   D   FM   A   P
     tree, squirrels. A pretty tree.   D   F   Pl
                                       The whole middle looks like a tree.
                                       I can't tell exactly why. It's just a
                                       tree where the squirrels are. (?) A
                                       head and four legs and it looks like
                                       the squirrels are climbing.

23"

Card IX

12" 1. ∨∧ Two animals in a swim-   D   FM   A
     ming pool. They are   D   CF   Water
     trying to get hold of   dr F   Obj
     each other by the   The green part looks like a a pool of
     hands. This looks like water. Here is the base. The animals
     the base of the pool. may be dogs or bears, I don't know
                            which.

36"

Card X

5" 1. This looks like a flower   W   CF   Pl
     garden.   Different colored flowers.
     2. A butterfly on the side.   D   FM   A
                                  He might be flying.

35"

INTERPRETATION

More creativeness was shown here than is characteristic of patients
with organic interference where ideational elements are involved (four
M's of good quality with elaboration). This finding supported the
impression gained from intelligence test that emotional instability might
be exaggerating difficulties. Few features could be interpreted as indicating organicity without the qualification that they are also found in
records of psychoneurotics with hysterical inclination. These include
limited number of responses, poor use of color, absence of good FC
(form-color) responses, emphasis upon concepts involving children, con-

fusion regarding the "squirrel" on Card VIII (patient did not miss tail), and variability in form level.

The relationship between movement involving human beings and color and texture was considered likewise more in keeping with depressive trends than organicity per se. Early use of texture, one reference to symmetry in the cards, and use of "black," would, on the other hand, be more suspicious of organic components. An interpretation of mild organic interference with thinking was made on the basis of Rorschach findings, with evidence for emotional instability and psychoneurotic components which, it seemed, tended to magnify the degree of difficulty present. The hospital discharge note read, Multiple Sclerosis: Psychoneurosis: Hysteria: Depression.

Case III   Early multiple sclerosis in a thirty-five-year-old man, with fever of unknown origin and chronic tonsillitis

THE CLINICAL PICTURE

History disclosed weakness of left arm appearing three months prior to testing. One month later came tremor of the left arm, numbness of the fingers on the left hand, and numbness of toes on the left foot.

A moving-picture projectionist with three years of high school education, the patient had been married for ten years.

EEG tracing was essentially normal at time of psychological testing, with some slowing. During the test session, the most striking feature of the patient's behavior was his difficulty in finding words, suggesting the possibility of a mild aphasia. Under pressure, movements of the hand became awkward, but most of the time motor coordination seemed good. What might be termed a happy-go-lucky attitude, closely allied to the early notion of euphoria, was noted. As he worked, he made an impression of being superior in intellectual ability under optimal conditions.

WECHSLER-BELLEVUE SCALE RESULTS

Considerable evidence for the presence of organic pathology was obtained on the Wechsler-Bellevue Scale, scores of which appear below:

Information	13	Picture arrangement	6
Comprehension	11	Picture completion	6
Digit span	7	Block design	3
Arithmetic	9	Object assembly	2
Similarities	8	Digit symbol	6

Verbal-scale quotient	103	Average
Performance-scale quotient	76	Borderline
Full-scale quotient	90	Average

Scores were consistently low on new learning, abstract thinking, and memory tests. Only the information rating, which involves remote memory, suggested at least a high-average level of former intellectual functioning. All scores obtained were believed to be minimal ones, not only because of impairment on an organic basis, but also because of co-existing or related emotional instability. Emotional overtones seemed indicated.

DRAWING OF A PERSON

After making two attempts and struggling hard, the patient finally stated that he had "no idea how to finish" the figure. What he did pro-

FIG. 11. Two figures of a person drawn by a 35-year-old man with diagnosis of multiple sclerosis, fever of unknown origin, chronic tonsillitis.

duce (Fig. 11) showed definite distortion of body-image concept and was considered pathological. It resembled most closely drawings of organic patients.

RORSCHACH RECORD

Performance	Scoring and Inquiry
Card I	
10″ 1. Well, that could be a fish. Maybe not.	W F A O Some kind of a—I don't know, I forget what I told you. Oh, yes a fish with a large body. I don't know what kind and it doesn't look much like one.
21″	
Card II	
11″ 1. Like a couple of dogs.	D F A P Two dogs. Just the shape of them. Noses, ears, and body.

Performance   Scoring and Inquiry

24"
Card III
25" 1. A couple of characters—so-   W   Fm   (H)   P
called characters—dancing.   So-called figures—puppets. They look
limp and crumpled up, sort of falling
over.

45"
Card IV
5" 1. That could look like an   D   F   Ad
animal, looks like a bull or   More like a bull's head.
something staring.

35"
Card V
10" 1. This could be a butterfly. I   W   F   Aobj   P
don't know if these are, yes,   This could be a dead butterfly.
a butterfly or a moth.

31"
Card VI
20" 1. This part up here. I'm con-   D   F   A
fused. No, I wouldn't know   I may be wrong, but the top part
offhand. I may think this   looks like some kind of an insect—
part here is some sort of in-   wings and body.
sect.

41"
Card VII
20" 1. Look like characters up in   dd→W   M   Fc   H
the clouds.   KF
There's a man up here in full dress
in the clouds around. (?) The fluffy
part looks like clouds.

34"
Card VIII
8" 1. Well, rocks and   — — — —

Can't find rocks.
2. A leopard.   D   F   Aobj   P
A leopard, something in the cat
family. (?) Kind of dead looking.

25"
Card IX
50" 1. Looks like a moose and over   d   FC'   Ad
on the other side, too.   A moose's head in there and here
is another one. (?) The shape and
color, I guess. (?) Gray.

87"
Card X
55" 1. Two so-called out-of-this-   D   FC'   A
world dinosaurs or some-   The grey things look like medieval
thing.   prehistoric animals.

Performance	Scoring and Inquiry
2. An airplane coming over and beginning to drop and go up in flames and smoke as it is descending.	D　Fm　CF　Obj KF This is a plane dropping and bursting into flames.
3. Offhand it looks like, I wouldn't say coral, but some sort of sea animals.	W　CF　N D　FM　A Coral or vegetation from the sea. These offhand look like a pair of monkeys stretching arms out.

90"

INTERPRETATION

Organic features are not so clear as in many other protocols. The meagerness of the record, presence of only one human-movement response, perplexity as shown in turning of the cards and in remarks, and the aeroplane crashing are features fitting an organic syndrome, but a large neurotic component is apparent, and many of these "signs" would also fit a neurotic pattern. Results on the Wechsler-Bellevue Scale and the drawing were more striking. The interpretation was organic damage, with psychoneurotic elements prominent. The hospital diagnosis upon discharge was: Multiple Sclerosis: Fever of unknown origin: Chronic tonsillitis.

Case IV　Early multiple sclerosis in a twenty-two-year-old woman college student

THE CLINICAL PICTURE

Presenting symptoms were paresthesias of the lower extremities and unsteadiness for seven months, blurring of vision for four months prior to testing. EEG tracing was normal.

Except that the patient complained of a bad headache during the psychological test session, behavior was excellent and she was cooperative and alert, with no signs of exaggerated affect. A right-handed preference was shown.

WECHSLER-BELLEVUE SCALE RESULTS

Wechsler-Bellevue test scores earned were the following:

Information	16	Picture arrangement	11
Comprehension	13	Picture completion	7
Digit span	11	Block design	13
Arithmetic	12	Object assembly	9
Similarities	14	Digit symbol	10

Verbal-scale quotient	122	Superior
Performance-scale quotient	99	Average
Full-scale quotient	113	High average

The pattern indicated much better functioning in some areas than in others. Digit-span rating, for example, was the lowest on the verbal section of the test, which seemed suspicious of organic interference in conjunction with more definitely lowered performance-scale quotient. Although the patient appeared to have much difficulty on performance tests in general, her block-design rating was very good. The possibility of blurred vision had to be considered in interpreting her low rating on picture completion. Scatter of successes on subtest scores also seemed to indicate the probability of emotional instability.

HOUSE-TREE-TWO-PERSONS TEST

More features of the evasive psychoneurotic seem reflected in the House-Tree-Two-Persons test (Fig. 12). Claims that the drawings are pathognomonic of organicity would be hard to defend.

FIG. 12. House-Tree-Two-Persons drawing by a 22-year-old woman college student with early multiple sclerosis.

RORSCHACH RECORD

Performance   Scoring and Inquiry

Card I

15″   1. Looks like a butterfly to me.   W   F   A   P
                                                All of it, the body and wings.

      2. An animalish-like thing. Just   D   F   A
         looks like a big animal.   In the center. The shape of the body.

Performance

3. Could be two men with a wing each.

Scoring and Inquiry

D   M   (H)

They seem to have their hands out.

2'01"

Card II

2"   1. Women with red hats holding the palms of their hands up with black coats and red dresses sticking out.

W   M   FC   H
        FC'
        Fc

They have a turban on. They are seated on something.

2. A spade.

S   F   Obj

The shape of a spade on cards.

3. Profile of two men—statues.

D   F   Art

Deep set eyes, Roman noses, protruding chins, just the head part—statues —chiseled.

4. Those are not the whole animal.

D   F   Ad   P

The heads of two bears—noses, ears— shape of them.

95"

Card III

8"   1. A man and a woman holding a package.

W   M   Fc   (H)   P

The woman—shape of the bust or upswept hair (left side). The man doesn't seem to have it. The woman has a jacket on, legs, end of skirt. Man has tie, trousers which end half way down. He shouldn't have high heels. They are both bending over. She has a pocketbook. I don't know what he has. Must be caricatures.

2. A red bow.

D   FC   Obj   P

Right between them. The center, side loops and tails that hang down.

3. A little pool of water.

dr   S   C'F   Pool
            mF

The blot is something in the way of obstructing the view. The white is where it has dried up and this (light gray) is the water.

2'08"

Card IV

25"   1. Part of this looks like the under side of petals of flowers.

d   Fc   Pl

Lines look like the petal has dew. These veins like. A flower that looks sort of dried up. It is closed.

Performance	Scoring and Inquiry

2. An X-ray of the backbone.

W   FC'   kF   At

Grayish color reminds me of an X-ray and this is the middle.

3. Two black-hooded figures.

dr   FC'   (Hd)
Fc

Two noses. I can see a little bit of face. The black looks like a shroud that goes with ghosts or goblins, or what have you.

4. Two icicles dripping down and turning over.

d   Fm   Icicles

Jagged edges and the way they bend down if the sun came out.

2'17"
Card V
9" 1. Two figures lying up against each other shrouded in black.

D   M   Fc   H
FC'

Here is their hair, elbows, legs. The clothes look like women.

2. Profile of a rabbit.

D   F   Ad

Tall ears and pointed snout.

3. Two, it looks like cherubs lying down on each side— like children, both identical, lying on their back.

W   M   Fc   H

Curly hair, eyes, nose-chin-legs. I really don't think the legs go well with them. The legs are more developed than children's.

4. An old man's profile with big nose and protruding chin.

de   Fc   Hd

Hum, did I say he had a long nose. This looks like there wouldn't be too many teeth. Or it could be one down here and here is another old man without teeth and hair.

2'45"
Card VI
34" 1. Some sort of bird or insect under a microscope.

D   Fc   A

Isn't very clear. This looks like feathers. Feelers. (?) Different shades on the feathers help.

2. Profile of two women back to back.

dd   Fc   Hd

Very small. I can tell by the black line. Pointed nose. (?) A little fuzziness would seem to be right here. More like a woman. I don't know really.

3. Like water.

D   KF→FK   Water

Pebbles and different shadings look like different depths of water.

Performance	Scoring and Inquiry

1'46"

Card VII

23" 1. Profile of two women facing
       each other with big hats or
       coiffures on.

     D M Fc H
They seem to be talking.

    2. Rain clouds.

     W KF C'F Clouds
The jagged edges and darkness and
other different shading of black and
gray.

1'15"

Card VIII

18" 1. Two bears pink-bodied like
       polar bears, only pink.

     D F/C FM A P
Curling up on a mountain ledge. He
seems to be missing some feet. Here
is his snout.

    2. Two fluffy pillows.

     D Fc Obj
Creases in a pillow after it has been
rested on a while. That's what it looks
like and it is sort of fluffy.

    3. An orchid, half orchid and
       half another flower.

     D FC→CF Pl
         Fc
Especially the pinkish part. It almost
looks like it has moisture on it. It has
the color and the shape of petals.

2'18"

Card IX

54" 1. Four pink vegetables of some
       kind.

     D CF cf Pl
Round shape and it looks leafy as
though they had layers.

    2. Two shrouded figures.

     D F Hd
Profiles of a shroud, here it is kind of
pointed.

    3. Head of a reindeer.

I can't find it now.

    4. False teeth, I think.

     dd FC' FC Teeth
White, divided in teeth-shaped sections. The pink is gums.

2'11"

Card X

12" 1. Two black bugs.

     D FC' Fc A
Some kind of bugs. They seem to
have hard black shells on them.

    2. Two green worms, and their
       heads are pointed, each one
       to the eye of the

     D FC A P
They seem to go from the eyes right
down. The shape and color.

Performance	Scoring and Inquiry
3. Head of a rabbit.	D F Ad
	The long ears and shape of the head.
4. Crabs.	D FC A P
	Mostly the color and crabs lend a seafish atmosphere.
5. Two yellow flowers.	D CF→FC Pl
	FC'
	Unopened flowers because the black down here holds the petals in. They could be rose buds. (?) The shape and color.
6. Shrimps.	D F A
	Just the shape of them.
7. Two islands coming out.	D F Geo
	Detached from the rest of the picture. It looks about the size of Madagascar.

2'34"

INTERPRETATION

Her responses showed more productiveness than those of many patients with organic disorders. This seemed in part due to high intellectual level and cooperative attitude. Organic features, nevertheless, were discernible: frequent reference to the redness and blackness of the cards, concern for symmetry, references to being "dried up," evasiveness, some degree of confusion (an orchid that is half an orchid and half another flower). Strong neurotic components, sexual conflict, and generally poor adjustment were unquestionable, and probably preceded the onset of symptoms. These are an unknown variable because pre-illness tests were not available. The hospital discharge diagnosis was: Multiple Sclerosis, early.

DISCUSSION OF CASES

Evidence for the existence of organic pathology was obtained in four cases of early multiple sclerosis, both from intelligence test and projective techniques. Degree and expression varied with the individual. In all, emotional instability was sufficiently prominent to interfere with functioning. Features commonly associated with psychoneurosis—hysterical inclination and depression—were those most evident. Results did not favor the inclusion of euphoria as characteristic, although within the individual some happy-go-lucky elements were detected. Findings are in keeping with those of other investigators who raise the question of whether emotional lability is an integral part of the disease process or an etiological factor producing neurological changes. The interweaving of emotional and organic factors on psychological tests may also suggest an explanation of multiple sclerosis as a psychosomatic syndrome based upon constitutional proneness to this type of regressive central-nervous-system disorder.

MULTIPLE SCLEROSIS AND NEUROPSYCHOLOGY

Varying degrees of intellectual and emotional interference in multiple sclerosis have been recorded on test. Significantly, reported intellectual and emotional deterioration follow closely the clinical course of the disease. The appearance of mental deterioration seems to shorten life expectancy, a fact suggesting a potentially greater contribution from neuropsychology, if careful longitudinal studies are made.

Although the combined presence of hysterical features plus organic interferences with thinking warrants a suspicion that multiple sclerosis may be a psychosomatic disorder, no psychological signs pathognomonic of it have yet been isolated. Future research will require a larger number of patients, as well as a more accurate selection. Pre-illness baselines, neurological correlations, and attention to irreversible changes attributable to the disease process offer interesting study possibilities.

BIBLIOGRAPHY

1. BALDWIN, M. V. A clinico-experimental investigation into the psychologic aspects of multiple sclerosis. *J. Nerv. & Ment. Dis.*, 115: 299–342, 1952.
2. BECK, S. Personal communication. Grinker, R. R., Ham, G. C., and Robbins, F. P. Some psychodynamic factors in multiple sclerosis. *Res. Pub. A. Res. Nerv. & Ment. Dis.*, 28: 456–460, 1950.
3. BING, R., and HAYMAKER, W. *Textbook of Nervous Disease.* St. Louis: Mosby, 1939.
4. BLATT, B., and HECHT, I. The personality structure of the multiple sclerosis patient as evaluated by the Rorschach diagnostic technique. *J. Clin. Psychol.*, 7: 341–344, 1951.
5. BRICKNER, R. M. Recent experimental work on the pathogenesis of multiple sclerosis. *J.A.M.A.*, 106: 2117–2121, 1936.
6. BROWN, S., and DAVIS, T. C. Mental manifestations and the emotional and psychological factors in multiple sclerosis. *Res. Pub. A. Res. Nerv. & Ment. Dis.*, 2: 75–82, 1921.
7. BURGEMEISTER, B. B., and TALLMAN, G. Rorschach patterns in multiple sclerosis. *Ror. Res. Exch. IX*, 3: 111–122, 1945.
8. CARTER, S., SCIARRA, D., and MERRITT, H. H. The course of multiple sclerosis as determined by autopsy proven cases. *Res. Pub. A. Res. Nerv. & Ment. Dis.*, 28: 471–511, 1950.

9. COTTRELL, S. S., and WILSON, S. A. K. The affective symptomatology of disseminated sclerosis. A study of 100 cases. *J. Neurol. & Psychopath.*, 7: 1–30, 1926.
10. DIERS, W. C., and BROWN, C. C. Psychometric patterns associated with multiple sclerosis. I. Wechsler-Bellevue patterns. *Arch. Neurol. & Psychiat.*, 63: 760–765, 1950.
11. FRIEDMAN, A. P., and DAVISON, C. Multiple sclerosis with late onset of symptoms. *Arch. Neurol. & Psychiat.*, 54: 348–360, 1945.
12. GRINKER, R. R., HAM, G. C., and ROBBINS, F. P. Some psychodynamic factors in multiple sclerosis. *Res. Pub. A. Res. Nerv. & Ment. Dis.*, 28: 456–460, 1950.
13. HARROWER, M. R. The results of psychometric and personality tests in multiple sclerosis. *Res. Pub. A. Res. Nerv. & Ment. Dis.*, 28: 461–470, 1950.
14. LANGWORTHY, O. R. Relation of personality problems to onset and progress of multiple sclerosis. *Arch. Neurol. & Psychiat.*, 59: 13–28, 1948.
15. LIMBURG, C. C. The geographic distribution of multiple sclerosis and its estimated prevalence in the United States. *Res. Pub. A. Res. Nerv. & Ment. Dis.*, 28: 15–24, 1950.
16. LOW, N. L., and CARTER, S. Multiple sclerosis in children. *Pediatrics*, 18: 24–30, 1956.
17. MERRITT, H. H. *A Textbook of Neurology.* Philadelphia: Lea & Febiger: 1955.
18. OMBREDANE, A. *Les Troubles Mentaux de la Sclérose en Plaques.* Paris: Presses Universitaires: 1929.
19. PUTNAM, T. J. Multiple sclerosis and "encephalomyelitis." *Bull. New York Acad. Med.*, 19: 301–316, 1943.
20. SCHUMACHER, G. A. Multiple sclerosis. *J.A.M.A.*, 143: 1059–1065, 1950.
21. SUGAR, C., and NADELL, R. Mental symptoms in multiple sclerosis. A study of 28 cases with review of the literature. *J. Nerv. & Ment. Dis.*, 98: 267–280, 1943.
22. WORTIS, S. S. Discussion of Grinker, R. R., Ham, G. C., and Robbins, F. P., Some psychodynamic factors in multiple sclerosis. *Res. Pub. A. Res. Nerv. & Ment. Dis.*, 28: 456–460, 1950.
23. ZIEGLER, D. K. Multiple sclerosis and rheumatic fever: related diseases. *Dis. Nerv. System*, 20: 221–224, 1959.

ADDITIONAL REFERENCES

1. ARNAUD, S. H. Some psychological characteristics of children of multiple sclerotics. *Psychosom. Med.*, 21: 8–22, 1959.
2. KAIM, S. G., SCHEINBERG, P., and STENGER, C. A. Correlation of the EEG with the Rorschach and cerebral metabolic tests in multiple sclerosis. *EEG Clin. Neurophysiol.*, Suppl. 3, 29, 1953.
3. McMORROW, F. T. Multiple sclerosis: a psychiatric approach to management. *J. Michigan M. Soc.*, 57: 1564–1566, 1958.

XII

>>

Geriatrics

Psychological and neurological investigations now reflect the increasing interest in geriatrics. Extended life expectancy, and improved methods of medical treatment, including recent advances in chemotherapy, offer an improved outlook for many elderly persons. At the same time, interest has sharpened awareness of how little is known about the nature of aging.

PROBLEMS OF DEFINITION AND VARIATION

The term "old age" is as deceptive as "mental deficiency," and implies an entity too broad in scope to be helpful clinically. Investigators do agree, however, that there are many calculable differences between the behavior of younger adults and those of seventy- or eighty-year-olds, which seem to be specie specific. These include a lowering in functioning ability, some memory loss, diminution of perceptive capacities, and slowing of reaction time. (Birren and Botwinick,[2] Clay,[4] Copple,[6] Friend and Zubek,[10] Griew,[11] Howell,[14] Kamin,[15] Pacaud,[22] Pacaund,[23] Singleton[27, 28] and others.)

Comfort[5] explains these alterations as a breakdown of "programs" fundamental to growth and based upon selective survival pressures. Reichenbach and Mathers[26] point out that irreversibility is a general characteristic of aging systems. Irreversibility, cumulation (mechanisms which register and accumulate effects) and limits of size, form, and function are mentioned by Birren[1] as universal factors. Because cellular degeneration in the brain has been demonstrated among children and young adults having prolonged cardiac disease, Wahal and Riggs[32] speculate that systemic cardiovascular insufficiency may contribute to alterations in neuroanatomic structures associated with senile mental symptoms.

The influences of exogenous insults added to genetic damage and biological change are inherent in irradiation theories (Curtis and Healy,[7] Landahl,[18] and Szilard[30]).

The roles which biological, psychological and social factors play in the aging processes are, however, still generally undetermined. Various studies have been undertaken to investigate, for example, relationship of parental to child longevity, of neuroanatomical, physiological, and psychological changes, or socio-cultural influences. Integration of findings is hindered by absence of a linear relationship between any two of the variables, making aging bases hard to determine.

Psychological expressions of aging are subject to wide variation, both within an individual and within results of any test selected. Usually normal degenerative processes occur very slowly and as extensions of the former self. These may become so slightly exaggerated that the personality is essentially intact. In other persons, marked mental and emotional changes appear over relatively short intervals of time and without overt signs of any distinct neurological disease. Time of onset, nature of changes, and degree of alteration are then important considerations. It is agreed that behavioral alterations are usually accompanied by feelings of frustration and loss of self-confidence. Most serious of all, feelings of uselessness often develop, with attendant depression.

Work to date shows that behavioral changes early in life are usually more disruptive to general adjustment than those occurring much later. Because most people lead more active lives with greater responsibilities at a younger age, more environmental pressures tend to be interrupted. Yet, as in other fields, the individual's total life picture should concern the clinician in geriatrics, because the patient's previous patterning will largely determine how he will handle old-age processes. Integral, therefore, to future investigation is the need for more adequate long-range studies such as are recommended by Nisbet,[21] Pressey and Jones,[25] and Lorge, Tuckman, and Dunn[20] as well as those based upon cross-sectional data. So far very few criteria exist for judging intellectual and emotional deviations due to aging phenomena.

When a pathological condition is superimposed upon neuropsychological changes already present, functioning is usually more rapidly and acutely disturbed. Further exaggeration of alterations may be noted, or, as is often the case, entirely new symptomatology may appear. Because so-called senile diseases such as Parkinson's for example, may make their appearance at anywhere from forty to seventy years, wide age ranges are involved.

Usually natural or expected age changes are estimated by the clinician and any excess assigned to organicity, i.e., to pathology. To date, only the most general statements have been validated, and detailed information is fragmentary and unreliable. Much more extensive and thorough work is needed.

SOME CLINICAL ASPECTS OF AGING

Thaler's[31] elaborate investigation dealing with relationships among the Wechsler, Weigl, Rorschach, EEG findings, abstract-concrete behavior, and concept formation, was limited to a normal old-age population of one hundred volunteers living independently in a community. In summarizing results, the following impressions of behavior and functioning were given:

1. A significant correlation was shown between better scores on the Wechsler subtests and more abstract performance on the Weigl Sorting Test ($p < .001$).

2. Increased meagerness of association on the Rorschach correlated positively with more concrete performance on the Weigl ($p < .01$).

3. Extremely concrete approaches to the sorting task were noted in 66 per cent of the group. This was thought to indicate limited capacity to think abstractly on test.

4. Advancing age did not correlate with any special EEG classification, although 62 per cent of the recordings were considered abnormal. Normal and focal recordings and higher total weighted scores on the Wechsler were found to be related ($p < .01$).

5. Increased age was associated with decrease in performance scores on the Wechsler subtests used ($p < .001$).

Homogeneity in individual cases and among groups is one condition inadequately met to date in reported results of neuropsychological studies. (This criticism applies as well to studies of elderly individuals without neurological disease, where many uncontrolled variables have been characteristic.) In the study of Hall,[12] for example, seventy patients between the ages of forty-one and sixty-five were used. The Wechsler-Bellevue and four conceptual tests were shown to be fairly unreliable under these conditions for differentiating between groups with depressive and/or organic complaints.

Busse, Barnes, Silverman, Shy, Thaler and Frost[3] reported on organic factors that influence the "psyche" of elderly persons. They studied 180 community and hospitalized subjects over sixty years of age. EEG tracings showed differential changes with a high percentage of focal dysrhythmia rather than diffuse abnormality, particularly in the left-temporal lobe. Where diffuse slowing occurred, it was accompanied by intellectual deterioration. Busse and associates also attributed depression to feelings of inferiority and loss of self-esteem, rather than to guilt feelings. Other findings reported were poor relationships with their children and a more favorable prognosis among subjects who worked than among those who were idle.

In the study of Williams[33] spatial disorientation in senile dementia was the major concern, along with psychological mechanisms disturbed. Some suggested methods of compensation were also reported. Subjects were between the ages of sixty-five and ninety-five years, and showed an inclination to wander. Intellectual impairment on visual-maze test was reported, with the comment that preliminary training tended to affect results favorably. Other factors influencing results were complexity of directions, clarity of goal, and amount of mental support.

Dorken and Greenbloom,[9] investigated psychological aspects of senile dementia. Sixty-seven patients with senile psychoses or psychoses with arteriosclerosis and twenty normal subjects of comparable age were given the Wechsler-Bellevue in an effort to determine different levels of subtest performance and the relation of age to extent of dementia. Dorken and Greenbloom reached the following conclusions:

1. Senile deterioration has no necessary relationship to, or dependence upon, normal process of aging.

2. Organization of abilities is different from that found in normal adulthood.

3. The per cent of discrepancies between verbal and performance scales on the Wechsler-Bellevue increased progressively from the normal old-age group to the high and low abnormal groups, normals showing greatest efficiency.

4. Copple's Senescent Decline Quotient provided a more valid index of the extent of senile deterioration than Wechsler's Deterioration Index.

5. In subjects over sixty-four years an Efficiency Quotient was better than an intelligence quotient as an appropriate estimate of intelligence in senile dementia.

6. Information, vocabulary, digit span, and picture completion were subtests of choice to include in a short form of examination.

In the report of Hopkins and Roth[13] on the performance of subjects over sixty, groups included patients with paraphrenia, arteriosclerotic psychoses, and acute confusion. Wechsler-Bellevue vocabulary, a shortened form of Raven's Progressive Matrices, and an information test composed of questions about personal information, orientation, and public events made up the battery.

Scores placed the paraphrenics and acute confusional cases with the affective group. Scores of arteriosclerotic patients fell somewhere between those for senile and affective groups. Senile psychoses were almost wholly distinct from affective psychoses, paraphrenia, and confusion.

Arteriosclerotic patients showed some overlap with affective and senile groups.

The Bender Gestalt test was used by Lakin[17] in a psychological evaluation of the aged. The most important evidences of impairment Lakin found are in distortions involving partial rotation of designs, marked perseveration of lines or dots, loss of detail, fragmentation, difficulty with acute angles, and overlapping of designs. Qualitative aspects of the study revealed exclamations of impotence, perplexity, and incompetence.

Although the Rorschach test is of value in differentiating between normal processes of aging and pathological conditions such as early senile psychosis with cerebral sclerosis, it has figured in relatively few studies; but those in which it is reported on show consistent and striking agreement.

Diminution of human-movement responses in normal older people, with higher animal-movement content, is observed by all investigators (Davidson and Kruglou,[8] Klopfer,[16] Prados and Fried,[24] Slosson,[29] and Light and Amick[19]). The same clinicians report increase in per cent of pure form responses, in contrast to decreased texture responses, which were noticeably scarce. Response to color varied. Either color was absent, or there was excessive emphasis upon the color-form (CF) and pure color (C) response at the expense of the more rational form-color (FC) reaction.

Klopfer[16] summarizes quantitative characteristics of old age as "considerable constriction" indicated by underemphasis upon color and movement responses and overemphasis upon form responses in the Rorschach test. When movement responses occurred they were chiefly of the FM type. Responses using k, m, K, and FK were minimal and variable. Stereotyping and overemphasis upon W at the expense of D were also striking. Qualitative aspects are reported by Light and Amick[19] as suspicion, anxiety, and evasiveness in response to the Rorschach.

Between the institutionalized and noninstitutionalized aged, no significant differences were found by Klopfer.[16] Davidson and Kruglou[8] on the other hand, believe that their institutional group showed evidence of "lower energy output," "greater rigidity of the personality," and "less emotional responsiveness."

A summary of Rorschach findings in terms of behavior suggests that in the normal aging process there are these elements:

1. Lower intellectual efficiency in general.
2. Diminution of capacity to use inner resources.
3. Narrowing of range of interests.
4. Decreased emotional responsiveness with little awareness of affective needs.
5. Feelings of anxiety, insecurity, and loss of self-respect.

Thus, differences in degree rather than in kind are typical of elderly persons without neurological pathology. With pathology, further exaggeration of existing changes and precipitation of new symptomatology are the major findings recorded to date. More specific evidence is scattered and fragmentary, showing an urgent need for further work.

CASE HISTORIES

Case I   Cerebral sclerosis and convulsions in a sixty-five-year-old woman

THE CLINICAL PICTURE

History was uneventful until the appearance of grand mal seizures at age sixty-two, with tonic movements, frothing at the mouth, and loss of bowel and bladder control. Unconsciousness lasted a few minutes. For two years prior to evaluation, seizures were completely controlled by a combination of drugs. During interseizure periods and periodically after the control of seizures, episodes of depression and hostility were reported. A diagnosis of cerebral sclerosis was made on the basis of neurological examination and abnormal EEG showing diffuse brain damage and convulsive features.

The patient was very apprehensive about psychological testing and very insecure. She repeatedly apologized for her performance, but at the same time seemed to resent the whole procedure as an unnecessary intrusion upon her private life. Apparently much of the material was very difficult for her to handle, so that feelings of inadequacy had some logical foundation.

Amount of schooling could not be determined. Her conversation and behavior suggested that she had probably been of average intelligence at an earlier age. She was evasive upon questioning and said, "Well, I went all the way through school, but that was a long time ago."

As she worked it became evident that she fatigued easily, but usually continued after an occasional momentary rest period. All tests were completed within one test session.

WECHSLER-BELLEVUE SCALE RESULTS

Information	3	Picture arrangement	3
Comprehension	4	Picture completion	3
Digit span	3	Block design	3
Arithmetic	3	Object assembly	3
Similarities	3	Digit symbol	0
(Vocabulary, not scored 8)			

Verbal-scale quotient	78
Performance-scale quotient	74
Full-scale quotient	75

All quotients show a functioning level of borderline. An exceptionally even pattern was obtained; only the digit-symbol score fell significantly lower than other ratings which comprised the quotients. It is of interest, therefore, that the vocabulary rating (not scored) is so much higher.

Findings were interpreted as showing a considerable degree of deterioration beyond that expected on a basis of age alone, with a former average mental level suggested. Interpretation is, of course, speculative because data were limited. Features in support of it are evenness of pattern with only simplest items passed, even though effort and attention were good; little variability in reaction time, which was slow; and the degree of confusion clearly apparent. All of these were consistent with rather severe pathology.

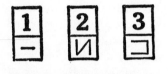
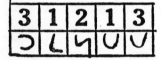

FIG. 13. Digit-symbol reproduction on Wechsler-Bellevue Scale by a 65-year-old woman with cerebral sclerosis and convulsions.

Evidence of distortion in the perception of spatial relationships is seen in the digit symbols reproduced below. Only two symbols were reproduced correctly within ninety seconds, although a total of five was completed (Fig. 13).

BENDER GESTALT TEST

About twenty minutes was spent on the Bender Gestalt test. Most figures were started twice. Dots and circles were counted several times, but the number reproduced was usually not accurate. All during the task the patient complained that she never had been able to draw and was ashamed of what she was doing. "I can't even copy this right," she kept saying, showing insight as well as impotence and perplexity.

Gestalten include many organic signs, such as rotation of the plane, inability to integrate parts, substitution of dashes for dots, poor judgment in placement, with lack of foresight, overlapping, imbalance, and increasing difficulty with more complex patterns. Serious interference on an organic basis was unmistakable from her work here.

DRAW-A-MAN TEST

When asked to draw a man the patient refused, saying, "No. I can't draw anybody. That would be too embarrassing. It's bad enough what I did already."

RORSCHACH RECORD

Performance	Scoring and Inquiry

Card I
23" 1. An animal that flies around in the trees.

W FM A P
All of the picture looks like a flying animal that flies around in trees. I don't know what kind.

29"
Card II
21" 1. Two animals together. They pick themselves something.

D FM A
Monkeys, it looks like.
Here they have something in their mouth.

25"
Card III
15" 1. Two monkeys.

W FM A
Here they are. The head and the legs. (?) The shape of them. They are standing somewhere.

19"
Card IV
19" 1. A bear.

W F A
This is an animal. I forgot what I called it. A bear? Did I say that? The legs and the shape of it looks like a bear with big feet.

24"
Card V
12" 1. A fly—a big fly flies around in the trees, too.
17"

W FM A P
It has wings, the fly, and it flies around in the trees.

Card VI
18" 1. A lamp—around the lamp. Something that built it up.

D W F Obj
Here (top) and this is something that it is built from. I don't know what.

24"
Card VII
14" 1. Two animals fly around together.

D FM A
These are birds flying around together. They have long necks.

	Performance	Scoring and Inquiry

25″

Card VIII

14″ 1. Two animals fly around on this thing.

D→W   FM   A   P

Two animals fly around on a lamp or what. (?) I don't know what kind of animals—maybe birds. (?) It looks like a lamp.

27″

Card IX

23″ 1. A lamp, too. They try to fly to the top.

D   F   Obj
D   FM   A

This is a lamp, too. Animals try to fly up to the top, too. (?) Birds, maybe.

29″

Card X

16″ 1. A bee. Bees. They suck the flowers. They like the flowers on this.

D   CF   Pl
D   FM   A

Here are some bees on the flowers. (?) I don't know the names of flowers. (?) They are pretty colors, too.

21″

When limits were tested, the patient could not see human movement, texture, or popular color responses, and said she couldn't find "more than I told you."

THEMATIC APPERCEPTION TEST

(Boy with Violin)

17″ He's looking at the violin. He's so anxious to know how to play. He doesn't know how to do it, but he will learn. Some day he will be a big violinist.

42″

(Farm scene)

10″ She stays for such a holy woman. A horse and a man. The man looks on the girl, too. I mean on the horse. She tries to look at it. She wants to look at it. She's very anxious.

33″

(Boy sitting with face covered)

14″ He fell. He doesn't know how to pick himself up. He's going to pick himself up.

30″

(Suggested intercourse scene or death scene)

19″ The girl is very sick. That man is very anxious. Very sick. He's very upset about it. (Demonstrates with hands.) Oh, God, what's the matter? (Long delay) She might be going to be well.

39″

(Blank card)

7″ There's nothing here. I have to make a story? I want happiness in my life. My daughter, children, and husband and everyone in my family.

27″

INTERPRETATION

The Rorschach and TAT tests show marked shrinkage of the personality structure and curtailment of creative thinking. No doubt anxiety plays a major role here, but exaggeration of limitation has sound foundations, since organic interference with functioning is definite. Of interest from the few TAT cards presented is her reiteration of how anxious the characters are, and her remark that she wants happiness. Clinically, she tends to become depressed easily and is quite pessimistic about the future course of her health.

Organic signs are unmistakable with practically all the most reliable ones present. Material presented differs from some of the preceding cases in that the neurological involvement has permeated all aspects of psychological testing.

Case II   Parkinson's disease in a sixty-three-year-old man

THE CLINICAL PICTURE

History was uneventful until one year before hospital admission for evaluation, when a sudden and progressive memory loss appeared. This loss was accompanied by personality changes, the patient's former active, assertive nature giving way to passivity, dependency, anxiety, and depression. Clinically, he appeared to have been of at least high average intelligence formerly.

Limited educational background (eighth grade), occupation given as a "partially retired merchant," married with two grown children.

During the psychological test session, patient expressed discouragement about his shortcomings and seemed frustrated and unhappy. He could not, for example, remember the names of the last two Presidents of the United States, which bothered him greatly. All intelligence test scores showed a loss of efficiency out of keeping with his vocabulary and conversation, but no particular area of dysfunction was noted.

As he worked he mentioned that he got lost frequently. This was verified when he was returned to his room after test. At the door he hesitated to enter, became confused, and did not recognize his surroundings.

WECHSLER-BELLEVUE SCALE RESULTS

Information	8	Picture arrangement	4
Comprehension	7	Picture completion	4
Digit span	4	Block design	5
Arithmetic	9	Object assembly	7
Similarities	7	Digit symbol	6

Verbal-scale quotient	96
Performance-scale quotient	100
Full-scale quotient	94

By pro-rating scores for age, the patient was still able to earn quotients within the average range. Observation of his performance, however, tended to contradict this degree of efficiency. In the writer's experience this is true of the performance of many elderly persons on the Wechsler; they seem to gain advantage with increase in age on a relatively poor performance. If quotients were interpreted literally in this instance, evidence for deterioration would be slight, contrary to the clinical picture and results of other tests. Subtest items also revealed significant loss of intellectual efficiency not reflected in the total scores.

RORSCHACH RECORD

Performance	Scoring and Inquiry
Card I	
3″ 1. A bat.	W F A P
	The shape of it. The wings and the face. The whole thing.
14″	
Card II	
7″ 1. Two bears.	D F Ad P
	The bodies are here, the shoulders, the waistline and the bottom. The shape of them.
19″	
Card III	
10″ 1. Two dudes.	W M Fc H P
	The faces, neck, shoulders, modelling, posing that way. They have stiff collars, evening dress, turning to each other.
	D FC Obj P
	A necktie because of the shape and color. I didn't notice it before.

Performance	Scoring and Inquiry

21"
Card IV
5" 1. A bear.

W Fc A

The face on top, the spine in the center. Looks like a baby bear between the legs. Furry bear.

24"
Card V
8" 1. A bat

W F A P

The shape of it.

Card VI
11" 1. A large bat.

W F A

The shape of it. The buttocks at the bottom and the legs on the side.

22"
Card VII
9" 1. Two puppy dogs.

D→W FM A

The face and body. They are both on a rock or the ground. I don't know which. (?) They might be turning around.

24"
Card VIII
11" 1. Two climbers, what they are I don't know. Animals I don't know.

D F/C FM A P

Pink animal of some kind. I never knew a pink animal altogether, with different color it could be a rat. (?) It is not climbing but are the kind that would.

28"
Card IX
17" 1. A hard-shelled lobster at the top, not a lobster, a hard-shelled crab.

W F A

The claws made me think of a crab and the shape of it.

25"
Card X
7" 1. Doing a dance.

D FM (H) P

Crabs dancing.

29"

When limits were tested, he could see ladies dancing in Card III and called the usual worms in Card X a cucumber because of the color and shape.

INTERPRETATION

Underproductiveness, minimal human movement, minimal texture, and avoidance of color except as an additional response, as well as more animal movement than human movement, are all features consistent with the old-age process and cannot be construed as indicating more serious organic interference. Six popular responses likewise suggest considerable contact with reality. Nevertheless, lapses in control are apparent, such as seeing the "buttocks" of a bat, and confusion about the "spine" and "a baby bear between the legs," which suggest more serious interference with thinking than the process of age alone.

On the basis of psychological test results the interpretation was organicity beyond the limits attributable to age. Discharge diagnosis of this patient was Parkinsonism, with EEG findings normal.

Case III   Right-sided Parkinsonism in a sixty-four-year-old man

THE CLINICAL PICTURE

Patient with marked manual tremor of right hand, who spoke in a hoarse whisper. He displayed pedantic and selfderogatory behavior alternately, sometimes bragging about former achievements and then about handicaps. Asked his occupation, he replied, "I'm a has-been physician." Following this comment, the patient seemed to enjoy enumerating incidents in his history, blaming "overwork" in the last war for his present difficulties. Superior intelligence as an optimal functioning level was unquestionable from his conversation.

WECHSLER-BELLEVUE SCALE RESULTS

Information	14	Picture arrangement	7
Comprehension	11	Picture completion	10
Digit span	10	Object assembly	9
Arithmetic	10	Block design	4
Similarities	14	Digit symbol	6

Verbal-scale quotient	119	Almost superior
Performance-scale quotient	107	Average
Full-scale quotient	114	High average

Weaknesses of reasoning ability were apparent on intelligence test and poor work on block designs. Slowness of reaction on tests requiring speed was also noticeable, with more disturbance than the scores themselves reveal. This was true also of distortions of reality which occurred. The latter confusion indicated the probable presence of more than the usual amount of interference, even though he was still able to function within the average range on performance test. Organic pathology seemed likely to account for this, since on the whole he appeared like an adolescent, obsessive-compulsive individual who was unable to maintain his former mental or emotional stability.

Performance	Scoring and Inquiry
2. This suggests a forest with a stream.	D FK Geo

Sometimes I remember flying over a forest and getting back. The mottling gives this impression.

74"
Card IX
23" 1. The coloring suggests my trip to the Virgin Islands to visit my daughter's family.

W C/F kF Geo
When you look at the topography of the landscape. The colors are beautiful.

2. The center part suggests the Crucifixion scene I saw in Lima, Peru.

D F Obj
All I saw was a cross.

2'20"
Card X
35" The right kind of colors.
42" 1. I think of the profile of Winston Churchill, of whom I'm very fond.

dr F Hd
The shape of the head and the facial features.

2. Christmas greens. Suggests our Christmas at home with all the family. Happy times.

D Csym Xmas
D F Obj
D F Obj
These look like candles. Those knockers on the door.

1'23"

INTERPRETATION

This record is included mainly because it is atypical of protocols reported by other investigators. Five human-movement responses, for example, are many more than are expected from elderly persons even without neurological involvement. Number of responses and general elaboration are also better than generally heard. Without doubt, however, regressive trends exist. Personal references to the past, uncontrolled and ineffective use of color, and infantile concepts intermingled with sophisticated reactions suggest weakening in control and inability to maintain his former efficiency.

One must be much more cautious, it is felt, in attributing this slackening to neurological involvement, inasmuch as such wide differences in ability to ward off age processes are known to be the rule. Features in the record more suggestive of organic interference would be the destructive concepts of the aeroplane and the intoxicated boys in costume, along with other signs which overlap the normal aging range. These factors combined with results of intelligence and drawing tests tend toward an interpretation of organic interference with thinking. Hospital diagnosis after neurological evaluation was: Right-sided Parkinsonism.

DISCUSSION OF CASES

Difficulties of estimating the nature and degree of organic interferences are illustrated in these three cases. Among features needing clarification are knowledge of normal aging processes independent of pathology, range of neuropathological expressions at the behavioral level, and pre-illness baselines for establishing losses pathognomonic of any disease entity.

Research is likewise complicated by the many aspects of old-age processes that themselves simulate organicity. Overlapping between non-pathological and neuropathological categories is dramatic. Since curtailment of possibilities for adequate adjustment is generally enforced by environment and socio-cultural pressures, a global approach to the whole individual is imperative in future study. Requirements are for longitudinal research as well as cross-sectional, with detailed analysis of the roles of neurophysiological, psychological, psychiatric, and socio-cultural influences. Oversimplification has been characteristic of earlier work. Even the concept of old age *per se* must be abandoned.

BIBLIOGRAPHY

1. BIRREN, J. E. Principles of research on aging. In *Handbook of Aging and the Individual: Psychological and Biological Aspects,* Ch. I. Birren, J. E. (Ed.). Chicago: Univer. of Chicago Press: 1959.
2. BIRREN, J. E., and BOTWINICK, J. Speed of response as a function of perceptual difficulty and age. *J. Gerontol.,* 10: 433–436, 1955.
3. BUSSE, E. W., BARNES, R. H., SILVERMAN, A. J., SHY, G. M., THALER, M., and FROST, L. L. Studies in the process of aging: Factors which influence the psyche of elderly persons. *Amer. J. Psychiat.,* 110: 897–903, 1954.
4. CLAY, H. M. Changes of performance with age on similar tasks of varying complexity. *Brit. J. Psychol.,* 45: 7–13, 1954.
5. COMFORT, A. *The biology of senescence.* London: Routledge and K. Paul: 1956.
6. COPPLE, G. Senescent decline of the Wechsler-Bellevue intelligence scale. *Univer. Pittsburgh Bull.,* 45 (8): 227–236, 1949.
7. CURTIS, H. J., and HEALY, R. Effects of radiation on aging. In *Advances in Radiobiology.* Edinburgh: Oliver & Boyd: 1958.
8. DAVIDSON, H., and KRUGLOU, L. Personality characteristics of the institutionalized aged. *J. Consult. Psychol.,* 16: 5–12, 1952.
9. DORKEN, H. J., and GREENBLOOM, G. C. Psychologic investigation of senile dementia: Wechsler-Bellevue adult intelligence scale. *Geriatrics,* 8: 324–333, 1953.

10. Friend, C. M., and Zubek, J. P. The effects of age on critical thinking ability. *J. Gerontol.*, 13: 407–413, 1958.

11. Griew, S. Information gain in tasks involving different stimulus-response relationships. *Nature*, 182: 1819, 1958.

12. Hall, K. R. L. Conceptual impairment in depressive and organic patients of the pre-senile age group. *J. Ment. Sci.*, 98: 256–264, 1952.

13. Hopkins, B., and Roth, M. Psychological test performance in patients over sixty. 99: 451–463, 1953.

14. Howell, R. Changes in Wechsler subtest scores with age. *J. Consult. Psychol.*, 19: 47–50, 1955.

15. Kamin, L. J. Differential changes in mental abilities in old age. *J. Gerontol.*, 12: 66–70, 1957.

16. Klopfer, W. G. Personality patterns of old age. *Ror. Res. Exch.* 10: 145–166, 1946.

17. Lakin, M. Clinical use of the Bender visual motor test in psychologic assessment of the aged. *J. Amer. Geriat. Soc.*, 4: 909–919, 1956.

18. Landahl, H. B. Biological periodicities, mathematical biology and aging. In *Handbook of Aging and the Individuals: Psychological and Biological Aspects*, Ch. 3. Chicago: Univer. Chicago Press: 1959.

19. Light, B. H., and Amick, J. H. Rorschach responses of normal aged. *J. Proj. Tech.*, 20: 185–195, 1956.

20. Lorge, I., Tuckman, J., and Dunn, M. B. Human figure drawings by younger and older adults. *J. Clin. Psychol.* 14: 54–56, 1958.

21. Nisbet, J. D. Intelligence and age: retesting with twenty-four years' interval. *Brit. J. Educ. Psychol.*, 27: 190–198, 1957.

22. Pacaud, S. Le viellissement des aptitudes; déclin les aptitudes en fonction de l'age et du niveau d' instruction. *Biotypologie*, 14: 65–94, 1953.

23. Pacaund, S. Experimental research on the aging of psychological functions. In *Old age in the modern world*: 279–289. *Proc. Intern. Assoc. Gerontol.* 3rd Congr. London: E. & S. Livingstone; 1955.

24. Prados, M., and Fried, E. G. Personality structure of the older age groups. *J. Clin. Psychol.*, 3: 113–120, 1947.

25. Pressey, S. L., and Jones, A. W. 1923–1953 and 20–60 age changes in moral codes, anxieties, and interests as shown by the "X-0 Tests." *J. Psychol.*, 39: 485–502, 1955.

26. Reichenbach, M., and Mathers, R. A. The place of time and aging in natural sciences and scientific philosophy. In *Handbook of Aging and the Individual: Psychological and Biological Aspects*, Ch. 2. Chicago: Univer. Chicago Press: 1959.

27. Singleton, W. T. The change of movement timing with age. *Brit. J. Psychol.*, 45: 166–172, 1954.

28. Singleton, W. T. Age and performance timing on simple skills. In *Old Age in the Modern World*: 221–231. *Proc. Intern. Assoc. Gerontol.* 3rd Congr. London E. & S. Livingstone: 1955.

29. Slosson, R. L. Rorschach reliability as secured by the test-retest method with seniles showing a memory loss. Personal communication to Klopfer, W. G. In Klopfer, B., *Developments in the Rorschach Method.* Yonkers, N.Y.: World Book; 1956.

30. SZILARD, L. On the nature of the aging process. *Proc. Nat. Acad. Sci.,* 45: 30–45, 1959.

31. THALER, M. Relationships among Wechsler, Weigl, Rorschach, EEG findings, and abstract-concrete behavior in a group of normal aged subjects. *J. Gerontol.,* 11: 404–409, 1956.

32. WAHAL, K. M., and RIGGS, H. E. Changes in the brain associated with senility. *Arch. Neurol.,* 2 (2): 151–159, 1960.

33. WILLIAMS, M. Spatial disorientation in senile dementia: the psychological mechanisms disturbed and some methods of compensation. *J. Ment. Sci.,* 102: 291–299, 1956.

ADDITIONAL REFERENCES

1. GLANZER, M., GLASER, R., and RICHLIN, M. Development of a test battery for study of age-related changes in intellectual and perceptual abilities. Report No. 56: 138. School of Aviation Medicine. Randolph Air Force Base, Texas, 1958.

2. HIMWICH, W. A., and HIMWICH, H. E. Neurochemistry of aging. In *Handbook of Aging and the Individual: Psychological and Biological Aspects,* Ch. 7. Chicago: Univer. Chicago Press: 1959.

3. ORME, J. E. Rorschach performance in normal old age, elderly depression and senile dementia. *Rev. Diagnostic Psychol. & Personality Exploration,* 6: 132–141, 1958.

Author Index

Subject Index